Yep — you can if I did!

Lois Anna Mark

Tortillas & Peanut ButteR?

TRUE CONFESSIONS
OF an AMERICan MOM
TURNED MEXICAN SMUGGLER

Dr. Linda Sonna
Lois Sonna Mark

 ShelfStealers Publishing + DrSonna.org

For information contact **www.DrSonna.org**

Cover design by Jacques Paul Lalonde & Dr. Linda Sonna

ASIN: B01FH51J66

ISBN-10: 1-61972-032-9
ISBN-13: 978-1-61972-032-9

ShelfStealers Publishing
Laredo, Texas
United States of America

First Edition, December, 2016

Cataloguing Data:

Sonna, Linda. 1950-
Tortillas & Peanut Butter: True Confessions of an American Mom Turned Mexican Smuggler /Dr. Linda Sonna, Lois Sonna Mark

1. Mexico 2. Biography/Memoir 3. Multicultural 4. Travel 5. Expatriate 6. Parenting 7. Spanish I. Sonna, Linda. 1950- . II. Tortillas & Peanut Butter: True Confessions of an American Mom Turned Mexican Smuggler. Tags/ Metadata: Mexico, Parenting, Hispanic, Multicultural, Expatriate, Travel, Spanish

10 9 8 7 6 5 4 3 2 1

TO MEXICO

*Thanks for welcoming
tourists, immigrants, and
assorted foreign interlopers
to your fabulous fiesta!*

ACKNOWLEDGMENTS

*"The most important thing in life
is not knowing everything,
it's having the phone number
of somebody who does."*

— *Anonymous, (521) 555-8225*

Thanks to those who lived the stories first hand:

William Lee Sonna, Larry Allen Sonna, Mark-Brian Sonna, Leno A. Sonna, Ferne Knize, Diane Elliston, Mrs. Kocmoud, Diane Gilliard, Frances Tornow, Fred Tuttle, Señor Osio, Señora Carrera, Terry Aldredt, Guillermo Sálazar, Dr. Responsable and Family, Greg St. Ville, Claudia Beatriz Arrieta Zamora, Patricia, Lupita, Estanislado, Francesca, Ricardo, and the students at the *Instituto de Estudios Bilingües* in Irapuato.

Thanks to those who helped unravel the mysteries of my mystifying mamacita:

J. Samuel Shimek, Barbara Gastwirth, Joy Urban, Dr. John Valcik, Thomas C. Agler, Beverly Agler, Dr. Stephen Scherffius, Diane Gilliard, Dr. Leroy Howe, Judy Goodstein, Dr. Henry Kaczkowski, Dr. C. H. Patterson, Gray Wolf, and Sheila San Felipo.

Thanks to those who provided support and encouragement:

Joan McCord, Vikki Davidson, Bob Henry, Charlotte Burns, Paula Howard, Don Whittington, Jan Weinbrenner, O. J. Bryson, Helena Pine, John Caswell, Madelyn Miller, Teresa Shaft, Mary Gugino, Michele Potter, Sandra Richardson, Jim Richards, Alicia Mayo, the Taos Writer's Group, Brinn Colenda, Vicki Mercer, the La Manzanilla Writer's Group, Pamala Field, Dr. Dr. José Luis Bañales Vázquez, Dr. César Gil Hoyos, and Gail Weiss.

Thanks to those who read, critiqued, and edited:

The LaGrange Library Writer's Group, Lynne Willard, Diane Gilliard, Carol Penn, Jim Minter, Dulce D. Moore, Roy Mullins, Susan Malone, Mimi Ayars, Wanda Horton, Joan & John McCord, LeRoy Clary, Susan McBride, Dolores Donner, Pat Snyder, Jack Ballas, Adolph Floryanowich, Glenn Bavousett, Andrew Miller, Ann Clark, Peter Rubie, Patrice Stanton, Ron Jackson, Lyn Phillips, Helen Hadsell, the Dallas/ Fort Worth Writer's Workshop, Abe Mark, Michael Seidman, Carolyn Williamson, Evan Fogelman, Katherine Naylor, Michele Potter, Mary Gugino, Colleen Finley, Tom Finley, Leroy Clary, Jim Schutte, Zion Gía Archuleta, Michelle Gía Gomez, Carol Rogers DeArmitt, Alicia Mayo, Nancy Anderson, La Manzanilla Writer's Group, Denise Brown, Julie Catton Amezcua, and G. Kaleo Larson.

CONTENTS

AUTHOR'S NOTE

NOW & THEN

*"The descriptions of smuggling are for informational purposes only.
Contact your contraband professional for recommendations and advice."*

— *Dr. Linda Sonna*

Serenades and chaperones have gone the way of the Walkman since my mother visited Mexico in the 1970s. American peanut butter has become plentiful. City folk sip soy caramel lattes at Starbucks. Some drivers stop for red lights. A word for "pet" has been added to the Spanish dictionary *(mascota).*Crime is up; family size is down. A few tourist restaurants serve nachos. Marijuana is legal.

Yet many things are the same. Broiled goat is still popular, moms are still saints, and bribes solve most every bureaucratic problem. Atheists remain Catholic at heart, and marijuana is cheap. The techniques for smuggling haven't changed much. Some tourist restaurants serve nachos.

If my mother's story inspires you to try your hand at smuggling contraband, I wish you a low-bribe, tax-free, un-incarcerated future.

¡Viva México!

Dr. Linda Sonna

CERTIFICATE OF AUTHENTICITY

"A little inaccuracy sometimes saves a ton of explanation."

— *H. H. Munro*

All events and characters in this book are real. No names have been changed to protect the guilty, except for government officials, which I don't recall. Maridél, the Student from Hell, is a compilation of my more devilish pupils.

OK, so maybe I didn't wear a red flamenco outfit on my first day in Mexico But my American mini-skirt drew as much outrage from the women and acclaim from the men as if I had tap danced through town, offering free peeks at my castanets.

Also, my daughter blew up the bathroom and accomplished the other plumbing disasters, not me. Linda also had the run-ins with the busload of Mexican males, Fernando the Fearful, and the hospital staff. She toned down some of my antics during my departure from Illinois. The truth, Linda insisted, was too strange for a nonfiction book.

Finally, after getting caught smuggling a water heater into Mexico, I stuck to smaller-sized, less conspicuous contraband.

I swear upon my blushing face, the rest is true.

Sincerely,

Lois Sonna Mark

Lois Sonna Mark
(AKA Lois Sonna, Batman, María Luisa González, Lois Mark)

CHAPTER 1

REVENGE OF THE DODO BIRD

*"They called me mad, and I called them mad,
and damn them, they outvoted me."*

– *Nathaniel Lee*

As I added macaroni to the pot of boiling water on April 1, 1968, my nerves were stretched tighter than my Playtex girdle. I glanced at the phone for the umpteenth time, willing it to ring. The clock was inching toward five-thirty, the end of Diane's workday. If she didn't call soon, my cliffhanger would last all night.

I was so focused on the phone, I startled at the sound of my daughter clomping into the kitchen on her three-inch platform shoes. "You're home early," I said with as much good cheer as I could muster.

Linda nodded vaguely. She set up the ironing board and plugged in the iron. Then, right before my astonished eyes, she did a backbend over the board, arranged her long hair like a skirt, lifted the iron over her head, and began pressing the kinks from her long, dark mane.

Within a minute her face reddened, her lips quivered, and her arms began to tremble. Her new hair-straightening method was apparently as difficult as it was ridiculous.

I tried not to laugh. "If you fall off those shoes and twist an ankle, you'll miss the audition at the Schubert," I warned the human pretzel.

"OK. I'll be careful, Mom."

No snide comeback from my testy teen?

"Dinner...smells...wonderful!" she gushed between gasps.

I sniffed the starchy cloud above the pot of noodles. "Yes, there's nothing quite like the luscious aroma of boiling macaroni."

Linda nodded, which caused her to press a crease into her hair. She grimaced but didn't otherwise react to this fashion disaster.

Something was definitely amiss. "What's up?" I asked.

"I... didn't... go... to... my... tap... lesson," the contortion artist replied between grunts.

I kept my tone upbeat as I braced myself for—for heaven only knew what. "You didn't feel like shuffling off to Buffalo today?"

Suddenly Linda jerked out of her backbend and spun around to face me. "I didn't go because I quit!" she shrieked.

"You WHAT?" Ah, but today was April Fools' Day! I decided to play along. "How will you give your regards to Broadway? Make a splash on the silver screen? How will you become a—" My words caught in my throat as I stared at her stony face. She wasn't kidding! "Then how will you become a Rockette?"

"I already told you, I'm too short. And dance lessons are too boring!"

I was so furious, I dropped the spoon, and it clattered to the floor. Without pausing to pick it up, I put my hands on my hips. "BORING!" I sputtered. "How dare you! I chauffeured you to and from your dance studio every week for ten very long years! I stayed awake though most of your lessons! I managed not to snore loudly during your recitals! You don't know the first thing about boring!"

Her eyes flashed. "Then why don't *you* take lessons?"

"Don't tempt me," I snapped. I picked up the spoon, rinsed it in the sink, and gave the noodles an overly hefty stir, splashing my hand with drops of boiling water.

I smeared some Parkay margarine onto my welts and managed to calm down while Linda disassembled her makeshift beauty parlor. "So what's next?" I asked. "If a career as a dancer is out, what will you do with your life?"

"Well, psychology is interesting."

"Listen to people's troubles all day? Talk about boring!"

As Linda clomped out of the kitchen, I collapsed into a chair. My life flashed before my eyes, and the pictures weren't pretty.

After years of driving Bill to piano lessons and conducting nightly nagging sessions to get him to practice, he had quit, dashing the experts' predictions for a concert career and my mother-of-Van-Cliburn hope.

At age six, Larry was already a T-ball dropout, so I hadn't been Cloroxing all those dirty uniforms for the next Babe Ruth.

When I scrubbed Mark's crayoned scribbles from a wall, was I prepping another canvas for a budding Van Gogh as I liked to think? Or just cleaning up typical toddler messes?

I had relinquished my plans to graduate from college, see the world, and take the world by storm in a high-powered career. Instead I had devoted my entire adult life to handing opportunities to my kids on a plastic platter, and for what? So they could follow in my dreary footsteps and become drudges like me?

That thought stopped me cold. A drudge? Was that what I was?

I tore off a piece of brown paper from a grocery bag, did some quick calculations, and stared in horror at the totals.

In the seventeen years since saying, "I do" to Lee, I had cooked 18,615 meals and washed the same number of loads of dishes, give or take some trips to McDonalds. I had vacuumed the house at least 2,652 times. Those numbers would double by the time Mark flew the nest.

At age thirty-eight I already felt as frumpy as a dodo bird. If something didn't change fast, I'd be a stark, raving cuckoo bird by the time I hit forty. I turned around and stared at the telephone. I needed it to ring. I needed for my best friend's news to be good—to save me.

As I stirred the packet of powdered cheese and a bit of margarine into the cooked macaroni, the phone's sudden shriek startled me. Once again the metal spoon tumbled from my fingers. Without pausing to retrieve it from the floor, I hurried across the kitchen to answer.

"Welcome to the firm!" Diane exclaimed. "You got the job! We'll be colleagues!"

My gasp muddled my reply. My words merged into a strangled roar as I inhaled through my mouth and emerged as a juicy snort when I exhaled through my nose.

I sank into a kitchen chair and listened as Diane spoke in exclamation points. "You'll have a top-floor office with a view of downtown! An executive salary with benefits! An expense account! You leapt straight from the kitchen to the top of our corporate organizational chart in a single bound!"

My mind was racing faster than a speeding bullet. I could hire a maid! Kiss my KP and diaper duties good-bye! I'd meet interesting people and do interesting work.

I plucked a bobby pin from the nape of my neck and re-positioned it under my hairnet. From now on, I'd get my hair permed at a beauty salon.

Diane lowered her voice to a conspiratorial whisper. "No offense, but one semester at Roosevelt College doesn't exactly meet the Ph.D. requirement for this job. A part-time local newspaper job doesn't quite satisfy the five-year marketing experience requirement. I sang your praises to my boss, but I'm frankly amazed that he even decided to interview you. I hope you didn't pad your résumé or lie on the job application."

"I didn't send a résumé. Probably my unorthodox answers on the job application piqued your boss's curiosity. Under 'Related Experience' I wrote, 'Yes!' When your boss asked for details during the interview, I told him about the marketing campaign I had spearheaded."

"I didn't realize! You led a campaign?"

"I marketed my plan for improving the educational environment to the PTA. I suggested re-painting the icky green lockers at Bill's junior high school a cheerful rose color."

"And the PTA went for it?"

"No. But your boss forgot to ask how my campaign turned out when he heard my slogan."

"What was it?"

"Hot Pink or Big Stink."

Diane chuckled.

I stretched the telephone cord to its curly limit, pulled some paper plates and plastic forks from the cabinet, and began setting the dinner table.

"Then your marketing VP asked my opinion about a campaign for spinach," I continued. "I suggested ditching the Popeye cartoon ads and shooting some footage of youngsters chained to a kitchen table, sitting in front of dinner plates heaped with canned spinach. As the youngsters weep and wail, a Dracula voiceover would intone, 'Adults hate the slimy green stuff, too, kids. But life isn't all Twinkies and Ding Dongs!' The VP liked my creativity."

"You're too much, Lois! Can you start on Monday?"

My husband's stormy face leapt into my mind's eye.

"I went out on a limb to get you that interview," Diane said darkly. "If you didn't want the job—"

"But I did! I mean, I do!" I had spent my entire adult life waddling around the house like a dodo bird, batting my useless wings against my suburban cage. Lee squawked if I left our metaphorical nest to do more than flit to the grocery store or church. Convincing him to let me fly like the eagle of my dreams would be the biggest challenge of my new marketing career. "I'll call you first thing tomorrow," I promised Diane.

To soften Lee's mood, I decided to jazz up dinner. I added canned tuna to the macaroni and cheese, arranged some Twinkies on a platter, replaced the paper plates with Melnac dishware, the plastic forks with metal flatware, and the Styrofoam cups with glasses. Lee's six o'clock dinner deadline was fast approaching, so there wasn't time to do more.

When I called the troops to the table, ex-dancer Linda teetered in on her clunky shoes. Next came ex-pianist Bill, his massive bell-bottoms on his faded jeans slapping at his thin ankles. Then ex-T-ball player Larry arrived followed by Mark the graffiti artist.

As I lifted Mark into his highchair, he shot me a big, drooly smile and crowed his one and only word: "Batman!"

"Why doesn't he say 'mama' like a normal kid?" the king of the castle grumbled as he lowered himself into his vinyl throne at the head of the table.

"Perhaps he's commenting on my unusual maternal essence," I said, stroking Mark's fine blond hair. Bill and Larry had also been towheads like me as babies. Their hair had since darkened, but Clairol kept mine golden.

Lee humphed and eyed the glop of tuna-noodle-cheese casserole on his plate. "What is this? Is this supposed to be FOOD?" he demanded, folding his arms over his chest.

Perhaps Mr. Grouch would find the fare more palatable if sweetened with a dollop of levity. I doubted he'd appreciate my line about life not being all Twinkies and Ding Dongs. I needed a different approach.

"Food?" I asked. I made a show of looking around the table, as if searching for some elusive edibles. Then I pushed back my chair, leaned over, and pretended to search under the table. At that moment Mark lobbed a tuna-noodle glob onto the floor and smiled at the splat. "Do you kids see anything resembling food around here?" I asked quickly, hoping Lee hadn't noticed Mark's breech of table etiquette.

"Dad means this *casserole*, Mom," Larry grumbled. He might be a genius according to the primary school IQ chart, but my humor rarely penetrated little Einstein's brain. Larry folded his arms over his chest like Lee, delivering the I-Won't-Eat-It-If-Dad-Doesn't Challenge. "This looks *gross*."

I reached across the table and prodded the lumpy orange mound on Larry's plate with my fork. "Well, it kind of looks like food, doesn't it? Though it also looks like chunks of dried up Play Dough smothered in orange Silly Putty sauce. Did you put away your toys like I told you?"

Larry nodded solemnly, not getting the joke. Linda and Bill glanced nervously at their father and pretended not to get it, either.

"Batman!" Mark crowed, preparing to toss another fistful of casserole onto the floor.

I caught his hand mid-fling and directed it to his mouth. "Mark, can you say 'yummy?' "

As he gummed his casserole glob, his squinty-eyed look of disgust suggested that "yummy" wasn't an apt adjective. Whenever my family tallied my many domestic failings, my cooking usually came in first. When Mark was old enough to vote, it would be unanimous, because I didn't like my cooking, either.

"OK," I said. "Let's find out if this is a Play-Dough-and-Silly-Putty casserole." I plunged my index finger up to the knuckle into the casserole mound on my plate, extracted my orange appendage, and sniffed it warily. "It has the distinctive reek of—" I sniffed again. "Could it be? Yes.

This smells like food!"

Larry smiled. Linda and Bill glanced at the storm clouds gathering on Lee's face and sucked the insides of their cheeks to contain their mirth.

"Batman!" Mark exclaimed, gracing me with a gooey orange grin.

The thundercloud burst. "WHAT DO YOU THINK YOU ARE DOING, LOIS?" Lee thundered.

I wiped my cheesy finger with my napkin. Tonight of all nights, I needed to turn our tired marital melodrama into a fresh, new comedy. "Come hell or high water," I decided, "I'm going to make him laugh!" I surveyed the stifled grins of my traitorous teens. "Them, too," I swore.

"What I'm saying, Lee," I said carefully, "is that this isn't just food—not mere physical matter that makes kids grow tall and parents grow flab. This is *soul* food, as our hippie son might say!"

Bill flipped his Beatle-length bangs from his brow, and I glimpsed a twinkle before his hair descended back over his eyes. The doctor had prescribed mealtime calm for his nervous stomach, which had now progressed to a pre-ulcer. A twinkle was good.

I leaned over Mark's highchair and lowered my face to within an inch of his tray. "Look here, Baby. See how your casserole is a bit burned and crunchy on the outside, and kind of cold and squishy on the inside? It's just like Mama used to make!"

"How dare you say that about my mother!" Lee began, repeating his lines even though I wasn't saying mine.

"Not like *your* mother used to make, Lee. It's like *this* mother used to make. Yes, I've been preparing this same lousy dish for years."

Lee looked confused. Progress!

I searched for a punch line. "Should we pass on my disgusting culinary tradition to the next generation? Or check out the kids' prospective mates first?" I wagged my index finger at Bill. "If you dare to marry a floozy, Son, I swear, I'll give her the recipe!"

Larry giggled and Bill chuckled. Linda's waist-length mane bobbed, so I guessed she was laughing, though only her pimpled nose showed through the part in her freshly ironed curtain.

Lee's eyebrows knit at the seam as he tried to fathom this twist in the plot. "This food tastes *rotten*, Lois."

"Rotten, no. Bad, yes. But either way, it's important for our children's future."

"Leftovers tomorrow? I work hard, and all you do is—"

"No, I mean the *recipe* is important. It provides essential non-nutritional value. One day Linda can march confidently to the altar, secure in the knowledge that her husband couldn't possibly be as appalled by her cooking as you are by mine. Our boys won't compare their dearly beloveds' meals to mine and find their wives lacking." I rose and lifted the Corning Ware bowl above my head like a trophy. "This casserole is a pound of divorce prevention! It guarantees children happy marriages!"

Linda, Bill, and Larry clapped, so baby Mark clapped, too.

Not so my cranky spouse. "If you stayed home like Mrs. Kocmoud, not to mention every other red-blooded wife, instead of gallivanting around town for that newspaper—"

I contained the urge to add the casserole to Mark's collection of orange mounds on the floor. "If I didn't work *a few measly hours a week from home,*" I hissed between clenched teeth, "we couldn't *afford* tuna or cheese for the macaroni casserole."

Lee's face darkened and hardened.

Oops. Mentioning his income had been a tactical error. "Imagine a world of macaroni-only meals, kids!" I said quickly. "The noodle makers would rejoice. Charley the Tuna could continue swimming the salty seas instead of floating in fresh spring water. Though the reduced cheese consumption might cost Elsie the Cow her job."

"Don't change the subject!" Lee said. "Your place is at home! If God had wanted women to work, He would have given them business suits."

What? Had he really said that? "Well, the Lord hath finally done it," I countered. "K-Mart now has a whole line of polyester outfits called 'pantsuits.' They're cuter and more practical than the fig leaf the Almighty designed for Eve way back when."

"I wear the pants in this family," my hopelessly old-fashioned hubby yelled. He pushed his chair from the table with such force, the sound scared Mark, and he started crying. Lee stamped off to the living room for his daily rendezvous with the *Chicago Sun Times*.

I stared bleakly at the messy table. After doing tonight's dishes, I'd still have 18,615 loads to go.

CHAPTER 2

GUILT ATTACK

*"I have yet to see any problem, however complicated,
which, when looked at in the right way,
did not become still more complicated."*

– Paul Anderson

"**B**ut lots of wives work these days," Diane said when I phoned my regrets to the firm.

"Yes, but none of them is married to Lee." I tucked the phone between my ear and shoulder and began sweeping the kitchen floor.

"Like the song says, 'The times, they are a-changin'.' *Have you read The Feminine Mystique?*"

"Is that the sequel to *One Fish/Two Fish/Red Fish/Blue Fish?* I mostly stick to Dr. Seuss these days. Though I did read *Coming of Age in Samoa* a few years back for Linda's social studies report."

"This kind of job doesn't come along every day. Not to someone with your—um—qualifications."

I couldn't even concoct a catchy comeback.

After I hung up, I turned on the radio and began slogging through dish load number 18,617. A bong on a Chinese gong signaled the arrival of my secret lover, but the customary tug at my heart failed to materialize when the silky-voiced adman invited me on a fun-filled trip to the Orient. Nor did my fingers itch when he announced the Northwest Airlines toll-free number for dialing now and paying later.

I strove to cast off the thick blanket of gloom by reminding myself that I'd already been to downtown Chicago a million times. The marketing job wouldn't have fulfilled my dream to travel.

After finishing the dishes, I walked into the living room to find Mark approaching a wall, crayons in hand. "That's a no-no!" I warned.

He dropped the crayons and ran howling to his room.

I had the urge to drop the dust rag and run howling to mine. What was wrong with me, anyway? My friends thought that freedom meant being at liberty to choose any brand of peanut butter their husband could afford and their children would allow. By that definition I was free as a bird. I could indulge my kids' preference for crunchy style Peter Pan.

In my heart I knew that the problem with me was Lee, and the problem with Lee was me. His moodiness and tantrums were undoing me and triggering Linda's migraines, eroding Bill's stomach, turning little Larry into a chronic crank, and erasing baby Mark's smiles.

All Lee wanted was to be a Father-Knows-Best husband to an everyday housewife. To please him I just needed to quit my little newspaper job, suppress the more unusual parts of my personality, and become a dedicated domestic artist. I wasn't ready to tackle the first two, but I could manage a happy homemaker project to mend last night's hole in our marital fence.

I didn't have to look far to find one. When I stepped into the hall, a Captain Crunch trail running from the kitchen to the boys' bedroom caught my attention. That mess would infuriate Lee and did need to be cleaned up sooner rather than later. I had vacuumed thousands of times, so what were a few thousand more?

I wrestled the state-of-the-art General Electric swivel-style canister model from the closet. It had been my anniversary present from Lee. His thought in choosing it had meant much more to me than the gift itself. That was why I didn't like it.

The vacuum valiantly slurped dust bunnies and linty crunchies into its gullet for a few feet. Then it refused to swallow and began regurgitating its meal back onto the carpet. I poked and prodded its long neck and fat belly to no avail. I checked its paper stomach, but it wasn't full.

I glanced at my watch and started to panic. Lee would return from his night shift in two hours. Would the crumby carpet prove his main charge against me—that he was a perfect Ozzie husband, and I was a failure as a Harriet? And if I succeeded as a Harriet for Lee, what about me? Was Harriet happy? Had she ever been to the Orient?

For the umpteenth time that morning, I felt the pressure of tears building behind my eyes. My ex-dancer daughter had been hailing *The Power of Positive Thinking* as the remedy for every bout of unhappiness, and I was desperate enough to give that method a try. I searched for a positive thought. I toyed with calling G.E. and threatening to expose the company in my newspaper column unless the vacuum's warrantee was extended, but that didn't help. I needed to talk to someone, but whom?

My mother came to mind, but I hated to blow her image of me as "uncannily cheerful." As a child I'd overheard her tell a neighbor, "If they hung Lois, she'd probably say she wouldn't mind being hung again." Besides, Mother had managed with two toddlers, a full-time job, and no husband. She'd probably tell me I should be grateful that I'd broken my vacuum and not my back.

I lacked personal experience with the blues, but Mother had said counting one's blessings was a good way to beat them back, so I decided to count mine. The project proved harder than I'd expected. I finally

SONNA & SONNA MARK

came up with Blessing Number One, that I'd broken the vacuum and not my back. I was too down in the dumps to come up with a Number Two.

A good cry helped the unhappy housewives on *As the World Turns*, so I retreated to my bedroom, hurled myself onto the chenille bedspread, and waited for the lump in my chest to squeeze past the one in my throat and unleash a stream of tears. Lee might be less angry if he found me with red-rimmed eyes and mascara smears. But I couldn't drip a drop of liquid sadness to save my sanity, much less my marriage.

Suddenly the words of my favorite philosopher came to mind. *"Oh well. I won't think about it today. I'll think about it tomorrow,"* Scarlett O'Hara had said. I rose to return to my chores but stopped at the doorway. If I stepped into the hall, I'd see the linty cereal mess and the anorexic vacuum. How could I not think about things until tomorrow that were in plain sight today?

As I pondered the fatal flaw in Scarlett's logic, a mysterious force propelled me toward the closet. I began heaping clothes into a suitcase.

While packing clothes for the kids, I reminded myself to iron Lee's shirt for work the next night.

While loading Mark into the Mercury, I debated whether to fix ham or chicken TV dinners for supper.

As I drove to Larry's school, I thought of ways to sneak the suitcases back into the house so that no one would know I had almost run away.

While waiting for Linda and Bill outside their high school, I pondered the mystery: my sanity had been shattered and my marriage destroyed by Captain Crunch.

"What happened?" Bill asked as he climbed into the car. "Did somebody die?"

"Me!" I wanted to exclaim. *"I joined the living dead about ten years ago."* Instead, I donned a happy-camper smile. "I'm pulling my lucky children

out of school in the middle of the day so they can start their Easter vacation early and spend it at Grandma's."

Whoops of joy rang out from the backseat.

While Linda, Bill, and Larry called first dibs on the beds in my childhood home, I took Mark into the kitchen. Mother sat him on the counter and handed him a beater of chocolate cake batter to lick.

"Thanks for taking the kids," I said. "I'll only be gone a few days."

"Days?" she asked. Her eyes narrowed. "Is this about Lee?"

I shrugged.

After a tense silence, she sighed. "Well, when I was no more than a slip of a girl, I left my sorry excuse for a family after my husband died in Missouri and took the train to Chicago. Back then, the city was real hard for a girl on her own with two babies in tow, so I thanked my lucky stars when another man done come along and took us in. By the time I saw my mistake, I had four kids instead of two, my courage was all used up, and I'd left too much scandal in Kansas to go back. When the womenfolk got the vote, I hoped my daughter wouldn't get stuck like back in my day. But it's a man's world still."

Relief poured over me. "I was afraid you'd tell me to count my blessings."

"If they don't add up to a hill of beans, you need a plan."

I wished I could hunker down in her lap for a couple of years.

As Mark waved bye-bye, the beater slipped from his grasp and clattered to the floor. "Batman!" he wailed, reaching toward me for comfort.

Mother waved me on. "There, there," I heard her cluck as I left the kitchen. "Give Grandma just a minute to whip up another batch of batter for her grandbaby."

The kids would be fine. The unanswered question was how I would fare.

CHAPTER 3

FLIGHT TO HOT TAMALE HEAVEN

"No matter how many miles a man may travel,
he will never get ahead of himself."

— *George Ade*

At the stoplight by the Stevenson Expressway entrance, I wondered where I was going. A jam of traffic was headed toward downtown Chicago, so I went the other way. As the suburbs gave way to cornfields, I thought about my brief note to Lee. How nasty would the scene be when I returned? I counted telephone poles to distract myself for a time, and then the blissful oblivion of highway hypnosis set in.

When I emerged from my trance, a huge sign overhead was welcoming me to Missouri. For some reason, that tickled me, and a bout of giddiness ensued. "I'll bet my lost Tupperware lids that Mrs. Kocmoud has never been to St. Louis," I said aloud. "Never again will I be ruled by Lee or bested by G.E.!" I loved that my motto rhymed. "And no TV dinner for me tonight. It's Kentucky Fried or die!" Those lines didn't quite rhyme but had a nice ring. Just a few hundred miles from home, and already I was discovering new talents.

After feasting on extra crispy and a Coke, I decided that a brief vacation would probably cure whatever ailed me. I checked into the St. Louis Holiday Inn. But as I drifted toward sleep, the audacity of my dastardly deed began to sink in. Why wasn't I home playing 'This Little Piggy' with Mark, listening to Larry describe the life cycle of a flea, yelling at Bill to lower the hi-fi's volume, and watching Linda iron her hair?

When I finally fell asleep, cute burros, men in colorful sombreros, and children eating sumptuous Taco Bell feasts danced through my dreams. On awakening I remembered my mother's tidbits about her trip to Mexico. "The Mexicans eat tacos instead of hamburgers," she had said. "The men ride burros and wear big hats."

I had pressed her for more details, but she had shaken her head. "To know Mexico," she said, "you've got to smell it yourself."

According to my map, that odor was a mere one thousand miles away.

As one town melted into the next, I rehearsed what I would say to Lee when I returned. "Every housewife deserves a vacation once every seventeen years, as I'm sure even Mrs. Kocmoud knows."

It cost twenty-five cents and all of my courage to drive onto the Laredo, Texas, International Bridge. As I crossed the Rio Grande, the bridge suddenly felt like a lifeline. Only runaway wives can know the fabulous feeling of crossing the flow below and setting rubber onto foreign concrete.

I crowed with delight. I had flown my peanut-butter-and-jelly coop and landed in hot tamale heaven!

A tangle of antique jalopies and newish American cars hiccuped along the narrow streets of Nuevo Laredo. The traffic lurched forward in a giant wave, only to screech to a halt a few inches later. At each intersection, horns shrieked and blared as drivers fought to gain a hair's edge lead in a race that seemed to be going everywhere and nowhere.

Amid the hustling, bustling car chaos, I felt more like one of Peter's little lost boys than a bold adventurer, and a wave of uncertainty swept over me. For the first time in as long as I could remember, no one was telling me how to drive, what to do, how to be. I slammed the car door on those thoughts and joined the pedestrian hubbub.

Outside the many rainbow-colored buildings selling jewelry and electronics, dressed-to-the-teeth tourists window-shopped while beggars with haunted eyes hovered at their elbows, hoping for handouts.

Street vendors hailed me in broken English to stop, look, and buy. Runny-nosed urchins, some who looked to be about four-years old, balanced two-year-old siblings on their hips while peddling tiny boxes ;of chewing gum. In an hour I bought enough to rot a beaver's teeth.

The Mexicans were obviously more touchy-feely than Americans. Parents and children, groups of teenaged girls, and even adult male friends ambled hand in hand, arm in arm, or hand on shoulder along the narrow slivers of crumbling sidewalks. Cuddly couples floated along with their arms encircling their partners' waist. When had I begun recoiling from Lee's touch? And how long had it been since Linda or Bill had let me hug them? Larry had declared himself too big to hold my hand at street crossings in first grade. In a few more years, Mark would announce that Mommy kisses contain cooties. Which meant I should be at home to receive his big drooly smacks.

But no!

I was fulfilling my lifelong dream to travel. I would stay put and have fun no matter how miserable I felt, darn it! And I needed to stay away for at least a week to make sure Lee got the point—which was, as best I could tell, that he would be better off loosening the chains than losing me forever.

Forever?

The thought made me tremble. I searched my memory for a role model—for some other woman who had traded the tried and terrible for the desperately different. Margaret Mead came to mind. I had read her book for Linda's social studies report. A publisher had bought Margaret's stories about Samoa; perhaps the *LaGrange Citizen* would buy mine about Mexico.

I took a street-side table in an outdoor café, ordered a Coke, and pulled a pen and pad from my purse.

At the next table, a Mexican couple was consuming quantities of chile like pickles—as if that were normal instead of just something to do on a dare. I wrote that down.

On the sidewalk, every post-pubescent male passerby paused to leer at me. I would bet my Maidenform bra that crummy casseroles and crumby carpets wouldn't dampen their enthusiasm for a blond-haired, green-eyed, pre-menopausal woman. I wrote that down.

Across the street, a man dragged a huge hunk of ice by a thick metal chain to a soft drink stand, where he paused to hack off a large, grimy chunk. The stand's owner paid him, chiseled off some ice slivers, plopped them into glasses, added soda, and served the drinks to his customers.

I looked at the shards in my own glass of Coke and decided I wasn't thirsty.

Once outside the café, I followed my nose around the corner to a series of open-air shops. The smoke spewing from aging vehicles leapt the curb and mingled with the mouth-watering sidewalk scents of spicy beef and fresh tropical fruit drinks. Those odors mixed with straw baskets, leather purses and belts, clay pottery, locals' perspiring underarms, and tourists' perfumed necks. The brew created a quaint if overly potent smell. I would need to write all this down.

The open-air shops ringed a huge building. When I stepped inside to explore, I crashed into a great shield of eye-watering, heart-stopping, stomach-turning Smell with a capital S. This must be what mother had meant!

I hastened back outside and paused by the entrance to recover from my breath-taking encounter with Mexico in the raw. Then I took a deep breath and plunged inside the indoor market's cavernous bowels.

When I was compelled to inhale again, the urge to flee was powerful. The fetid cologne was a potent brew of unrefrigerated meat from a thousand barnyards, fish from a thousand seas, fruit from a thousand trees, flowers from a thousand gardens, vegetables from a thousand fields, sweat from a thousand shoppers, and a thousand spices from people's gardens.

The olfactory assault was strong enough to make me wince, though the faint scents of flowers and spices somewhat softened the blow.

As my nose adapted to the smell, I was delighted to discover that my bravery had paid off. My status as a tourist attraction had suddenly disappeared. The vendors were too busy selling to notice me unless I was buying or looked like I might.

A wrinkled woman followed my gaze across her table of hand-carved curios to an onyx cat. "¡Ocho pesos!" she yelled, thrusting the figurine into my hands.

I checked my conversion card. Eight pesos was just sixty-four cents! But I'd heard that bargaining was the way to shop in Mexico, so I held up five fingers.

The woman roared as if I had struck her. She leapt from her chair, tore at her wiry hair, groaned, and doubled over as if my stingy offer had triggered an angina attack. "Go to Acapulco," she screamed in English. "Go to Taxco! Never will you find this cat for five pesos! You insult me! You insult the artisan who made it! You insult Mexico!"

Embarrassed, I looked around. Amazingly, no one was paying us heed. "I–I didn't mean to insult you," I stammered. "I don't have much money to spend. I guess I could pay—maybe six pesos?" I backed away in case she tried to bludgeon me.

"My children will starve on the streets!" she wailed. "With no money

SONNA & SONNA MARK

for medicines, my uncle will die! They will bury my mother in a pauper's grave!" Her black eyes scrutinized my face. "Sold!" she declared.

When I opened my wallet, I saw that I was out of change. My smallest bill was a ten-peso note. I hated to expose my vast wealth. "I'm sorry about your starving children, sick uncle, dead mother, and the underpaid artisan. I don't suppose you'd happen to have—um—change?" I asked.

She pulled a bulging wad of bills from the pocket of her tattered apron and graced me with a toothless grin. "You have very good bargaining ways. Like a Mexican, not a North American," she said as she handed me four pesos.

I hadn't felt so proud since I won first place in my third grade spelling bee.

At a table of used books, I bought a dusty Spanish/English dictionary. I looked up *adios* and found that it literally meant "to God." Throughout the day, strangers had been showering me with blessings. My puny hill of beans had turned into a big mound of frijoles!

As I passed a booth filled with guitars, a vendor thrust a burnished wooden beauty into my hand. "Thees one, she is beauteeful, Mees. Handmade. She makes the beauteeful music. See?" He brushed the strings and unleashed a tinny twang.

Bill had been wanting a guitar. Maybe this one just needed to be tuned. "Is it a real guitar? Or just a toy?" I asked.

"Thees guitar, she ees for the maestros, Mees! I give you special price." He eyed me sharply. "Six hundred pesos."

A great bargain! But did I dare spend forty-eight dollars? "I guess not, Señor. But *gracias*." I forced the guitar back into his arms and walked away.

"One *momento*, Mees," he said, following me down the aisle. "Today

I make special price for pretty lady. Price only for today, OK? Five hundred pesos."

But Bill loved rock music, so he probably wanted an electric guitar. I shook my head. "*No, gracias,*" I said.

"OK. Just four hundred pesos. A geeft from my country to your country, Mees."

I declined and walked away, but the vendor followed me. "How much, Mees?" he asked. "Two hundred pesos? No? OK. One hundred fifty pesos!"

I spun around to face him. "But that's just twelve dollars! It must be a toy!"

"*No comprendo.* What, Mees?"

"You said the maestros play guitars like this. You lied to me!"

He knit his brow.

"I wanted a real guitar, not a toy."

He scratched his head.

"This guitar is too cheap!" I exclaimed.

"OK! *No problema,* Mees. Don't worry, I raise the price."

A table of brightly colored flamenco dresses at another booth caught my eye. What a great souvenir for my dancer daughter! Well, maybe a lovely costume would rekindle my ex-dancer daughter's interest in the soft shoe. I bargained the vendor's initial fifteen-peso asking price down to seven pesos. Shopping at the market was definitely more fun than K-Mart!

Overall, Nuevo Laredo was smelly enough to make my eyes water, poor enough to make me want to cry, and dirty enough to put the fear of typhoid into me. When I got back to the car, I wrote all of that down. I'd heard that border towns attract the worst elements of two countries without giving the true flavor of either, so I decided to throw pesos to the wind and drive south. Lee could wire me money for gas if he wanted me back. And if he didn't?

I decided to save that thought for tomorrow.

By the time I pulled into the Saltillo Holiday Inn that night, I was brain-dead from exhaustion. The clerk at the front desk was sound asleep. After awakening him, we conversed in sign language. I began by clicking my fingers to wake him up. I pointed to him and then to myself, gave an exaggerated yawn, and pointed to the rooms behind me.

Instead of handing me a registration card, the young señor smiled broadly, exposing a gleaming set of ivory choppers. Then he nodded and leap-frogged over the counter. "*Sí, Señorita. ¡Sí!*" he said happily. He picked up my suitcase and ushered me down the hall.

The room looked exactly like the St. Louis Holiday Inn. It had the same beige bedspread, the same Formica bureau, even the same seascape print hanging near the same lamp.

When the clerk closed the curtains and turned down the bedspread, I calculated how much to tip for such attentive service. When he began helping me out of my clothes, I reduced his tip to a slap on the face. Apparently my sign language had gained something in the translation.

Although I did my best to frown while showing him to the door, the unadulterated adulation of Mexican males tickled my ego. I hadn't felt so attractive since—how long had it been? At least twenty-seven stretch marks and several dozen applications of Clairol ago.

But there was no rest for the weary. In a tortured dream that seemed to last all night, I relived the actual, blow-by-blow horrors of an incident that had happened back when I had served as a Brownie leader.

The dream began with my promise to take Linda's troop on a picnic to a nearby park. Mrs. Kocmoud contacted the Girl Scout office to point out that I lacked the required credential to lead a wilderness expedition. During the subsequent investigation, I assured the scout administrator that the traffic sounds and smog penetrated the entirety of Bemus Woods, so its status as "wilderness" was suspect. The scouting administrator remained adamant. I either had to pass the required fire-building course or cancel the outing.

During the course's final exam, I had used up an entire box of matches without generating enough heat to toast a marshmallow, much less to warm the required wiener. When I waved my perfect hot dog stick at the teacher to impress him with my whittling talent, my frigid hot dog broke free, catapulted into my cold fire pit, and scattered my tidy pile of tee-peed twigs. When they collapsed, the Kleenex I'd surreptitiously tucked inside to boost the flickers was exposed. The instructor gasped on glimpsing my illegal kindling.

"Isn't it terrible the way some people litter?" I had clucked while retrieving the singed tissue. "I want to reassure you, Professor, that you can in good conscience pass me. My attempt to cheat failed, so you can't accuse me of a crime I couldn't manage to commit. Additionally, if I can't get the charcoal going in the Bemus Woods' grill, the girls can snack on potato chips to stave off starvation during the five-minute hike to a restaurant."

A circling fly, which was far more attracted to the instructor's breath than I (he'd been grading wieners all morning), landed on his lip. I offered him a stick of sugar-free Trident gum in hopes of brown-nosing my way to a D. He accepted the gum but failed me anyway.

I awoke from my nightmare in a pool of sweat, with the image of Linda's tearful face still before me. Canceling that picnic had broken six little Brownie hearts. Linda still brought up this when listing my past crimes.

I was drifting back to sleep when a strange sensation overcame me. The room felt somehow askew, off balance, out of kilter. I sat up and peered anxiously into the darkness. I sensed the presence of something distinctly un-American in the room. I turned on the bedside lamp and looked around but didn't see anything amiss. I decided to check the bathroom and solved the mystery the minute my toes touched Mexican tile instead of carpeting.

There was no need for vacuums on this side of the border! I caressed the cool floor with my tootsies before lying back down. Faster than I could say, "¡*Viva Mexico!*" I fell asleep.

CHAPTER 4

EXPLORING NEVERLAND

"Logic is in the eyes of the logician."

— *Gloria Steinem*

I awoke in Saltillo's Holiday Inn, refreshed and ready to explore my Mexican Neverland. Surely fantastic adventures were lurking in every barrio, mine for the taking. Maybe I'd meet a tall, dark, handsome adventure!

I quickly banished that frivolous thought so as not to lose sight of my new plan: I needed to gather enough tantalizing tidbits to convince Fred Tuttle, the publisher of the Citizen newspapers, to buy my travel articles.

Saltillo turned out to be a spruced up, toned down, squeaky-clean version of Nuevo Laredo, as if the city fathers had plied the border town with tranquilizers, given it a face lift, and transported it south. Saltillo bustled without as much hustle as its northern neighbor. The street vendors waited for business instead of ambushing it.

Or so it was until I ambled across the central plaza and a tall, unkempt, very brawny man suddenly planted himself in front of me. He carried a beat-up, breadbasket-sized metal box from which two frayed chords dangled.

He raised his index finger. *"Un peso,"* he began.

I didn't understand the rest, but I didn't care to donate if he was begging or pay the eight-cent U.S. equivalent for whatever he was selling. *"No, gracias,"* I replied.

But the persistent vendor or beggar didn't budge. I stepped to the side and tried to walk around him, but he moved at the same time. We spent an awkward moment two-stepping before I extracted a coin from my purse, handed it to him, and tried to walk on.

The man pocketed the peso but instead of stepping aside, he thrust a wire into each of my hands and patted them to let me know I was to hold on. Then he pressed the red button on his metal box.

I felt a sudden hair-curling, spine-jangling wallop of a jolt, heard my strangled roar as if from far away, and willed my spasming hands to drop the wires. When I was finally able to let go, I glared at the horrible man who had tried to electrocute me in the middle of town in broad daylight.

His smile dissolved, and he hastened to mime an explanation. He pointed at the box, pulled up his shirtsleeves, and flexed his hefty biceps. Next he rippled his meaty triceps while pointing to the box and smiling. Then he pinched the drooping flesh on my upper arm and frowned.

Apparently he had zapped his way to a better physique and had intended to tighten my flab. Finally, he pulled at his crotch and nodded enthusiastically to indicate that even that muscle could be electrically toned.

I nodded curtly and walked on, but my heart was singing. If someone could make a living by zapping, business opportunities in Mexico must be unlimited!

Suddenly anything seemed possible. The chains anchoring me to Lee felt a bit looser.

A large sign with a picture of a telephone and the word *Telefónica* caught my eye. I entered the storefront, wrote my mother's phone number on a form, paid the clerk an exorbitant sum, and joined the crowd waiting on rickety metal folding chairs. A long hour later, the clerk called my name, raised four fingers, and I entered booth Number Four.

I lifted the phone's heavy black receiver and heard Linda's faint voice behind noisy, insistent static.

"Can you hear me?" I asked.

"Is that you, Mom?"

There was a loud hiss, crackle, and pop. And then silence.

I pantomimed the problem to the clerk. She mimed that I'd have to pay again to call again. I decided to try from elsewhere later.

Outside the *Telefónica*, a poster next to an aging Greyhound bus advertised guided tours of Saltillo. I jumped aboard and joined the sweating crowd of Americans inside. Judging from their sunburned hairless pates and parts, they had been overdosing on Mexican sunshine.

As the bus began bumping down the cobblestone street, I struck up a conversation with a blue-haired woman and her gray-haired husband from Iowa. "How do you like Mexico?" I shouted above the grinding gears, shrieking brakes, and coughing engine.

Mrs. Iowa mopped her brow. "It's wonderful," she said, "if a bit too hot. The hotel accommodations leave a lot to be desired, though the ceiling fans are a cute touch. Still, they should have installed air conditioners."

"I like the Holiday Inn. It has lovely floor tiles."

"Do the clerks speak English?" the husband asked.

"Not even sign language."

"That's the problem," he groused. "If Mexicans want our business, they should learn English."

His wife looked a bit green from so much bouncing and jostling. "They should cement over these cobblestones," she said. "And why did they build the streets so narrow? Good gracious!" She clenched her dentures, and the entire crew of sightseers gasped as the bus's front tires leapt the curb and headed straight for the side of an office building!

The brush strokes in the adobe facade filled the windshield before the driver spun the steering wheel and completed the hairpin turn.

"The biggest problem with Mexico is the food," Mr. Iowa said. "I'd give anything for a regular American meal—pizza, spaghetti, or chow mein. I'm all taco-ed out."

"We do love Mexico," his wife added. "It's just that we'd like it better if it were more, well…"

"More like America?" I asked.

They nodded.

As we toured museums, cathedrals, forts, and statues by squinting through the grimy bus windows, I toyed with the possibility of working as a physical anthropologist. Surely those museums held enough broken pot pieces to land me an assistant professorship at DuPage Junior College. I'd just need to learn enough Spanish to decipher the placards.

While I tried to fathom a future for myself, the corn-belt couple worried about less esoteric problems. "When are we going to make a pit stop?" Mr. Iowa blustered.

I also felt cranky after spending hours cooped up inside the ancient vehicle, which seemed to belch as much smoke into the aisle as onto the street. At least, I assumed the foul odor emanated from the engine. American digestive systems being as they are, it was hard to know for sure. My new Iowa friends, Henrietta and James Collins, glanced over their shoulders whenever a puff of fetid air wafted in our direction, deflecting suspicion toward the back of the bus.

Apparently some of our tourists had eaten on the street before hearing our tour guide's lecture. He warned us about consuming snacks containing dangerous microbes that could lead to our demise, though not necessarily physically. Apparently the Mexican bug made the afflicted pray for a quick transition to the hereafter but rarely provided transportation there.

The Collins were nice enough people, but when they frowned at beggar children, held their noses outside the native market, and induced the driver to stop so they could shop at the local Woolworth store, I saw them for what they were: tourists. They oohed and aahed over the picture postcard vistas on the outskirts of town while I filled my pad with notes about the climate and topography.

Worse, their flashy Mexican sandals, giant sombreros, and cactus-patterned shirts made them as obtrusive as cockroaches in an American kitchen. Every time they disembarked from the bus, the locals gaped at them.

My red flamenco outfit was drawing a lot of attention, too, but donning the souvenir dress I'd purchased for Linda, to hopefully reignite her love of dance, had been a necessity. I was out of clean clothes. At least, that's what I told myself.

In my heart I knew that by wearing the flamenco dress in public, I had crossed the line from a bit peculiar to brazenly bizarre, but I felt entitled to indulge this looniness. After all, I had just walked out on everything I knew and loved, plus everything I didn't. I was on the rebound, not from love but from my life.

When our guide released us for a short break, Henrietta and I stared uncertainly at the *Damas* and *Caballeros* signs on the restrooms' doors. "Why don't they just write Ladies and Gentlemen?" Henrietta asked. "Do you think they are trying to trick us?"

The literal translation of these terms, according to my dictionary, was "Dames" and "Horseback Riders." I chuckled as a distinct visual image presented itself. I would need to investigate further to learn whether these strange designations described the natives' sexual behavior.

After finishing in the *Damas* room, the line of tour-group ladies waiting to do their business was long. I went outside and collared natives for woman-on-the-street interviews to add a little local color to my research. After a few fruitless attempts at conversation, I found an

English-speaking taco vendor.

"How do you like living and working in Mexico?" I inquired.

Glad for the chance to practice his English, he chatted amiably. When I had won his trust, I unleashed my inner investigative reporter and sought revealing answers to tough questions. "Have you ever considered moving to the land of milk and honey to pick grapes?" I asked. "Do you have plans to become a wetback?"

The man proved long on hot sauce but short on answers. He kept trying to sell me a taco, going so far as to offer me a free sample with my choice of *cabeza*, *mejilla*, or *lengua*, which my dictionary translated as head, cheek, and tongue. I strove to contain my grimace when declining.

I was still waiting for the rest of my tour group to finish the restroom break when a tremendous din broke out from an approaching city bus. At least twenty men were howling and wailing while leaning so far out of the windows, a small pothole or street bump could easily tumble someone to the ground.

The men drummed frantically on the bus's metal frame, which jerked to a stop in front of me. The men clawed at the smooth exterior for non-existent handholds. By some miracle, no one fell out. As they regained their balance, the frantic drumming and wrenching wails resumed.

I couldn't guess what drove their frenzied SOS. Had the bus been hijacked and its passengers kidnapped? Was a bandito holding them at gunpoint?

Looking around, I wondered how their compatriots on the sidewalk could ignore the desperados' deafening din. Wasn't there a single Good Samaritan in the whole Catholic crowd?

As I debated what to do, about twenty pairs of beseeching eyes riveted onto the only person who was paying them heed: me. If I spoke

Spanish or could operate a pay phone, I would call the police. Given the circumstances, there was only one decent thing to do.

I took a deep breath and stepped toward the bus, ready to break down the door and free the captives from whatever torture they were being subjected to. If they were prisoners en route to the quarries, I would embarrass myself; but I didn't question the wisdom of meddling in a foreign country's affairs. I slid into my role as the world's watchdog as if my American heritage had bred me for it. Which it had.

On seeing their savior approach, the clatter of fists on metal stopped. Great, ear-splitting whistles filled the air as the men heralded my arrival by blowing through their teeth.

"What's the matter?" I called out.

The men began beating on the bus again, but now in the slow, coordinated rhythm of a death march. Obviously their situation was truly grim. A man at the nearest window called out, "*¡Por favor!* Please, Mees!" Two friends lowered him from the window by his ankles until he was dangling upside down at my eye level.

"What is it?" I asked.

The man's handlers were having trouble managing his weight. He dipped to the level of my chest and swung like a pendulum. "Speak!" I exclaimed. "Before they drop you!"

"Eet ees thees, Mees, that breaks my heart. Your *chi-chis.*"

"My what?"

"Your *chi-chis.* Your beauteeful knockers!"

My knockers? I finally got the message. Worse, I got the whole picture. My face turned red as the light turned green. As the bus lurched forward, I hoped his friends would lose their grip and drop him on his smart-alecky head.

I noticed a small brown leather lump at my feet and stooped to pick it up. "Oh, Mister!" I called, waving the wallet above my head. "It is this that breaks my heart: that a man would pay such a price to compliment a lady!'"

"*¡Ay!* Mees!" he wailed, extending his arms out the window.

Even for an experienced T-ball pitcher mom like me, I knew my lob wouldn't reach home plate. I reached into my blouse, placed the wallet between my beautiful knockers, and blew the man a dramatic farewell kiss.

Then I examined the tattered wallet's contents. There was no money or identification, only a black and white photo of the scrawny man with his plump wife and seven children. In losing his wallet, the shameless married flirt got what he deserved.

At that moment, the lessons of the Bay of Pigs, Viet Nam, and Chile were driven home to me. I suddenly sympathized with all the American presidents who had tried to right a foreign wrong, only to end up with egg on their interventionist faces. Why, I wondered, did the U.S. keep trying to save the world, only to discover time and again that it didn't need saving?

But politics was beside the point. What mattered was whether Mexico could save me.

When our tour bus disgorged the passengers for the midday meal, I sat at a table with my Iowa friends. I soon regretted my decision. While waiting to be served, they not-very-surreptitiously pried their Mexican sandals from their swollen feet and rubbed them on the tile floor to cool their blisters and bunions.

Even before our waiter handed out menus, I knew what they would order: *hamburguesas* (hamburgers), *papas fritas* (fried potatoes), *agua purificada* (purified water), and *Coca-Cola* (Coca-Cola).

I, on the other hand, was ready to broaden my culinary horizons with an authentic Mexican meal. I couldn't read the menu, so I let my fingers do the walking. When my food arrived and I surveyed the unsavory assortment, I realized that the hunt-and-point method hadn't quite worked. My waiter brought me chicken rice soup without the broth *(sopa de pollo)*, lumps of some sort of meat in icky sauce *(mole a la poblana)*, raw eggs *(huevos a la natural)*, and gaseous water *(agua con gas)*. The latter tasted like club soda, so I was at least able to quench my thirst. When requesting a refill, I asked the waiter to bring the water and hold the gas, but his English wasn't up to it.

Henrietta and James spent the meal longing for corn-fed Iowa beef and philosophizing about the problems of the Mexican nation, which could be solved by placing a jar of French's mustard and Heinz Piccalilli on every restaurant table. My meal was terrible, but at least I hadn't had to cook, spar with Lee while eating it, or pull the plug on Mr. Ed to get a kid to carry out a KP assignment.

When I finished my fare-thee-wells to my compatriots at the tour's end, I worried about what to do next. Already a pattern was developing: everything was fine as long as I was busy; between activities, a voice in my head shouted, "What in heaven's name are you doing? You can't support four children on your own. You should be at home, working things out with Lee!"

Since no new activities presented themselves to drown out the disturbing thoughts, I became somewhat nervous about my situation. After reviewing my last journal entry, "Few trees, many cacti; data suggest arid climate," I lost confidence. My money was running out. No matter how loath I was to sell out to crass commercialism, I needed a job. Or I needed to go home.

Home.

For a moment I thought my congealed tears might melt. Suddenly I missed the smell of dirty diapers. The sight of Linda's unmade bed and messy room. The sound of Bill's blaring rock music. The crunch of Mark's cereal beneath my feet when I staggered down the hall at night to whisk nightmares from Larry's mind so he would stop yelling.

I longed to curl up on the sofa with the kids and a bowl of greasy popcorn to watch a Batman rerun. And Lee?

I couldn't stand being his wife, but what was the alternative? A couple of years back, when Lee had correctly guessed that I wanted out of the marriage, he had declared that I wouldn't make it on my own. Did he really believe I couldn't? Or was he afraid I could?

I pictured myself walking through the door of our blond brick home and being greeted by Lee's terrible tirade, which would end with a question, "And if the neighbors find out about your little trip, what will they say?"

I shivered at the thought. But then I remembered the words of my second favorite philosopher, Rhett Butler: "Frankly, my dear, I don't give a damn."

Any tears that might have exited their ducts slid back into my sockets. My courage bucked up, propelling me forward.

I folded myself back into the car and headed south.

CHAPTER 5

DESTINY CALLS

"Sanity is madness put to good uses."

— *George Santayana*

It was nighttime when I nosed the Mercury up the narrow streets of the small mountain town of San Miguel de Allende. I stopped at the first hotel I could find, pried my stiffened fingers from the steering wheel, staggered inside, pantomimed my need for a room but not a roommate, and collapsed into bed.

My body was ready to rest, but my mind refused to drop into dreamland. A crazed cacophony of church bells chimed midnight, as if to remind me that I was out of tomorrows. If I didn't start for home in the morning, I'd have to push the car north.

And then what? To leave Lee, I'd have to find a job. To land an interview, I would need a lobbyist to advocate for me. I couldn't ask Diane to help after the recent fiasco.

At the very least, I'd need references. Would Frances Tornow be willing to provide one? We were friends, but as the senior editor of the *Citizen Newspapers*, she sometimes had trouble with my creativity—like when my hard-nosed investigative journalism had uncovered the information that Lee's favorite housewife, Mrs. Kocmoud, would be in charge of the elementary school carnival's popcorn booth. Mrs. Kocmoud had a reputation for being overly harsh when disciplining her poor children, so in my article I had described her as the school carnival's "head popper." My pun drew chuckles from my PTA, Brownie, and Boy Scout leader friends, but an anonymous ingrate called the paper to complain. Frances had insisted I stick to straight reporting, but time and again, the temptation to use my funny bone to tickle readers got the best of me.

All of my other friends were full-time mothers. I didn't know anyone else I could ask for a job lead, much less a reference. I had years of experience and was an expert at washing dishes, serving meals, cleaning house, and caring for kids. Besides the lack of pay, the other problem was no prospects for advancement. The only way up was out.

After breakfast the next morning, I walked to the central plaza to peek at San Miguel de Allende's world-renowned cathedral.

I was expecting pretty or appealing, but no. With its garish pink façade and sweeping spires, the gothic monstrosity was a perfect replica of Walt Disney's cartoon castle. I carefully scrutinized the bizarre building, but Tinkerbell was nowhere to be seen. In the courtyard out front, churchgoers chatted cheerfully, apparently not put off by a mad architect's grand gothic joke. I wished the people in my world weren't put off by my little modern ones.

On my way back to the hotel, I stepped inside the *Instituto Allende* to explore. Bunches of flyers and announcements had been tacked to a tree doubling as the school's bulletin board. Most of the notes were in English; and most had been penned by students seeking roommates, tutors, and textbooks. One note writer was looking for transportation to an upcoming peyote party. A three-by-five inch notecard caught my attention:

> ENGLISH TEACHER IS WANTED. DEGREE NO IS NECESSARY. EXPERIENCE NO IS NECESSARY. SPANISH NO IS NECESSARY. CALL FOR FURTHER INFORMATION IF IS NECESSARY.

I fit the job description perfectly! Destiny was calling; I knew I should call back. I managed to use a pay phone. A secretary scheduled my interview to start in fifteen minutes.

When I walked into the office and said, "Good afternoon" in perfect English, Señor Osio recognized my qualifications and hired me on the spot!

"I attended school for over a dozen years," I said. "So I obviously have a ton of classroom experience. Nevertheless, because I am so exceptionally conscientious, I would be interested in attending a workshop or course about being on the other side of the teacher's desk. Should you hear of one, please let me know."

"I will give the training to you in this instant," Señor Osio said. He handed me a textbook. "You tell to the students, 'Open the books to the Page One.' "

"I can do that."

Instead of continuing, he sat in silence.

"And then?" I asked.

Suddenly suspicious, he peered at me over his reading glasses. "Then you tell to the students, 'Go to the Page Two.' "

"I can do that," I said, adding a confident smile.

"Now I give to you your orientation." He extracted a scrap of paper from his desk drawer and proceeded to draw bunches of little lines, big arrows, and squiggles. "I give to you this map for you to find the *Instituto Norteamericano de Estudios Bilingües.*"

"What does that mean?"

"The North American Institute of the Bilingual Studies. You report to Irapuato."

"Is that my boss?"

"No. It is the town where is my new school. I have already one school in Toluca." He pointed to his little map. "Irapuato is one hour to west of the town of San Miguel, more or less. One hour to south of the city of Guanajuato, more or less. Three hundred fifty kilometers to north of Mexico City, more or less. Also, do you know how to write on machine?"

"Type? Yes. I do newspaper page layouts and paste-ups, too.

"Good. My schools are for the preparation of the bilingual secretaries. Can you write short?"

"Shorthand? I took a course in high school."

"Good. Can you write the business letters?"

"I wrote a cover letter when I applied for a marketing research position. I was going to write one to General Electric's customer service department, but—"

"Good. You will teach the English, the typing, the shorthand, and the business letters."

"How many teachers work there?"

"One."

"Just me and the principal?"

"Do you have any experience with the disciplining of the students?"

"I have four children."

"Experience communicating with parents?"

I decided not to mention my seventeen years trying to talk to Lee, but I mentioned my PTA membership.

"Experience with the administering?"

When he heard about my Brownie and den mother activities, he made me the school's principal and director, and added another sixty pesos to my weekly salary!

That was five dollars more, according to my conversion chart. "It sounds wonderful, Señor Osio. Can I support four children on this income? I will need a babysitter for my youngest child."

The phone rang. Señor Osio nodded, though it wasn't clear whether he was issuing an affirmation or a dismissal.

I waited a long while for his telephone conversation to end and then rose to find a restroom. He waved good-bye, so the interview was obviously over.

I floated back to the car. In less than an hour, I'd gone from runaway housewife to English professor, principal, and director of an institution of higher education. Instead of just a brief foreign vacation, I would live abroad! I'd been handed a whole new life on a platter, and this one was silver, or at least ceramic. Best of all, I'd be free of Lee!

It took me just a few minutes to check out of the hotel and jump into the car. I couldn't wait to get back to LaGrange to collect the kids and start my new life.

CHAPTER 6

A STAR IS BORN

*"If you can't control your peanut butter,
you can't expect to control your life."*

– Bill Waterson

Linda stared at me in disbelief. "Move to Mexico? You've got to be kidding. What about college?"

Of course she needed to graduate with her Lyons Township high school class, take two summer courses at the local junior college and attend the University of Illinois in the fall as planned. She could visit Irapuato during her university vacations.

Bill acted as if I were asking him to give up his tie-dye shirts and don ironed blue jeans without holes or frayed hems. "Live in Mexico?" he said. "No way."

"But just consider the advantages." I hadn't seen Irapuato, so I could only guess. "Unlimited burro rides!" I ad-libbed.

He didn't dignify Advantage Number One with a response.

"A chance to learn to play the marimba!"

"The what?"

"It's a Latin American musical instrument, kind of like a xylophone."

Or was the marimba a dance?

He rolled his eyes.

"A top-of-the-line, handmade Mexican guitar, like the maestros play, costs just twelve dollars. You can take lessons."

Bill tossed his head to clear his long, brown bangs from his eyes. "Huh?"

A spark of interest! "And then you can join a mariachi band and learn the classic Mexican songs. The singers are great, but the instrumentals are kind of strident, because each band member tunes his instrument separately by ear instead of everyone tuning to the same note."

"You're kidding! That must sound awful."

"I prefer to think of it as quaint. All of the mariachi songs sound the same to my American ears, just as all Beatle songs sound the same to my mother ears. But as a mariachi, you'll get to wear a giant sombrero with spangles and a sparkly tux."

He rolled his eyes and resumed leafing through *Mad Magazine.*

I shouldn't have said "tux" to a teen. He might refuse to move now, but he wouldn't do well without me at home to hold Lee at bay. I was confident that Bill would change his mind and join us later.

As I was packing, Lee stormed into the bedroom. "I forbid you to leave!" he announced, introducing the scene I'd been dreading.

"I'm sorry, Lee, but your days of ordering me around are officially over."

"You won't leave without Larry and Mark. If they stay, you'll stay."

"But they're not staying."

"We'll see what a judge has to say about that!"

Surely a court wouldn't prevent a mother from leaving home with her children? Though technically, I supposed they might be considered half Lee's.

He began to pace. "I fixed the vacuum. What more do you want?"

"The vacuum is just one small part of a much bigger problem."

"OK, have it your way. I'll buy you a new one, an upright or another canister. Take your pick."

I laughed before realizing he was serious! "I'm past the point where you can sweet-talk me into staying," I said.

"You're not going, and that's final. I'll get a court order to keep Larry and Mark here. Or at least in the U.S."

I added a pair of shoes to my suitcase, willing my hands to stop shaking. How to convince him that a separation was best for both of us? The way to a man's heart was via his stomach. Perhaps a special dinner would convince him.

Lee remained silent while sawing away at the blackened crust of his macaroni casserole with his plastic knife. When he finished eating, he did the unthinkable: he carried his paper plate, cup, and napkin to the trash.

Suddenly I was terrified. If he would go to such an extreme length to hold onto me, what other desperate act might he commit? I dared not wait to find out.

After Lee left for work the next day, I jotted a note telling Linda and Bill that I looked forward to them joining us soon. Then I put Larry, Mark, and the suitcases in the car and drove south.

Larry and Mark didn't grieve for their father and siblings. Or if they did, I was too busy counting telephone poles to stave off thoughts about the past, too busy telling them about my newfound Neverland to notice any trickling tears.

I knew Lee would miss me for a time, or the me he wished I would be. But I doubted he would miss the children. He had shown a bit of interest in them as infants, but as soon as they had learned to say "no" he declared them "brats." After that, he pretended they didn't exist, and any reminder that they did enraged him.

I was sure Lee would be happier without us. He'd find a special woman who didn't mind hellacious halitosis or foot fungus, and who liked king-of-the-castle tyrants. Someday he would tie a knot with the next Mrs. Sonna, and they would walk off into the Chicago smog to live miserably ever after. Because Lee was such an accomplished killjoy, unremitting misery would be his version of happily-ever-after.

As for me, instead of languishing in the vacant theater of my life, I would play a lead in a juicy Mexican drama. With Larry and Mark cast in supporting roles, Linda making cameo appearances, and Bill waiting in the wings to join our troupe, I was bound to be a star.

CHAPTER 7

SPANISH LESSONS

"Pendejo [pen-day'-ho], n., m. 1. Hair over the pubis and groin."

— *Velázquez Spanish and English Dictionary*

Larry and I practiced Spanish during the one thousand seven hundred-mile drive from LaGrange to Irapuato. I hadn't learned much in my lone high school course twenty years previously but had subsequently picked up some of the language on my own. By the time we arrived at the border, we could say *buenos días, adios, adobe, bravo, matador, tortilla,* Chiquita Banana, and Old El Paso Taco Sauce so fast it made our heads spin.

Larry had been reading since age two, so when car crankiness set in, I handed him the Spanish/English dictionary. He spent hours poring over it between restroom breaks!

Meanwhile, our chatter jump-started Mark's English. When he was thirsty, he pointed to the canteen and said his first full sentence: "Wa-wa, Batman!"

When the boys napped, I contemplated my future as a professor. I saw myself standing at the classroom podium like a modern Socrates, tossing pearls of wisdom to my adoring disciples. They would record my words in shorthand, type my gems into their lecture notes, and laugh at my jokes. They would be eternally grateful when I elucidated the mysterious intricacies of business correspondence and office memos.

On arriving in Irapuato, I followed Señor Osio's napkin squiggles to the *Instituto.* I paused in front of its battered wooden door and crumbling façade, and then pulled back into traffic to apartment hunt.

A few blocks away, under a large sign that said *Doctor Responsable,* a hand-written note taped to the window said, *Se Renta Apartamento.* That looked suspiciously like "Rent Apartment." I parked and went inside to check.

The handsome, middle-aged, white-coated man behind the pharmacy counter didn't speak English, so I pointed to the note. After a quick tour of the furnished apartment next door, I took out my wallet. He wrote a number on a scrap of paper, and I checked my conversion chart. The price was definitely doable. I paid him. Mission accomplished! We had a home!

But as I began unloading the suitcases, I grew uneasy. I had assumed the quoted price was for a month. If I had only paid for a week, we would soon be living in the car. Once again, Scarlett O'Hare came to my rescue. I decided to save all rent worries for seven tomorrows from today.

While arranging the boys' clothes in a bureau, someone knocked on our front door. Outside stood a poorly dressed, four-foot eight-inch woman with large dark eyes, dark chocolate skin, a long mass of wavy black hair, and an upper row of large buckteeth. While I stared and wondered how to proceed, Larry stepped forward and said, *"Hola."*

"Buenas tardes," she replied.

My genius child had completed an entire conversation in Spanish!

All we gleaned from the woman's subsequent stream of Spanish was her first name: Francesca. Once we had established the impossibility of conversing, she began a self-guided walking tour of our apartment, peeking into each room while I trailed behind her in helpless dismay.

When she arrived at the kitchen, she walked in, picked up a dishrag, pointed to a glass in the sink, and looked at me with raised eyebrows.

I didn't need a maid, but I did need a babysitter. I pointed to Mark and nodded enthusiastically.

She wet the dishrag and began washing Mark's face.

She was sort of on the right track, so I held out my wallet, and she took out some money. I glanced at my watch. If I hurried, I could check out the Instituto and return in an hour. So I nodded, smiled, and waved good-bye.

Francesca waved good-bye and took Mark's hand. As I was retrieving my car keys and purse, Francesca walked him out the front door, closing it behind them.

"What is going on?" I wondered aloud.

Larry chuckled. "I think you just sold Mark."

"Oh my God!"

After they were safely back inside, I looked up the words for "baby," "sit," and "here" in the dictionary. "¡Niño sentar aquí!" I told Francesca.

After several repetitions, Francesca picked Mark up and sat him on the floor at my feet.

I switched to "sit baby" by exclaiming, "¡Sentar niño!"

After several repetitions, Francesca tried to sit on Mark.

"I won't be gone long," I told Larry. "Don't let either of them out of your sight."

Like the outside of the *Instituto's* building, the inside had seen better days. Its front wooden door opened near a room with peeling paint and a dilapidated wooden bench. I guessed it was the waiting room.

The next small room held a dilapidated wooden desk, which contained a

SONNA & SONNA MARK

cash box and some registration forms. So this must be my office.

The next small room contained two dozen aging student desks, a blackboard, and a battered metal bookcase. I was delighted to see *Gregg's Shorthand* emblazoned on the red book spines. When I pulled a copy off the shelf, I recognized the cover. This was the very same textbook I had used in high school! But when I flipped through the pages, they were filled with inscrutable squiggles and Spanish words.

Why had I thought I could teach shorthand, or even English for that matter? I would stand at the blackboard like a dolt, while teenagers hurled incomprehensible insults at me, and I wouldn't be able even to reprimand them. I could send the kids who misbehaved to the principal, but that was me.

Could a deaf mute handle this job? If not, what would become of us? At least Lee had kept a roof over our—

"No!" I interrupted myself, slamming the mental door on my doubts until later. The thoughts awaiting my attention until tomorrow were piling up fast.

In the next classroom, a dozen antique Smith Corona typewriters squatted on small rusting metal tables. Two or three chairs were crammed in front of each one. Did that mean one student typed while a classmate or two watched?

The last classroom contained two-dozen aging student desks, a worm-eaten teacher's desk, a blackboard, and a shelf of tattered English/Spanish dictionaries. The teacher's desk drawers didn't even have essentials like chalk or an eraser. Señor Osio was running the school on a shoestring!

When I returned to the office, several mothers had squeezed onto the waiting room bench. When they saw me, they smiled and extended their hands to shake mine. That was very good!

None of them spoke any English. That was very bad!

After exchanging smiles and names, they wagged their tongues at me for a while. I gave them registration forms, but they left without enrolling their children. If the school failed, I would be out of a job and back in the States faster than I could say "welfare."

When I arrived home two hours later, Francesca pointed to my wallet. I held it open, and she extracted the equivalent of two dollars and departed. At a dollar an hour, that was about double the cost for a babysitter in the U.S.!

I slumped onto the sofa. We couldn't survive if I had to spend half of my monthly income on a babysitter. But as I was changing Mark's diaper, Francesca returned with bags of groceries and change! She then proceeded to cook dinner, wash the dishes, bathe Mark, and tuck both boys into bed.

I checked the babysitting problem off my mental list, but on her way out the door she rubbed two fingers together and pointed to my purse. I strove to steady my trembling hands as she extracted some coins. The many sudden drops and precipitous inclines on this emotional roller coaster were exhausting. But when I saw how little she had taken, I hugged her. Apparently the cost of a full-time sitter and maid was about two dollars per day!

Now our survival depended on enrolling some students. I worked on my marketing campaign until the wee hours of the night.

"Spanish no is necessary," Señor Osio insisted when I phoned him in San Miguel de Allende the next morning.

That was my cue! I began my speech about the usefulness of clerical support personnel. Señor Osio displayed a glimmer of interest in Benefit Number Three, "Getting Parents to Pay the Tuition." He said that I was welcome to hire a bilingual school secretary and pay her out of my salary.

I spent the rest of the morning looking up the Spanish words for "cheapskate," "miser," and "stinker" in preparation for our next conversation.

I also looked up *pendejo*, which I'd heard Mexican men mumble under their breath or exclaim loudly during heated discussions. The dictionary defined *pendejo* as a "pubic hair"—definitely a five-star insult! But Señor Osio was safe. I couldn't insult the only pubic hair in the country to consider me worthy of a paycheck.

I dealt with the mothers trickling into the *Instituto* that morning by smiling and handing out registration forms. Hopefully they would complete and return them with the tuition money soon. At lunchtime I closed the office early and headed off to hunt down a school for Larry.

In the public school's second grade classroom, fifty ragged waifs chatted, laughed, and bounced around the room while the teacher sat at her desk reading a book.

In the private Catholic school's second grade classroom, sixty boys wiggled and whispered at their desks. Although the monk was relaxing at the teacher's desk, his classroom was far more controlled. Learning would be possible if he decided to teach. The tuition was pricy, but this was an essential expense. I wrote a check.

On rising the next morning, I was shining as if my life depended upon it. When Francesca arrived, I showed off my new-and-improved attitude. First I nodded and smiled to let her know that I agreed wholeheartedly with whatever she was saying, and then I shrugged helplessly to let her know that I had no idea what I had just agreed to and was at her mercy. On my way out the door, I gave her a sweet, friendly smile in the hopes that she would take good care of Mark and wouldn't steal all the belongings of her sweet, friendly boss.

En route to Larry's school, I strove to combat his new-school jitters by slathering him with doses of my phony-as-heck courage. "Everything will be fine," I repeated again and again to try to convince him as well as me. Meanwhile, I mentally inventoried our food supplies to calculate how long we might last if the *Instituto* folded before it opened.

At the *Colegio Pedro Martínez*, I found Larry's classroom and introduced him to his monk. As I turned to leave, I was too preoccupied to issue the traditional maternal hug and admonishment to be a good boy. Without thinking, I slapped him on the shoulder and blurted, "Give 'em hell, Son."

Larry's shocked look got my full attention. I glanced nervously at his teacher, but fortunately the monk hadn't comprehended my English profanity. Before I could figure out how to transform my "buck up, Buddy" injunction into wise words of motherly advice, Larry's face relaxed. "You, too, Batman!" he said, returning my shoulder slap. "Give 'em hell!"

At the *Instituto* I smiled and nodded until each mother's or couple's prattle petered out. Then I handed over a registration form and pen, pointed to the tuition cost, and held out my hand. A few parents paid! By week's end I had perfected my pantomime, and the cashbox was filling up.

My Marcel Marceau pantomime worked well in person, but I couldn't adapt it to the telephone. Each attempted conversation ended with me apologizing, *"Perdón. No hablo español,"* and hanging up. But my lack of phone fluency apparently reassured callers that their kids would learn English at my school, if only by osmosis, because more parents arrived to watch my mime and pay. Still, my stomach continued to knot every time the telephone rang, until I solved that problem with some Yankee ingenuity: I kept the receiver off the hook whenever I was there.

By the end of the following week, I had enough students to put two or three at each typewriter. I hoped Señor Osio wouldn't eliminate my five-dollar director's salary once classes began. I decided to create a marketing plan to sell him on the idea of letting me keep that job—as soon as I figured out what directors did the rest of the year.

I need not have worried. During our next phone call, Señor Osio assigned me more tasks. "Your next duty as the director is to do a meeting with the parents to bolster the school spirit."

"*¡No problema!*" I told him. "Faster than you can say 'parent/teacher association,' the Instituto will have one. Faster than you can say 'fundraiser,' our PTA will be holding car washes, carnivals, and garage sales. Perhaps we can use the profits to repaint the classrooms. Hot pink would be nice."

"Hot? No, we cannot risk to burn a student. And garage sales? I do not understand. The PTAs in the United States sell the garages?"

Some things lose a little in the translation; some lose a lot.

Señor Osio continued, "The students must develop the good attitude for the school."

"The PTA can sponsor a pep rally," I suggested.

"Yes, rally their pep! We will do this with the school uniforms. The students will wear the gray skirt, the gray socks, the white blouse, and the red sweater. And the gray pants for the boys."

"Do the parents know where to buy uniforms?"

"My new company will fabricate them and will deliver them to the *Instituto*. To pay for these clothes, I will do you the favor of taking the money from your paycheck. Then, when the parents pay, you can keep the money."

This was the man for whom the word *pendejo* had been invented.

Fortunately, the parents paid promptly. Pricy uniforms, I learned later, cost less than the kind of wardrobe fashion-conscious teens and young adults require. And for some unknown reason, the students were proud of the drab, shapeless clothing.

The best solution to any problem, I always believed, is the one that makes everyone smile. The uniforms had the parents grinning, the students beaming, and Señor Osio laughing all the way to the *banco*. To rally my pep, I began adding a small fee as compensation for my time and trouble. When no one objected, I increased my charge. Soon I was smiling, too.

CHAPTER 8

PASS THE BREAST

*"It is a cheering thought to think that god is
on the side of the best digestion."*

– *Donald Marquis*

The *Instituto's* enrollment bulged to the point that I hired two additional teachers, Señora Carrera and Terry Aldredt. I continued to handle the administrative and school uniform duties as well as teach. More students and teachers meant more administrative work, which meant that I deserved a raise.

Señor Osio wasn't receptive to the idea. Rather than hold a grudge against my superior, I decided to take personal responsibility for solving my problem. My school uniform handling fee had worked out well, so I tacked an administrative fee onto each student textbook. And *voilà!* Problem solved.

While doing paperwork in the office one morning, I noticed that something was wrong with the silence. It hovered over the *Instituto* like a thick blanket, unruffled by the usual student murmurs, foot shuffles, and paper rustles. When I went out to see what was happening, every classroom was empty—the entire student body and the teachers had disappeared!

I found Terry Aldredt on the patio, sipping a soda and reading a book. "Where is everyone?" I asked.

"They left. I guess they went home."

"What? Why?"

"Maridél went from room to room with your announcement, that you had declared a school holiday."

"WHAT?" Whenever there was trouble involving more than one student, Maridél was the ringleader.

"A holiday in honor of—"

I hurried outside and spotted a cluster of red sweaters down the block. A crowd of curious pedestrians and motorists had created a jam of sidewalk and car traffic as they paused and craned their necks to peek at my uniformed truants.

On approaching I saw that the *Instituto* students had encircled a marimba band.

An inner ring composed of naughty ne'er-do-wells gyrated to the xylophone music in an ecstasy of adolescent abandon.

The students in the middle ring egged on the dancers by clapping, hooting, and shrieking.

The students in the outer ring wore uncertain smiles and cast guilty glances over their shoulders.

When the outer-ring girls saw me coming, they sounded the alarm. The dancing, shrieking, and clapping stopped by the time I reached the group.

I strode into the center of the circle. "*¡Silencio!*" I yelled as the marimba band blared on. "I demand to know—"

Before I could finish my sentence, Maridél gave a signal, and the band began an exceptionally loud rendition of *Las Mañanitas,* the Mexican

Happy Birthday song. The students joined arms in their respective circles, swaying as they serenaded me.

"It's not my birthday!" I protested, but the din drowned out my words. I glared at Maridél, who gave me the "Gotcha!" grin as she and her followers belted out verse after verse… after verse… after verse. As they neared the end of what must be the longest song in the history of music, a van swerved from its lane and screeched to a stop at the curb.

A reporter jumped out, notebook in hand. "*¿Qué pasa?*" he asked.

"It's the birthday of our dear director," Maridél replied. "We are honoring her with a small fiesta."

I grabbed the reporter's arm to stop him from taking notes. "*¡No, no es mi* birthday!" I stammered.

He shrugged apologetically. Between my poor Spanish, the raucous music, and the street noise, he couldn't understand what I was saying.

When *Las Mañanitas* finally ended, the band switched to Happy Birthday, and the students serenaded me in English. I waited impatiently for the final note and prepared to chastise the group. I would threaten to call their parents if they pulled a similar stunt ever again. But when the song ended, Maridél planted a kiss on my forehead, and the reporter's light bulb flashed before I could speak.

I shooed the students back into the *Instituto* and summoned Maridél into my office. I was livid. "You know perfectly well it's not my birthday!"

"*¿No?*" Maridél extricated a mirror and tube of lipstick from her purse, and began adding color to her ruby lips.

"You are in big trouble, Señorita!"

She blotted her lips with a tissue.

"And all of your classmates are in trouble because of you."

"Oh?" she asked.

"As the instigator, your punishment is… Well, I'll tell you tomorrow. You can spend tonight worrying about what it will be."

I don't know how Maridél fared, but I spent a sleepless night wondering how to punish a student for giving me a birthday party.

The next morning the picture of Maridél kissing my cheek appeared on the front page of the newspaper under the headline, "*Instituto* Honors School Director at Street Party." That's when I had my answer. I couldn't punish Maridél or any of the other students.

"Once again, Maridél will get off scot-free," I complained to Larry. "Otherwise, I wouldn't put it past her to contact the paper with an update. The next headline would be, '*Instituto* Ingrate Punishes Students for Birthday Party' or some such."

Larry was studying the back of the cereal box. "Maridél, the Student from Hell," he intoned.

"Larry! I may hope she ends up there, but that's not nice to say."

"You tell me to ignore kids who bother me, Mom. You should take your own advice."

"Teachers can't just ignore students."

"My teachers do."

"They do what?"

"They ignore the students."

I had supposed that the monks kept kids in line by ordering up lightning bolts from the Heavenly Head Honcho. "Then how are you learning so much?" I asked.

"I sit in the back and read the *World Book Encyclopedia*. That was the best gift Linda ever sent us. I'm on *Volume A*. Ask me about anything that starts with 'aa.' Ask me about aardvarks."

As Larry relayed facts about the ugly critters, I formulated a new disciplinary strategy. That very morning I announced to the students that I would begin teaching as soon as they quieted down. Then I sat at my desk and waited. A week later the students were doing each other's nails and make-up, and I was memorizing the conjugations of Spanish irregular verbs.

When I described my new classroom woes in a letter to Linda, she replied that punishing students actually caused more behavior problems than they solved. Instead, progressive U.S. schools dealt with misbehaving students by ignoring them.

"This classical conditioning technique developed by Pavlov," Linda wrote, "has been proven effective for extinguishing unwanted behavior."

Thus assured that I was using a cutting-edge U.S. educational method that had already been adopted at Larry's prestigious private school, I felt no qualms about ignoring my *Instituto students.*

Meanwhile, my nemesis in the north had devised a new method to try to control my behavior, as Linda informed me in another letter.

> *Dear Mom,*
>
> *Dad filed for a legal separation, and the judge awarded him temporary custody of Larry and Mark.*
>
> *Now Dad can have you charged with kidnapping. He said he will press charges if you don't go back to him, and that if I cared about his welfare, I would give him your address so he can bring Larry and Mark home, because then you will return, too. I think his custody move was just a ploy to get you back.*
>
> *But I do worry about the boys being in Mexico. I'm sure they would be better off in the U.S. Have you thought about returning?*
>
> *Missing You!*
>
> *Linda*

A chill ran up my spine. Was she worried enough to give Lee our address? Our phone number? I immediately penned a reply.

> *Dearest Daughter,*
>
> *Mark and Larry are fine in Mexico! They watch as many cartoons in Irapuato as in LaGrange, albeit in Spanish. We eat mostly Mexican food, but I shore up their diets with regular infusions of*

U.S. peanut butter, candy bars, and Gansitos, the Mexican version of Twinkies.

I confess that Mexican chocolates aren't up to American standards, and that Gansitos are stuffed with jam instead of whipped cream. But when we go to the border, I immediately take the boys to McDonalds, Burger King, and to a pizza parlor.

Larry and Mark also have all the inessentials at home: a TV set, a record player, a radio, an electric organ, a dozen battery-operated toys, and enough board games from the U.S. to stock a toy store.

Irapuato has enough people and cars for the boys to acquire a proper appreciation for city crowds and traffic gridlock. And rest assured that the monks teaching at Larry's private school use cutting-edge educational methods with the students. There's no need to worry about his academics.

Come visit! Larry will share what he's learned about aardvarks, and you can chat in Spanish and English with Mark, your bilingual baby brother!

Hugs & Kisses,
Mom

In my spare time during school and in the evenings, I applied Larry's encyclopedia technique to conquering Spanish. I started on Page One of the Spanish/English dictionary and began memorizing all of the words.

Cramming my head with nouns, verbs, adjectives, and adverbs also helped stave off loneliness for Linda and Bill while crowding out thoughts about the bridges I'd burned to my past. Shortly after I reached the letter B, Bill arrived on our doorstep.

My heart thumped with joy. "*¡Bienvenido!* Welcome! What a wonderful surprise! I'm shocked that Lee let you come."

"He didn't exactly let me. I couldn't take the old man any more."

"But he gave you money for the bus ticket? I'm surprised he'd let a young teenager travel so far alone."

"I didn't tell him where I was going." He stuck out his thumb.

My little boy had hitchhiked two thousand miles!

I reached out for a hug, but Bill thwarted my embrace by fussing with his army-style duffel and a guitar case. Nevertheless, I got close enough to smell him. The clean-cut, fourteen-year-old lad I'd left in LaGrange had become a stinky, lanky adolescent with shoulder-length, matted hair. He needed a bath and, as I soon discovered, better manners.

I wasn't sure whether Bill's surly, sassy attitude stemmed from age or anger. To find out, I tucked Larry and Mark into bed, made a giant bowl of popcorn, and joined Bill on the sofa in the living room. "Here," I said, handing him the bowl. "Have some *palomitas*."

He reached for a fistful of kernels with his grimy hand.

I managed to stick to my cutting-edge behavioral management technique by pretending not to notice. "*Palomitas* is my favorite Spanish word," I said. "Palomas are doves. Tacking *-ito* or *-ita* onto the end of a word adds the meaning of "cute" or "little." So each popcorn kernel is a cute little dove. Isn't that sweet?"

Bill humphed.

He obviously wasn't up for small talk. I supposed we needed to have The Conversation. "I know the family breakup has been hard for you," I began. "But in time, we'll all be better off."

"Oh? Mark and Larry will be better off as spics?"

"Bill!" I exclaimed. That language obviously came from the Big Bad Bigot back in LaGrange. I rose and went to bed.

The next day Bill's behavior was even worse. He responded to my requests to hang up his wet towel and turn down the hi-fi with threats to return to LaGrange. To ease tensions and convince him to stay, I decided to wow him with the local wonders. The problem was, there weren't any.

If beauty is in the eye of the beholder, the blind might appreciate Irapuato. For those with decent vision, it was harder. There was a notable absence of streams, mountains, shores, and trees. A dreary desert skirted our 175,000 inhabitants' urban sprawl.

"But," I noted when I took Bill out for an impromptu welcome wagon tour, "as deserts go, Irapuato's is quite lush. It receives just the right amount of rain for growing…well…" I pointed to a thriving clump of weeds. "As you can see. Crab grass."

"Boring," Bill intoned.

"And strawberries! The fields are outside of town."

He yawned.

Undaunted, I explained how Irapuato had transformed itself from the sleepy Indian village of bygone days into a polluted metropolis. "Legend has it that an Indian was munching on strawberries and spitting out the seeds while walking along a sandy path. The seeds sprouted, took root, and grew. I cannot attest to the truth of this fascinating story, since I cannot imagine why, much less how, anyone would spit out strawberry seeds. But the fact remains that the surrounding desert is full of strawberry fields. We can go for a look-see, if you'd like."

He didn't like.

"But Irapuato is the strawberry capital of the world."

He rolled his eyes.

"Those juicy bites of sunshine form the basis of the city's entire economy. Most every strawberry you've eaten in your entire life came from Irapuato. Did you know that?"

"Nope."

"Aren't you glad you know now?"

"Nope."

He wasn't into topography or commerce. Perhaps sociology? I pointed out how the locals walked arm in arm, hand in hand, or hand on shoulder, including mothers with sons, fathers with daughters, sisters with brothers, and friends of all ages.

"Looks like a bunch of queers."

Lee's terse conversational style and parochial vision had obviously been warping our son. That made it even more imperative that I win the LaGrange-versus-Irapuato competition. "Irapuato's plaza may not have mountains, flowers, or statues like other Mexican towns," I said. "Admittedly, our plaza looks like an empty parking lot. But if you return on Sunday afternoon for the major social event of the week, this expanse of cement will be brimming with people."

"What's up on Sundays?"

A spark of interest! A full sentence! Was his sulking at an end? "While the adults gossip and the younger kids play, the teenaged boys walk clockwise, two and three abreast, around the perimeter of the plaza. Meanwhile, the teenaged girls walk counterclockwise, two and three abreast, in a somewhat smaller circle. The teens flirt as they pass one another, and some pair off. The couples then walk clockwise, arm in arm or hand in hand, in an even smaller circle near the center."

"So?"

"So then there are three circles instead of two."

"The boys go one way, the girls go the other, and the couples walk together in the same direction as the boys? Wow. Fascinating." He gave a noisy fake yawn.

"Arm in arm, Bill! The couples walk arm in arm!"

"No shit."

"WHAT DID YOU SAY?"

"I mean, wow, Dude."

"Don't you think that's pretty racy for a Catholic country?"

"Practically lewd."

"Forget it. Well, the next stop on my tour is Woolworths."

He gave me the teenaged eyeball roll.

"But imagine a five-and-dime store in Mexico! Do you remember

Kresge's in LaGrange? Irapuato's Woolworths has a real soda fountain."

"No sh–. I mean, far out."

"Of course, some items cost more than a dime. But Woolworths carries socks, four pairs for ten pesos. That's less than a dollar."

Bill gave a long, low whistle. "Cheap socks!"

He was acting like a *pendejo*, but I wasn't going to give him an excuse to head back north. If he left, I might feel compelled to follow to save him from his father or from himself. I wracked my mind for something that would appeal to an American teen. "I know! How about if we 'check out,' as you say, the movies."

"Groovy."

After checking the placards outside the cinema, Bill said that the films also looked boring.

"But the Hollywood reruns are dubbed in Spanish, Bill. Though some just have Spanish subtitles."

"So?"

"Imagine Julie Andrews opening her mouth to sing, and out comes somebody else's voice singing in Spanish! It's a hoot! I don't mind seeing Mary Poppins again if you're interested."

"Nope."

"Do know how to say 'supercalifragilisticexpialidocious' in Spanish?"

"Nope."

"*Supercalifragilisticoexpialidoso.* Isn't that funny?"

He rolled his eyes.

When Linda had entered adolescence, my mother had reassured me that "Sooner or later, almost every teenager turns into a civilized human." Now the word "almost" worried me.

We passed a restaurant spewing the delicious scent of smoky meat into the street. A window placard advertised *cabrito asado.* Maybe a juicy prime rib dinner would achieve what a four-hour cultural encounter with Strawberry City had not.

Bill snorted. "Eat in that dive? You must be kidding."

"Card tables and folding chairs plastered with Coca-Cola logos can be deceiving. Some of the best restaurants in Mexico are furnished like this."

After being seated, I checked the dictionary and uncovered the shocking news that *cabra* meant "goat" and *asado* meant "roasted."

"Would you like some cute little kid for supper, Bill?" I asked.

"You said prime rib."

"I didn't say prime rib of what. I thought goats were just at kiddy zoos. But they're probably great with tortillas." I hoped.

"What are my choices?" he asked.

"You can order *pierna*. That would be goat leg, Bill," I said with a smug smile. I'd learned the word for leg from the chicken vendors at the local market. "Or you can have *pechuga*." I checked the dictionary. "Hmmm… it says *pechuga* is 'breast.' " Was *chi-chis* a slang term? Had I been ordering chicken knockers at the market?

Bill snickered. "Breast sounds good to me!"

"Of a GOAT, Bill. Like a chicken breast." My adolescent would send me to an early grave even if the goat didn't. "Or you can have *machitos*, which are…" I thumbed through the dictionary. The closest word I could find was *macho*, defined as "masculinity." And of course *ito* was a diminutive suffix. "How interesting," I marveled aloud. "I didn't know people eat a goat's cute little masculinity!"

"What in the world!" Bill exclaimed.

"I'm probably misunderstanding."

"Ask the waiter. If he points to his crotch, order something else."

I signaled for service and pointed to the menu. "*¿Qué es?*" I asked.

The waiter answered in English. "Well, Señora, how I explain? They are of the boy goat, not the girl goat. You want I bring you a pair?"

"No! We'll take an order of *pierna*, an order of *pechuga*, and two Coca-Colas."

When he left Bill asked, "What happened? The waiter didn't blush, but you did."

"I don't wish to discuss this further."

Bill smiled. "You look kind of queasy. I'll bet I know what's wrong. You're afraid the cook will switch the order as a practical joke, right? Or as vengeance? The gringos stole a hunk of their country, and the chefs serve us goat balls as revenge?"

"Enough!" I said. "I'm not finding this conversation particularly funny."

But I couldn't cast out the seed of doubt planted by my trying teen. When the waiter approached with heaping platters of goat something-or-others, I lost my appetite. "Let's just go home," I suggested. "I can fix you a special snack that has staved off rickets and malnutrition while we've been mastering Spanish. Have you ever tried tortillas and peanut butter?"

"Nope."

"Then you must. It's the specialty of the casa, *chez moi.*"

"Sounds about as appetizing as roasted goat balls."

"Bill!"

"You know, Mom, Dad's really bent out of shape about Larry and Mark living down here. So is Linda. Dad's hassling her for your address."

"Oh?" I asked, trying to sound disinterested even as my heart picked up speed until it was hammering at my chest.

"Maybe if Linda knew about the great things about Irapuato, she'd be OK with them living in Mexico. You know, like being able to hear Mary Poppins say 'supercalifragilisticexpialidocious' in Spanish, to buy cheap socks, and to eat goat balls, maybe..."

Bill was suddenly distracted. I followed his gaze to a svelte señorita at the next table, and then I did a double take. It was none other than my least favorite student, Maridél! She smiled and blew me an exaggerated kiss. I had to put up with her haughty glares and uppity stares at school, but I wasn't about to tolerate her sarcasm after hours. If looks could kill, the one I shot her should have sent her straight to the hereafter.

"Gee, Mom. Is that how you treat your students?" He locked eyes with the young miss. She primped and smiled flirtatiously. "How do you say, 'I'll try anything once' in Spanish?" he asked.

"Why in the world do you want to say that, Bill?"

"Because I couldn't help but notice that girl's *pechugas*, like on a CHICKEN, Mom. Her *piernas* aren't bad, either. Those are LEGS, like on a GOAT. I guess this town isn't so bad after all. Some of the sights make my *machitos* tingle. *Machitos*, like on a—"

"Enough! I get the picture."

"Don't freak out! If I'm going to live here, I need to practice Spanish, right?"

He was planning to stay! And he was speaking in compound sentences instead of in humphs and grunts, even if I didn't like what he had to say. "Let's go home, Bill," I said. "You've learned enough Spanish for one day."

He snuck a peek at Maridél. "Aww, Mom," he whined. "Do we have to?" He sounded more like his baby brother than the father he had been trying to emulate since he arrived.

"Yes, let's go. We can drop by the plaza after church on Sunday, and perhaps that pretty señorita will be there. If you walk the laps with the boys, you can see her on each trip around the square. Maybe you two will decide to walk arm in arm. That's not quite as good as an American orgy, but—"

"Arm in arm? No way! I'd be too embarrassed."

"Embarrassed?"

"Somebody might see me. And what if she turned me down?"

I didn't want Bill to get involved with my nemesis, but I knew better than to fan the Romeo-and-Juliet flames by attempting to smother adolescent embers. "I know what you mean, Dude. But like, what if she agreed? Wouldn't that be groovy, Man?"

Bill's face pinked, and he hunched his shoulders as if wishing he could disappear.

"I could invite Maridél over for a genuine American meal if you'd like."

He shook his head. "You said we were going home, so let's just go." He stood up and headed for the door.

I trailed after him, blowing an exaggerated kiss in Maridél's direction as I passed her table. She had the gall to smile, as if my air-borne kiss were affectionate rather than sarcastic. She really was a cool cookie. Besting her was going to be a *very* big challenge.

CHAPTER 9

THE PORCELAIN CHALICE

*"If at first you don't succeed, try, try, again. Then quit.
There's no use being a damn fool about it."*

— *W.C. Fields*

To win the hand of a mythical king's daughter in days of yore, noble adventurers sallied off in quest of a golden chalice. Along the way they had to slay some fire-spitting dragons.

When modern travelers visit a foreign country, most of our adventures are like life itself, which can be incredibly petty and insufferably banal. The chalice we covet is porcelain. The royalty we seek to appease are Lady Bladder and Lord Bowel. The dragons we must vanquish are the maddening maze of cultural quirks that send travelers with less hardy systems fleeing for home.

No knighthood awaits us at the finish line, either, or king to bestow a happily-ever-after reward. After locating a toilet, I felt relieved but not especially enriched or ennobled by my accomplishment.

I wish I could say that while fighting the battle of the Mexican bathroom, I came to appreciate this cultural challenge. But no. I continued to prefer the American way of flushing.

Our landlord first introduced me to Mexican plumbing. He lived above his pharmacy, which was cluttered with mysterious hand-packaged herbs and elixirs. The sign said, *"Doctor Responsable,"* so I assumed that Responsable was the doctor's last name. I didn't dawn on me until years after I became adept at Spanish that the literal translation was "responsible doctor," which referred to his character.

After Bill moved in with us, the water shortage in our apartment became intolerable. I suspected the landlord was limiting our supply as a money-saving maneuver. I knocked on his door and tried to beg for an increase in our daily quota.

He walked me back to my apartment, led me to the bathroom, gestured at our bathroom fixtures, and wagged a warning finger at me. *"No hay mucho agua,"* he said.

I flashed him the smile I used whenever I had no idea what someone was saying. *"¡No hay mucho agua!"* I repeated.

He must have caught the blankness behind my friendly frozen smile, because he switched to charades. First, he squeezed his thumb and index finger together.

"Small!" I exclaimed.

He nodded. He either understood some English or had concluded from my confident tone that I was on the right track. Next, he pointed under the sink. *"Tubos,"* he said.

"Copper?" I guessed.

He shook his head.

"Tubes?"

He nodded. Then he pretended to hobble on a cane.

"Grandmother? Grandfather? Old woman? Old man?" I guessed. "Old!"

He put his finger on his nose.

"So far we've got 'small tubes, old tubes.' "

He held up ten fingers, paused, and then flashed his hands at me twelve times.

I did the math and came up with one hundred twenty.

Then he crawled around on the floor, mooing like a cow. Next he pretended to milk a cow. Finally, he poured imaginary milk into imaginary jugs.

I finally put it all together. The small tubes under the sink—make that the pipes—were small and old. They only dispensed one hundred twenty jugs of milk. He must have meant gallons of water.

The next round was harder. I eventually understood "He who loses it carelessly didn't deserve it in the first place." The light bulb in my head finally flipped on. "Waste not, want not!" I said.

He marked a point on an imaginary chalkboard and departed.

At dinner that night, I studied the bottle of milk and began to wonder. Had Dr. Responsable meant one hundred twenty gallons of water, or liters?

"How many liters make a gallon, Larry?"

"About four."

"You're only in second grade. How do you know about liters—or about gallons, for that matter?"

"I'm a genius," he answered simply.

I patted his light brown hair. At least Mexico hadn't damaged his self-confidence, though given his smarter-than-everybody attitude, I wasn't sure that was a benefit.

I pictured a gallon of milk and mentally multiplied the quantity by thirty. What a tremendous amount of milk! I put the idea of a water shortage out of my mind.

But later that night, when the water ran out while Larry was bathing, I learned that milk lasts longer. "You should have told us what Dr. Responsable said!" Larry said as shampoo dripped into his eyes, and I explained that thirty gallons of milk lasts for over half a year. He wasn't enough of a genius to follow my logic. "What are you going to do about the toilet?" he demanded, as if I could conjure water.

"The more important question, boys, is what we can learn from this cultural experience," I said. "Every story has its moral, and that must be true of this one, too. In fact, there must be several good lessons for such a dramatic story."

"Such as?" Larry asked.

"Well, Lesson Number One: we must ration water."

Larry looked at me expectantly.

"Well, do you understand Lesson Number One?"

He nodded.

"That's the most important moral to this particular story. If you remember Lesson One, you'll automatically grasp Lesson Two."

After testing the faucets and failing to get another drop to drip, I rinsed Larry's head with our expensive bottled drinking water.

We soon mastered the art of bathing in two inches of water. We didn't waste, but we continued to want. More worrisome than the water shortage was what Linda would say if she found out that her brothers were being deprived of American comforts. I hoped I could solve the problem before she arrived for her spring break visit.

Our water shortage reached a crisis shortly after Bill arrived. He along with Mark, Larry, and I suffered four cases of Montezuma's Revenge at the same time.

During my Saltillo bus tour, the guide had explained that tourists contract this abominable abdominal malady because of an ancient curse. Long before the Pilgrims were munching turkey up in Plymouth Rock, Hernán Cortés had hosted the first European cruise to Mexico. The Aztecs welcomed the light-skinned Spanish visitors as gods, but soon the bargaining over the natives' golden trinkets turned nasty. The tribe's head honcho, Montezuma, decided the tourists had overstayed their welcome, and he ordered them to drop their souvenirs and leave the continent. In the ensuing fracas, Cortés and his small tour group brought ten million locals to their heels with a few guns and a case of smallpox. To avenge the bio-terrorism, Montezuma placed a curse on the intestines of every party pooper present, as well as all future visitors. The dysentery's nickname had survived through the centuries: Montezuma's Revenge, AKA *turista*.

Now, in modern-day Irapuato, I was facing the ominous truth that thirty gallons of water wouldn't be enough for one stricken tourist to get well, much less four. I suggested we limit our flushing to once every four toilet uses.

"That's gross," Bill said.

Larry was against my plan, too. "Improper hygiene will make us sicker!"

That seemed pretty advanced for a second grader. "Hygiene?" I asked. "Are you up to *Volume H*?"

"I don't need to read the encyclopedia to know about common-sense disease prevention."

"Well, consider how unhygienic this bathroom will be if we run out of water before we run out of the runs." I giggled at my word play.

Because I was the mother and they were the children, Bill and Larry insisted that it was my job to come up with more water. My mission impossible was to find a way to convince the commode to keep flushing throughout the night.

I had never looked inside a toilet tank before. I half-expected Mr. Clean to emerge from the murky depths and assault me with his ammonia crystals. But there was nothing scary or disgusting inside, just a small chain, a rubber stopper, a floating bulb, a few tubes and gadgets, and clean water.

I used the toilet, flushed, jumped up, and studied the goings-on inside the tank.

My observation resulted in a hypothesis, which I tested with an experiment. I pulled the short chain, and it lifted the red rubber stopper, which covered a hole in the tank's bottom. Water escaped from the hole and filled the toilet bowl. When I released the little chain, the rubber stopper covered the hole and stopped the flow of water.

"Come here!" I called. "See what I found in the toilet!"

After a pause, Bill called back, "That's *gross!*"

"I mean, I found a solution. Come!"

Bill and Larry joined me in the bathroom.

"Don't flush if you do Number One," I said. "If you go Number Two, pull the chain inside the tank just long enough to rinse the toilet bowl."

"Great," Bill said. "Can we like, go back to bed now?"

"First I want to be sure that you two comprehend some important lessons."

They nodded wearily.

"Number One: The human brain has an amazing capacity for original thought. Properly used, our minds can subjugate modern technology and bend it to our will."

"Great," Bill said. So what's Lesson Number Two?"

"Number Two? Well, don't forget Number One, and you'll do fine with Number Two."

"Sure, Mom," Larry intoned.

Their attitude of ingratitude soon changed. Whenever nature called, the boys awakened me from my fitful slumber and induced me to rise by appealing to my pride. "Mother, *please*," Larry and Bill said time and again. "You're so good at subjugating the toilet."

Not only was the water shortage a problem, but our hot water shortage made our water shortage seem worse. After all, if you're not going to have water, wouldn't you rather it be hot? After being left in the cold several times, I set aside a chilly weekend afternoon to unravel the mysteries of the water heater.

The instructions engraved on the side of the tank said "Danger!" in

TORTILLAS & PEANUT BUTTER

four languages. The rest were in Spanish, so I resorted to tinkering. I pulled a little metal handle, and a small door near the bottom of the tank popped open. Inside was a flame about the size of a birthday cake candle. The fire was obviously too small.

Larry paused at the bathroom door. "Way to go, Josephine!" he cheered. Like his siblings, he was always delighted to see me up to my elbows in a domestic endeavor.

I gritted my teeth. "To heat all this water, we need more fuel. Maybe charcoal."

Larry's face darkened. "Sure, Mom. Blowing up the house would fix everything."

I didn't like his sarcasm. "And the moral to the story is, 'If at first you don't succeed—' "

"Try, try again." He yawned noisily.

"I was going to say, 'If at first you don't succeed, hang in there.' "

After Larry walked on, I pushed the little button that Dr. Responsable had instructed me to push twenty minutes before we needed hot water. I heard a whoosh and a big blue flame appeared. That little flame was just the pilot. Pushing the button started the flow of gas.

"Bill! Larry! Come here," I called. "You, too, Mark!"

They crowded into the bathroom.

"Whose turn is it to take a bath tonight?" I asked.

"Mine," Bill answered.

"And you will have plenty of hot water! All you have to do is follow a few simple steps. Number One: every time you pass by the bathroom, listen carefully. If the water heater is completely silent, push this little red button. That will start the gas so the water can heat. You, too, Mark." I showed him how.

The boys regarded me expectantly.

"So what's Number Two?" Larry asked.

"Well, does everyone understand Number One?"

"Yeah, we know, Mom," Bill said. "There is no Number Two."

"Number Two is—from now on we will have hot baths."

Bill and Larry rolled his eyes, so Mark rolled his, too.

I don't know about the boys, but I pushed the button about a dozen times that evening. Bill put a toe in his two inches of bathtub water and smiled. "I'm impressed," he said.

"It was nothing," I gloated. I touched the side of the metal tank. It was hot enough to burn my hand. I gave the button another push and left Bill to his bath.

A few minutes later, I heard a blood-curdling scream. Larry, Mark, and I ran to the bathroom. When I opened the door, clouds of steam rolled out. Bill was standing up in the tub, clutching a towel to his waist and pointing to the water heater. "It's going to explode!" he yelled.

The tank rumbled like a lava-filled volcano. Boiling water hissed and sputtered through the heater's metal joints. The heater trembled and shook as if it were about to break free of its moorings and catapult itself from its corner.

"Hurry, Mom!" Larry yelled. "Subjugate it!"

I grasped the little door's handle and burned my hand on the scorching hot metal. I pulled the plastic button we'd been pushing, and it fell out in my hand. I grabbed a wet washcloth and pulled on the metal door handle again. Inside I saw the big flame. Suddenly it disappeared. The little candle-sized flame remained, so I blew it out. It took some time for the tank to stop hissing, sputtering, and shaking.

"It's fixed!" I announced.

I thought Bill and Larry would congratulate me. But no.

"Look!" Bill said. He was shivering so hard his teeth chattered. I followed his gaze to the bathtub. His two inches of water had escaped through the leaky plug.

Larry's face was white. "You nearly killed us!" he yelled.

Suddenly Mark let out a loud howl. "Batman!" he cried, pointing at the water heater, afraid it would start shaking and making scary noises again.

"Buck up, boys. We can learn some important lessons from this," I said quickly. "Number One—"

Bill interrupted me. "The only thing worse than cold water is NO water. And there is no Number Two."

If my sons' faith in my plumbing ability was somewhat tarnished that night, it completely rusted over the next evening. I didn't think to relight the pilot before pressing the little red button (only one time) in preparation for my bath. While waiting for the water to heat, I went into the kitchen and turned on the stove. My plumbing career and three-quarters of the kitchen went up in smoke. I was unharmed except for singed eyebrows and lashes, minor finger burns, an hour-long echo in my ears, and a serious blow to my ego.

Larry surveyed the rubble with a haughty look of disgust that reminded me of his father. "How could you?" he demanded. "What will Linda say if she finds out you nearly killed us twice in two days?"

I was too young to claim senility, too smart to claim ignorance, too proud to claim dingy-ness, and too afraid of what Linda would say to argue. "All that matters is that we learn the important lessons that fate has seen fit to provide for us," I said.

"I can't wait," Bill said. He sounded like Lee.

"Yeah. Me, too," Larry growled. He sounded like Lee, too.

I'd had it with their sassiness and sarcasm. "It's this way, boys," I said. "Number One: SHIT HAPPENS! And there is no Number Two."

There was a stunned silence. "That's no way to talk in front of children!" Bill exclaimed.

Larry issued his standard threat. "I'm telling Linda what you said!"

My heart skipped a beat and my hands went clammy. But when I looked up, Bill was smiling.

"Actually, Mom," Bill said, "your bathroom references were backwards. It should be Number Two: SHIT HAPPENS! And there is no Number One. Get it?"

The three of us laughed until tears streamed from our eyes, so Mark laughed, too.

Lesson Number One for me was that I didn't have to be a conventional mom to be a good one. I was starting to grasp Lesson Number Two: perhaps it was OK to be me.

Mark pulled on my skirt. "Shit h'ppen, Batman!" he said, grinning.

Oops.

When our landlord toured our disaster area the next day, he looked and sounded like our shaking, sputtering water heater. I thought I would have to subjugate him to avoid an on-the-spot eviction. *"No problema,"* I said. Having exhausted my Spanish, I continued in English. "I don't like to cook, anyway," I said. "I could make do with a hot plate."

A few days later, maintenance workers flooded in to re-paint the hallway, bathroom, and kitchen, and to replace the stove. A few weeks later, the bills arrived, addressed to me. I took on extra classes at the *Instituto* to earn more money and began flailing about for ways to tighten our belts.

I later used my intimate knowledge of Mexican plumbing to emerge unscathed from the worst water disaster ever to strike an inland city in Mexico. But that earth-drenching catastrophe happened several years later.

In the meantime, I had other, more pressing business to attend to: honing my linguistic skills so I could communicate with the people who inhabited my world, and so I could subjugate Maridél, the *Instituto* student who had become the bane of my existence.

CHAPTER 10

BATMAN SPEAKS

"Never miss a good chance to shut up."

— *Will Rogers*

I finally learned enough Spanish to limp through the school days, but crossing the language barrier in my personal life was harder. The phrases I had memorized, such as "The fee for the course is fifty pesos," and "You can finance the school uniform for our low monthly rate or pay cash" didn't keep the party invitations rolling in. After having been voted The Girl Most Likely Never to Lose an Argument in high school, I couldn't even start one. It was a lonely time.

During my semester of high school Spanish, the teacher had said the best way to learn was to live in a foreign country. Because infants progress from miniature mutes to babbling blobs to talkative toddlers in three years, I figured that three months would be enough for me. I was wrong. My adult brain proved more handicapping than helpful.

Larry was fluent enough within a few months to correct my errors. Mark's English vocabulary quickly expanded beyond "Batman," and he was soon communing in Spanish with other little *chicos*. Meanwhile, my battle to unite my mind and tongue dragged on and on.

I fastidiously wrote verb lists and did self-assigned homework at night. I couldn't think fast enough to get the right word in the right place during a live conversation, but I could write the second person singular of the past perfect tense of any regular verb. All I needed was paper, a pen, and a lot of time. Without a social life, I had time aplenty.

I practiced Spanish with Francesca. When I asked, "*¿Cuántos años tiene usted?*" I was astonished to learn that my babysitter, cook, maid, and language tutor was not in her late forties as I had guessed. Apparently raising six children without a husband in a hovel without running water had accelerated the aging process to warp speed: she was only twenty-four! The physical hardships hadn't dulled the sparkle in her dark brown eyes or put a damper on her merriment, however. The boys loved her as much as I did.

After a few weeks in Irapuato, Bill reverted to the easy-going lad I had known in LaGrange. But when I said he needed to attend school, get a job, or pull his weight around the house, tensions between us heated up. When I directed him to pick up his messy room one morning, he packed his duffel bag, departed in a huff, and disappeared.

A month later Bill was back on my doorstep. It turned out that he had hitchhiked to LaGrange and stayed a few weeks until Lee made a similarly outrageous demand. Then Bill left and hitchhiked back to Irapuato.

Bill stayed with us for several months. An upset over the decibel level of the record player ended his third Irapuato visit. He stamped out, and I later found out that he had once again made his way back to Lee, where he lasted for a few months.

I eventually realized that Bill's sudden departures for LaGrange didn't have to do with which country he liked best, as I thought at first, or which parent he loved most, as I later feared; he was trying to hold onto both of us. He had dropped out of high school after I'd moved to Mexico and had been adrift ever since. Did I need to return to my old life for Bill to move forward with his? If so, that was a child-rearing test I would have to fail. I buried my pesky conscience by doubling my Spanish dictionary studies.

When I was on the letter M of the dictionary, Bill showed up on our doorstep once again and announced, "Dad might start dating any day now. You need to move back before he marries someone else."

His statement was so ridiculous, I laughed. "We're not even divorced yet. At least, not as far as I know."

"I just mean...I'm sure the old man would take you back in a flash. Hell, he would probably move to Irapuato if you wanted. I'm just saying you'd better do something before it's too late."

His earnest expression and pleading tone caught me up short. "I'll think about it, Son."

"Great! When?"

"Tomorrow or the day after. For sure when I finish my dictionary studies."

Fortunately he didn't ask when that might be.

"Linda thinks—"

"I get her letters! I know what your sister thinks!"

As I proceeded through the alphabet, I grew increasingly apprehensive about what might await me on the other side of Z. I feared the loneliness would be too intense for comfort. But when I reached the last page of the dictionary, I had friends and a social life. And lots more Spanish to learn. My dictionary, as it turned out, didn't include a lot of words.

Mark and Larry had to teach me that Mexican roosters don't cock-a-doodle-doo, they say *quiquiriquirí;* American hearts thump, but Mexican hearts *tic-toc.* I learned that that only English bells ding and dong; Spanish bells *tin* and *tan.* The TV taught me that cartoon combatants like Batman and Superman yell "Pow!" when punching enemies, but their Mexican counterparts yell *"¡Zas!"*

Eventually I could shoo a cat, goo at a baby, and hiss to flag down a waiter like the natives. I even became brave enough to utter accepted courtesies. I said, *"Mi casa es tu casa"* ("My house is your house") without worrying that a guest would accept my generous offer and move in with me. I responded to compliments about a new dress or blouse by saying, *"Es tuyo"* (It's yours) without worrying that I'd have to strip and hand over my outfit on the spot.

Finally I progressed beyond words to communicate with gestures. With a flick of my wrist or toss of my head, I could communicate "Hi there, Handsome," "Bye-bye, Fellah," and "Up yours, Buster."

However, I could never bring myself to answer the question, "Do you have any children?" properly. I found the hand and arm movements that accompanied the verbal answer too off-putting. Frankly, the gestures seemed gross. Mexican women responded by turning up a palm, curling the hand into a fist, and extending the middle finger skyward. Then they repeatedly jerked the hand up and down while listing each child's age, raising their hand a bit as they worked their way up from the youngest child to the eldest. The rhythmic jerks of the infamous raised middle finger looked like a faithful reenactment of how the man had planted each seed. When acquaintances asked if I had children, I kept my hands busy and just used my voice.

Despite my impressive linguistic accomplishments, conversational confusions continued to arise from time to time. When I awaited treatment for an abominable abdominal illness in Irapuato's hospital emergency room, the nurses ignored my noisy indications of distress and continued ministering to other patients. I finally climbed onto an empty gurney, and then several workers came running. But instead of discussing whether to call a priest or a doctor, they conversed about the strange noises I was making.

I searched my handy pocket dictionary for "ouch." It wasn't listed, but I found "to groan." "I am groaning," I explained in Spanish.

The nurses and aides stared at me blankly.

I looked up "to moan" and announced in Spanish, "I am moaning." No reaction.

"Oooohhhh!" I exclaimed.

They giggled.

I tried an "owwww."

A severe Mexican Nurse Ratched signaled me to get off the gurney. I feigned ignorance of her gestures. Then an English-speaking nurse arrived and ordered me back to the waiting room. I quickly described my symptoms, and she explained, "In Mexico, a dying person says, *¡Huy!* or *¡Ay!*"

"*¡Huy! ¡Ay!*" I cried.

She gasped and summoned a doctor. *El doctor* diagnosed *turista*, welcomed me to Mexico, and sent me home with a prescription.

Through the hours of my long, sleepless night, I pondered the linguistic incongruity: for a Mexican malady, *huys* and *ays* should be better pain relievers than oooohhhhs and owwwws. But they weren't.

CHAPTER 11

CONTRABAND CONFESSION

"Wickedness is always easier than virtue for it takes the short cut to everything."

— *Samuel Johnson*

Our six-month tourist visas were about to expire. I needed to turn them in to the Mexican immigration office at the border and remain in the U.S. for twenty-four hours. Then we could get new six-month visas and return home.

The prospect of such a very long road trip wasn't thrilling, but at least Mark was fully potty trained. And I would be able to stock up on American goodies at my favorite stores such as K-Mart and Target, and on American groceries at supermarkets like Kroger and the A&P. I couldn't wait to spend a day or two perusing long aisles filled with every type of consumer good imaginable and stocking up on the high-quality, low-cost brands I knew and loved!

As I was planning our trip, I received a newsy letter from Linda. Lee had filed for divorce (he really was letting go of me—hurray!). The judge had set a court date, though Linda didn't know when (but freedom was on the horizon!). Lee was asking for permanent custody of Larry and Mark and a stipulation that I couldn't take them out of Illinois.

There was a possibility that none of that was true. Linda lived in a campus dorm in Champaign-Urbana, so she hadn't actually seen any court documents. Her information about Lee's alleged legal maneuvers came during their telephone conversations. He wasn't a litigious sort, and he was so cheap I couldn't imagine he had hired a lawyer. He might have invented the story, trusting that Linda would relay it to me as part of his strategy to force my return.

Bill lived with Lee for long stretches but knew nothing about his legal affairs. Apparently several seemingly casual conversations about me had quickly escalated to violent confrontations over Bill's refusal to divulge my whereabouts. As a consequence, Bill said he had drawn strict lines around their discussions, leaving the room if Lee so much as mentioned me. He only knew that Larry, Mark and I had left LaGrange to go to Mexico, but not which city or state. For all he knew, we were in Timbuktu.

What to do about renewing our visas? If Lee had gone to the trouble of getting custody, he might have also contacted the police and pressed charges against me. If a U.S. immigration official investigated our passports, would a kidnapping charge from Illinois be revealed? If a Texas policeman stopped my car, would a check on my Illinois driver's license turn up problematic information? That was a lot of ifs.

I'd never had to present our tourist visas in Mexico, so I wasn't sure that keeping them current would matter. And if a policeman asked to see them during a traffic check, I could probably avoid a fine and deportation by paying a bribe. That was only one if.

After almost six months without access to American stores, all three of us were outgrowing our clothes, and my blue-light special withdrawal symptoms were intense. There were no ifs about that!

I decided to head north to shop.

My hand shook a bit as I handed our passports to the U.S. border marshal, but I needn't have worried. Larry, Mark, and I share last names and look a lot alike, so the official didn't doubt they were mine. And he apparently didn't think it unusual than an American mom had taken her child on a six-month trip through Mexico when he should have been in school.

I drove to my favorite U.S. stores with exceptional care. I passed several police cars but wasn't stopped.

After two delicious days of shopping, we crossed The International Bridge back into Mexico. My next challenge was to get four illegal items through Mexican customs: two humans on full display (Larry in the passenger seat; Mark stretched out in the back), and two carefully concealed jars of peanut butter (one jar of Jif crunchy style tucked behind the flashlight and Kleenex box in the glove compartment; one jar of Peter Pan creamy style wrapped in a hand towel and tucked under the front seat).

I knew the Mexican officials wouldn't question Larry and Mark's presence in my car, but I wasn't sure whether my packets of Lipton Chicken Noodle Soup and other edibles were in danger. Hopefully the hidden peanut butter was safe.

When the customs official just nodded and waved me on through, I realized I'd been holding my breath. I felt as proud of my peanut butter victory as if I'd smuggled in gold bullion.

On returning to Irapuato I learned that there had been a lot less risk than I'd imagined. Though on the U.S. side of the border I could have been taken into custody and transported to the Cook County jail if I'd been caught with the boys, my peanut butter hadn't been in jeopardy at customs. Importing wrapped food for personal consumption was perfectly legal.

That was wonderful news, because although I eventually found peanut butter for sale in Irapuato, I still preferred to import it from the U.S. The problem with Mexican peanut butter was all in the name. Roses may smell as sweet as *rosas*, but I couldn't make the mental leap from peanut butter to *mantequilla de cacahuate*. My Spanish/English dictionary defined *mantequilla* as "butter"; *de* as "of"; *caca* as "doo-doo," as in shit; and *ahuate* as "the hair of sugar cane." I might have managed to down sugar cane hair, but I couldn't bear to serve doo-doo butter to my kids or to eat butter of shit myself. So I continued to buy American.

Teresa Aldredt unwittingly planted the seed that got me into disorganized crime.

"*Ay*, Lois," she begged. "The next time you go to the United States of America, would you please bring to me a bottle of that most beautiful toilet water by Jean Pateau? The prices in Mexico are too dear for a mother supporting five children on the small salary you pay to me."

Señor Osio set the salaries, but how could I refuse? Terry was a good teacher and had become a close friend.

At the K-Mart in Brownsville, TX, the cologne Terry wanted cost five dollars a pint. At the border, the customs official looked at the receipt and said the import tax cost six dollars. Yet Terry happily paid the total, glad for the chance to smell like an American for a few weeks.

Other friends soon got wind of our transaction, and they requested that I bring them special items. As word continued to spread, the demand for U.S. goods escalated from a bother to a nuisance to an out-and-out hassle. On each trip north, I spent more time shopping to satisfy their insatiable appetite for made-in-America originals such as Revlon nail polish, Timex digital watches, Wrangler jeans, and G.E.

mix masters. Because the import taxes were so hefty, I couldn't tack on a commission for myself. However, personal items were duty free, so I began removing the store tags, tossing the receipts, and passing off the purchases as my possessions. I could then charge my friends for the import taxes and keep the money. I thought of my profits as the cost of shipping and handling.

Soon my trips to the U.S. to renew our visas seemed to be as much for my Mexican friends as for me, so it seemed reasonable that they pay my travel expenses. Besides, it was their government that required me to put in regular appearances at the border in the interest of red tape. Having to renew my visa every six months was expensive and degrading. It placed me in the same category as the weekend tourists who don't know a *torta* from a *tortilla*. (A *torta* is a ham sandwich on a *bolillo* hard roll. A *tortilla* is a flat, thin disk of stone-ground corn meal that tastes like moldy cardboard until you're addicted. At that point, *tortillas* still taste like moldy cardboard, but you have to eat them to eliminate withdrawal cravings.)

I had an ax to grind with the American bureaucrats, too. We saved the U.S. government a lot of money by living in Mexico. We didn't use U.S. libraries, schools, fire departments, courts, roads, or any of the other services funded with tax dollars. It seemed to me that America should pay me to live abroad. And by selling U.S. products to a foreign market, I was supporting the U.S. economy. Nevertheless, the feds expected me to file and pay U.S. income taxes.

Although Mexico was my beloved foster mother, I didn't want to sever ties with my mother country or alienate her IRS. Someday, I might want to live in the U.S. again. According to Linda, the U.S. government was busy linking their various and sundry computers. Someday a passport check at the border could reveal whether a citizen had failed to file taxes. For all I knew, the computers at the border could already tell.

Linda had always been a nervous child, and when she learned about my smuggling sideline, her letters became litanies of worries and warnings. In addition, she even managed to upset Bill with her doom-and-gloom predictions of disaster. When he arrived in Irapuato for a visit, he had barely dropped his duffel bag when he asked, "So how's the gun-running business these days?"

"Guns!" I exclaimed. "Never!"

"Oh. So the big money is in heroine and pot?"

"You've been watching too many movies, Bill. This isn't a seedy, underworld business populated by Mafiosos and thugs."

"Then what is this, Mom?"

"This is Mexico!"

"I'm supposed to believe the whole country is into smuggling?"

"No. Few locals could afford to travel to the border or finance the merchandise. If I paid the Mexican import taxes, and if I declared my profits on my U.S. income taxes, my business would be legal. It's not like I'm exposing Larry and Mark to a criminal element."

"Mom! YOU are the criminal element."

Had my own son said that? "Enough!" I commanded. "I do not wish to discuss this further!"

But Bill was armed for an argument. "Maybe Dad needs to come down and check things out for himself."

I hoped Bill didn't detect my shaking knees as I said, "Put this message in your duffel bag the next time you head north: I'll take Larry and Mark to visit Lee in LaGrange if he promises to return them afterwards. But he won't. His goal is to get me back. And he thinks the way to do that is to get hold of them."

Bill didn't say that my fears were unfounded, that Lee had moved on and I needed to do the same. Instead, Bill nodded.

Mark burst into the room, curtailing our discussion.

Bill lifted him into the air. "Looks like the littlest crook has grown," he said.

Mark giggled. "*Ay,* Biggest Brother! Such stuffs you are telling to me!"

Bill didn't bring up the contraband subject again. He was back living with Lee the next time Larry, Mark, and I went to the border. I packed our suitcases lightly when we went to the U.S. so we would have more room in the car for contraband on our return trip.

After a few more trips north, we only took the clothes on our backs so that our empty suitcases could hold more merchandise. To increase the likelihood of a smooth passage when crossing back into Mexico, I traveled under cloak of daylight and made it a point to arrive at the International Bridge during the height of the tourist rush, when the customs officials were too busy to search many cars. I got in line behind a hippie couple whenever possible. After the Mexican guards had spent an hour rifling through a crammed VW van to search for drugs and had finished haggling over the price of admission to the country, the officials gladly accepted a middle-class mother's small donation and waved us on through.

I didn't understand why the Mexican authorities thought hippies might try to smuggle drugs into Mexico. Wasn't everyone's goal to get them out?

Once I asked a border official why the authorities were so intent on searching for marijuana and other illicit medication. He mumbled something about keeping out transient types so they didn't become a drain on the Mexican economy. Apparently paying a big bribe proved a traveler's financial independence.

After a dozen uneventful border crossings, a barrel-bellied border guard with beady eyes and exceptionally heavy eyebrows spied the gift-wrapped box I had hidden in plain sight on the back window ledge. I was sure the box was far too conspicuous to arouse suspicion, but the Sancho Panza look-alike waddled to my car window, pointed to the box, and asked in English with only the faintest trace of a Spanish accent, "What's that?"

"Which that?" I asked.

"That that! Step out of the car."

As I hastened to obey, I felt unaccountably rattled. Maybe the bone-wearying drive and south Texas heat had undone me. Maybe it was Linda's last doom-and-gloom letter. "Sooner or later your luck will run out," my eternal pessimist had warned. "If you end up in jail, what will happen to Larry and Mark?" The answer, of course, was that the authorities would contact Lee, and he would swoop in to claim them. Once that happened, I might have to move back in with him until I could kidnap them back.

I got out of the car as instructed. "That package, Señor, is a gift, as you can clearly see. It's a birthday gift. It's for—for poor little Bobby."

The official reached around Mark in the backseat and extricated the box from the window ledge. My pulse raced as he reached for his leather holster. Instead of pulling out a gun, he extracted a giant pair of gleaming metal scissors.

"Surely you wouldn't open someone else's birthday present!" I protested.

He didn't even look at me as he slid the scissors under the ribbon.

"Shame on you!" I said. "If you want to know what's in there, just ask."

He snipped off the bow.

I switched tactics. "Better yet, come to Bobby's party," I said lightly. "It's in Irapuato this weekend. I'll draw you a map."

As per my instructions, both boys had always remained quiet and looked bored when I tangoed with a border guard. Today Mark stared out the window and yawned, clearly bored. But Larry covered his mouth, his upper torso shaking with stifled giggles.

I adopted the severest tone I could muster, hoping Sancho Panza wouldn't notice the quake in my voice as I said, "What's your name, Señor?"

"Pablo."

"Well, Pablo. Didn't your mother teach you it's impolite to spoil someone's surprise? How would you like it if someone cut the wrapping off of *your* present?"

He pulled off the ribbon.

"When is your birthday, Pablo?"

But he was not to be distracted.

Why had I started on the Bobby's-birthday-present story? It was going to be tough to connect to the box's contents. "Wait!" I shrieked. My voice was louder and shriller than I had intended. Paying a hefty bribe or tax would wipe out my profits, which would cover a month of Larry's school tuition.

I pulled myself up to my full five-foot-one-and-one-quarter-inch height and thrust out my chest. "I'm warning you, young man. Poor Bobby is suffering from—from cancer. From cancer of…" Of the what? "Cancer of the chest. Yes, he has chest cancer. This could well be his last birthday. When I asked poor Bobby what he wanted me to bring him from the U.S., he had only one wish. He didn't care about a present, *per se*. As a poor child from a poor family, he didn't want to burden me by requesting an expensive gift. Bobby said that all that mattered was that his present be wrapped in Snoopy-the-dog wrapping paper. I searched all over Texas to find it. And if you cut it, I'll, I'll…"

We eyeballed one another. If the bulge under his jacket was what I thought it was, he could have his way with all the little Snoopy dogs, and I was helpless to protect them. "If you cut that wrapping paper, I'll be sad!"

I heard a strangled chortle from Larry.

The border guard grasped the paper with his meaty hands and ripped it off. Then he opened the box and stared at my two hundred tubes of mascara. "*¡Caramba!*" he exclaimed, his eyes gleaming in anticipation of a bribe.

"Now Señor, believe it or not, those aren't for sale. I'm not planning to sell even one tube."

His hairy eyebrows curved into an arch.

"Would you believe…this is a gift for a prostitute friend?"

He shook his head, and his eyebrow hairs waved in the wind.

"Would you believe I'm a compulsive shopper who can't resist a sale?"

His brows knit at the seam above his nose.

"Of course you wouldn't, wise man that you are. The truth is, I'm a collector. I collect mascara. It's a fascinating hobby. I recently attended a convention where thousands of tubes dating back to Cleopatra's time were on display, and I was fortunate to be able to buy all of these Maybelline originals. Well, they're not terribly original, because each and every tube is slightly used, and therefore not subject to taxation."

He stared, as if considering.

"Would you believe any of the above for two hundred pesos?"

His face contorted and he snorted. As his nostrils flared, I saw that God had graced him with a bushy nose as well. Now here was a man I could relate to! I considered my ability to grow hair one of my special talents, though I weeded unwanted sprouts from my face.

"Would you believe all of the above for two hundred pesos and a free sample of mascara for your wife, mistress, or favorite friendly lady of the night?"

He agreed, but I was peeved. My mother had never said "no" to me, and she hadn't let my father or teachers say "no" to me. I had tried to continue mother's tradition by always getting my own way.

Once I had paid a bribe to the customs official, my only recourse was to get even. I set my sights on scoring a bigger hit on my next border crossing.

CHAPTER 12

A SMUG SMUGGLER

"Money was never a big motivation for me….
The real excitement is playing the game."

– Donald Trump

Guillermo placed an order for a dozen American toilet seats for his motel. He was sufficiently wealthy, intelligent, and attractive that I was eager to have him as a customer.

On my next trip to the border, I found toilet seats on sale at K-Mart. When I exited the store and met up with Larry and Mark in front, they were not amused. They took one look at my overloaded shopping cart and began acting like tyrannical parents dealing with a wayward child.

"No, Mom," Mark said sternly. "I am telling 'no' to you."

"Are you asking for trouble?" Larry asked. "You need to get a grip."

"I have a score to settle," I explained.

"Right. With toilet seats," Larry said.

I didn't like his sarcasm.

In tandem, the boys set their jaws and crossed their arms over their chests. They trailed behind me as I pushed the shopping cart through the parking lot.

When we got to the car, I tried another tack. "These toilet seats are incredibly lucrative. We'll use some of the profit to do something special. Maybe eat at a nice restaurant? See a movie?"

They exchanged glances.

"Just a Wendy's hamburger is fine," Larry said.

"I am not liking anymore the movies," Mark said.

"Good!" I said. "Because I really need to use the money from this sale to pay your school tuition."

"Public school is fine with us," Larry said.

Both boys sat in the car instead of helping me remove the boxes from the toilet seats, arrange them under our suitcases in the trunk, and wheel the refuse to the trash.

"Ready for an adventure?" I asked as I started the ignition.

No reply.

"Lighten up, you two. This will be fun."

"No. It won't," Larry said.

I glanced in the rearview mirror. "So much fun that you'll end up laughing."

"No way."

"I'll bet your school tuition on it. Are you ready to put your money where your mouth is? Or perhaps I should say, 'put my money where your school is?' So here's the deal. If you don't laugh about this after we clear customs, you can attend public school. So Larry, do you accept my bet?"

"Sure," he said with a notable lack of enthusiasm.

"OK. You're on!"

We arrived at the border during the changing of the guard. A tired, distracted official began asking me the standard customs questions without appearing to even care about my answers. I had almost finished the brief interview when he glanced at his watch, told me to wait, and disappeared. None other than Pablo, AKA Saint Sancho of the Eyebrows, waddled out to inspect my car.

"Uh-oh," Larry said.

"Not to worry," I replied. Surely thousands or even tens of thousands of tourists had passed through his meaty mitts since our last encounter. And I had been wearing sea green mascara. Today my eyes were ringed in sky blue. "It's been six months," I whispered. "He won't remember me."

Sancho Panza squinted at me. "Have we met before?" he asked, his bushy brows alternately arching and knitting as he leaned on the driver's side window.

So as not to jog his memory, I refrained from blinking my blue eyelashes. "I don't think so, this being my first trip to Mexico and all," I said, hoping my failure to blink would come across as a wide-eyed look of innocence.

He continued to stare at me.

Fearing that his seed of doubt might sprout into a full-fledged memory, I hastened to explain. "If I look familiar, it's probably because—well, have you ever been to the movies?"

He nodded.

"I look very much like a famous actress, so I appear familiar to most people. Some of her fans go so far as to hound me for her autograph. Sometimes I give it. I mean, I don't actually sign her name, because that would be forgery, and I'm very law-abiding. I sign my name and explain that I'm traveling incognito to hold down the crowds. But then I reveal my true identity, because I'm very honest. Would you like my autograph?" My eyeballs itched from the strain of keeping my lids up, but I dared not rub them for fear the mascara trail would lead Sancho to our shared past.

"Which actress?" he asked.

"Actress?" I was having a hard time following the thread of my own convoluted yarn. "Oh, Sarah James. She's very famous, but no one has heard of her."

He scratched his head.

"I mean, Sarah plays a lot of bit parts, just minor roles. She sort of seeps into people's memories while they're munching popcorn and drooling over the big-name stars. Usually Sarah plays a maid, though I've noticed her in a lot of crowd scenes. Did you see *The Ten Commandments?*"

He shook his head.

"No? I thought everyone had. How about—have you ever seen a John Wayne movie?"

He nodded.

"That's it! Sarah often played an Indian maiden. No one special, just one of the tribe. Such an observant man you are to have recognized me—I mean her!"

"An Indian?"

"I know. Hollywood should hire authentic cast members, instead of giving Caucasians all the juicy roles. The director must have dyed Sarah's blonde hair and darkened her white skin. Imagine me with black hair and brown make-up, I'm the spitting image of Sarah."

"Make-up?" He blinked both eyelashes and pulled at an upper set as if to pluck out a memory. Either the remembrance of my mascara stash was at his fingertips or my unblinking stare was getting to him.

"But I shouldn't be taking so much time from such an important man! I'm sure you have better things to do than chat with a Sarah James look-alike. You have a job to do; I have a country to see. I'll move along so you can get back to work."

He walked to the back of the Mercury, signaled me to open the trunk, and began rummaging through it.

"Listen, you're more than welcome to tell your friends that you met a bona fide Sarah James double. Well, what the heck? Tell them you met Sarah in the flesh. I'm sure she won't mind. I'll give you her autograph as proof."

"*¡Ay!*" he exclaimed when he peeked under the suitcases in the trunk. The closest English translation is, "Ouch," but with an upward lilt of the voice at the end, the meaning changes to "I gotcha!" He held up a toilet seat.

"Now that may look like—um—like a toilet seat. And, in fact, it is. Yes, it is exactly what it looks like. A toilet seat. You can stop searching now."

He ordered the boys out of the car but continued plucking toilet seats out of the trunk and placing them on the ground. If I didn't do something *rápido*, I'd be in deep, very expensive *caca*. I squared my shoulders, thrust out my chin, and blinked the moisture back into my eyes. "Just so you know, every item in this car is for my personal use. I don't owe any tax."

He stared incredulously at the tower of toilet seats. "Twelve?" he asked.

"Well, you see…Americans and Mexicans have different restroom habits."

"Twelve?"

"American families are small, so we don't have to hurry in the bathroom. Which means we can 'do our thing' at our leisure. Which means we wear out a lot of—. But this is such an indelicate subject. It's not something for American ladies to discuss with others, especially in mixed company. But yes, these toilet seats are all my personal possessions, and each is slightly used. Therefore, they aren't taxable items."

"Twelve?"

"It's amazing how quickly they wear out. I'd hate to be caught without a spare. It can be hard for a man to understand, but it's a very dangerous situation for a lady, if you know what I mean."

"Twelve?"

"Well, Auntie Em wore hers out and nearly drowned."

His eyes widened in surprise.

"It was a close call, but Auntie Em is fine."

"Twelve?"

Now I pitied the man. I was feeding him great lines, and he kept repeating the same, stupid question. "Of course, I haven't used all twelve toilet seats as, um, as toilet seats. Some have served as, um, as picture frames. They add a three-dimensional touch to artwork. My youngest son, a budding artist, will confirm that."

Mark usually came through for me in sticky situations, but he was having trouble with this one. "These stuffs," he said vaguely. "Frames... decorations for going around the pictures." To boost his credibility, I ran my hand through the back of his hair, caught a clump in my hand, and helped him nod.

Sancho Panza scratched his head.

"You're right," I said quickly. "Twelve is undoubtedly more than I need. I'm sure I could make do with eleven. Perhaps you'd like to take one home to your wife. If hers wears out and she doesn't keep a spare, she could end up like Auntie Em."

His blank stare suggested he wasn't thrilled by my generous offer.

I placed the toilet seat in his arms. "My toilet seat is your toilet seat. The next time your wife is fresh out, give it to her as a present. Then watch her eyes light up with relief. And with love for her thoughtful husband."

Sancho stood blinking in the sun, staring at the toilet seat in his arms. If he were trying to make sense of my story, we would be stuck for heaven only knew how long. I ordered the boys back into the car, tossed the remaining toilet seats back into the trunk, and started the engine. As I drove off, I wondered how this story would end. Would Sancho gift wrap the toilet seat and give it to his wife for her birthday or anniversary? If so, I hoped their marriage would survive. I didn't like to think of myself as a home wrecker.

Mark leaned forward from the backseat. "I was not realizing of the women's problems with the toilet seats, Mom. I am glad I am being a boy! I promise to you, I will be putting down the seat like you are always insisting to me."

I was strict with Larry and Mark about lying and hated to lie in front of them, though I had explained that because the Mexican border officials don't play by the rules, we don't have to play by them, either. But in this case, having Mark absorb a bit of misinformation was worth it if he'd remember to put the toilet seat down. Some future wife would thank me.

"And I was not knowing that the toilet seat can be for the framing of the pictures," Mark said.

Now that one was harder to justify. Maybe Linda and Bill were right when they said that Larry and Mark shouldn't be exposed to the kinds of creative conversations smuggling required.

Before I could think of a response, Larry winked at me and said, "Well, Mark, what can we say? You probably never realized that Mom is a Sarah James double, either."

"I did not. Who is this Sarah?" Mark asked.

"An actress," Larry said. "Next time you see a film with a cast of thousands, ask Mom to point her out. By the way, Mom, can I have one of those toilet seats?"

"Whatever for, Larry?"

"I want to frame a picture and hang it in the living room." Larry grinned and chucked me on the shoulder. "A picture of you!" He laughed at his great joke.

I didn't find his punch line funny. "Well, Larry. I bet you would laugh, and you did. I won. You must continue in private school."

My best prize was being able to counter Linda and Bill's claim that my contraband business was harming their brothers. I would tell my eldest children that being exposed to my creative conversations and phantasmagorical fibs was nurturing Larry's sense of humor.

As an optimist, I was willing to bet an imported toilet seat that Linda and Bill would someday laugh about my unusual business. The only question was whether I'd live long enough to hear them say "professional smuggler" without a growl, and maybe even glimpse a gleeful smile.

CHAPTER 13

THE BEEF BATTLE

*"Victory goes to the player who makes the
next-to-last mistake."*

— *Savielly Grigorievitch Tartakower*

Determined to experience all aspects of Mexican culture, I set out one sultry summer afternoon to witness the life-and-death struggle between man and beast at Irapuato's *corrida de toros.*

My kids refused to go. Mark didn't want to see blood. Larry didn't want to see the matador get killed. Bill didn't want to see the bull get killed. "Enjoy the massacre," he said as I headed out the door alone. I shouldn't have told him that *matador* means "killer."

During the walk to Irapuato's arena, I wondered about my turn to perversion for diversion until I arrived. The huge crowds decked out in their Sunday best reassured me that bullfights offer more than an opportunity to ogle some offal. For that, the locals could watch Jaws mangle swimmers in the Hollywood reruns at the downtown theatre, *¿no?*

"One ticket," I told the cashier in Spanish.

"Twenty pesos for the shade, ten for the sun."

"What?"

She explained that I could choose a bleacher seat in the sun for a pittance or spring for a pricy place in the shade. I decided to work on my tan.

After teetering up the bleachers in my high heels and settling onto a wooden plank, I saw that more than thrift and pallor separated the ticket holders. The well-heeled locals cooling their high heels on the bleachers in the shade wore sunglasses; the poor peons perspired and squinted in the blazing light.

The seating arrangement made no sense. The Indians on my side of the arena already had great tans but no sunglasses. The shady-side señoras had rouged and powdered faces. Why didn't they sit where the sun could paint roses on their pallid cheeks?

A burst of cheery brass band music drew everyone's attention to the ring. Coronets and saxophones blared, almost together and almost in tune, while the tubas umpah-pahed in the lower registers.

As pretty señoritas in fluffy skirts paraded across the sand, my companions in the sun stamped their feet, catcalled, and whistled. They whooped and hollered as the other members of the cast made their way across the ring: the flag-waving *banderilleros*, the mounted *picadores* with their long spears.

Finally, the slender matador strutted in, resplendent in his flashy suit of lights. The sunny-side crowd leapt up and roared. At the conclusion of the short parade, the shady-side bunch politely applauded.

Then the bull entered the ring. He turned out to be an exceptionally lily-livered, chicken-hearted type. I nicknamed him Fernando the Fearful because he huddled up next to the arena wall, with his back end toward the center of the ring and looking down at the sand as if trying to hide. Meanwhile, the short, slender matador in the skin-tight pants and sparkly top pranced and postured in the ring's center, twirling his cape to try to get Fernando's attention.

Fernando was too busy battling with the flies to notice the cape. He bit at his side and swished his tail, but wasn't making much progress. When he stamped the ground to shiver the pesky insects from his front legs, the matador dashed from the ring as if fleeing mortal danger. Three assistants ran in and frantically swished their capes in Fernando's direction to divert any bovine wrath that might develop. None did.

In the stands on the other side, the shady-side crowd watched in silence. My sunny-sider pals punctuated their disapproving howls by hurling empty beer bottles into the arena.

As I mopped sweat from my streaming brow, a *banderillero* rode in on horseback to try to provoke a charge from Fernando and prevent a stampede from the stands. By swishing a giant flag, the equestrian managed to shoo Fernando closer to the ring's center. When the horse and rider exited, Fernando followed them. A door slammed shut to keep him from leaving the ring. He stood with his chest pressed against the wooden gate for an inordinate amount of time, as if hoping his friends would come back for him.

Then the matador returned to see if his furry opponent now grasped the game and was willing to participate. Fernando didn't and wouldn't. As the matador advanced, Fernando walked over to greet his old friend, apparently expecting to be fed or petted. But when they met at the center of the ring, the matador twirled his cape in Fernando's face, forcing him into reverse until his rump hit a wall.

Unable to go forward or backward, he took a hard left and took a leisurely stroll around the ring's entire perimeter. En route he tried to escape through all six exits, but each was quickly blocked. I crisped in the sun as Fernando ambled on and on and on. When he finally completed the circle, he huddled near his shady-side fans. Some spectators leaned over the arena's wall and tried to pet him.

I hid my eyes as a spear-toting *picador* entered and began punishing poor Fernando. I introduced myself to the man seated on my right

119

and asked why the *picador* was being so mean. Julio explained it wasn't personal—flags and stabs were part of the show.

After the bored sunny-side bunch had spent an hour drowning their disappointment in beer, the men got tired of tossing their empties at the matador and started throwing them at one another.

Suddenly some loud English shrieks for help penetrated the conversational buzz. A young American tourist high in the stands on my side of the economic divide had probably chosen to wear short shorts and a halter-top to minimize her tan line, but the men thought her outfit signaled her interest in sex rather than sun. They were giving her more attention than she had hoped for.

Some policemen lumbered up the bleachers to contain the fracas. As a full-blown brawl broke out, the matador lifted his sword and struck the fatal blow. That re-focused the audience's attention. As Fernando sank to his knees, the sunbathers aimed their ire at the ring. The sweaty-side spectators booed and torpedoed still more beer bottles into the sand, while the folks in the shade tossed their seat cushions.

The officials did not award the usual trophies to the matador during the concluding ceremony, according to Julio, because it had been such a sorry spectacle. Instead, the spoils were severed from Fernando's head and sold to the highest bidder.

I was appalled. "What will the buyer do with Fernando's ears?" I asked Julio.

"Put them in the freezer."

"But why?"

"So they don't spoil."

My arms, upper back, and face were so sunburned, every movement hurt as Julio and I inched down the bleachers. My heart hurt as much as my burned skin.

I had wanted to embrace or at least accept all aspects of Mexican culture, but the match had been too unfair. The matador had a cape to distract Fernando, assistants to dizzy him, flag-waving *banderilleros* to frighten him, *picadores* to wound him. And the matador had a spear to kill him and six ways to exit from the bullring. To hold his own, Fernando would have needed an infusion of bravery like the Cowardly Lion received from the wily wizard in Oz.

"The *toro* didn't stand a chance," I mumbled through my sunburned lips.

"A chance?" Julio asked. "No, Señora. The *toro* always dies. A bullfight is not a competition."

"Then what is it?" I asked.

"Es un ritual." He paused to consider. *"Es arte,"* he said.

I had heard of performance art; this was apparently the Mexican version. Not a winner-take-all sport but a ritual re-enactment of our ancestors' struggle to survive the wilds of nature. Because Fernando had failed in his role of ferocious antagonist, the drama had been about a man battling his own ego. No wonder the onlookers had been so irate. No one wanted to spend time watching the same tired melodrama they lived each day.

Outside the arena I offered to buy Julio a taco. We followed the heady aroma of charcoaled broiled steak to an outdoor grill. On arriving, I saw Fernandoburgers in the making and fainted. Julio caught me before I hit the ground.

After we parted and I began walking home, I felt simultaneously hungry and queasy. Was my stomach still reacting to the sight of those Fernandoburgers? Perhaps the meat in the taco I'd consumed in the stands had been rancid. Yikes! While ruing poor Fernando's demise, I'd been munching on his kith and kin! How disgusting! I was swearing off meat!

But less than a block later, another hunger pang hit, and I wondered whether I could make my animal fast last. My resolve receded as my stomach growls grew, and I began to question my veggie vow. Would eschewing animal protein reduce pain and suffering in the world? I'd never heard a carrot cry, but there might be more to a tuber than meets the ear. It wouldn't help to give up meat if I took to mass murdering cauliflowers and lettuce to pick up the nutritional slack.

Bullfights seemed cruel to Americans because we didn't like to think about the beings behind our burgers. Maybe the masses of human carnivores mindlessly masticating meat north of the Rio Grande needed to be force-fed an occasional bullfight to grasp the source of their protein.

To develop compassion for the poor vegetables bringing up the bottom of the food chain, Americans and Mexicans should both be forced to eat at a Benihana Restaurant now and then to witness the ritual hacking of veggies. Though bullfights and Benihanas might traumatize children, so they could instead be forced to say grace to honor the flora and fauna who sacrificed their lives so that humans might live.

My stomach settled down once I was home, cooled off, and had soothed my sunburn stings with lotion. I felt hungry enough to eat a horse but too tired to catch and cook one, so I settled for some leftover tortilla chips and peanut butter.

As I crunched my first bite, I began thanking the corn and peanuts for their gift. But after the first mouthful of the stale, unsavory snack, I cut my prayer short.

It was unfortunate that slain vegetables had died for such an ignoble cause, but it was too late to stir them into something savory. All I could do was give them a proper funeral.

To that end, I buried them in the trash and cooked myself a hamburger.

CHAPTER 14

INTERNATIONAL INTRIGUE

*"There is no stronger bond of friendship
than a mutual enemy."*

— *Frankfort Moore*

My Mexican friends said that after creating the world, God stepped back to review His handiwork and realized He'd forgotten Mexico. "Oops," He said. "I'll tuck it under the United States and give it the last thing I have: the best climate in the world."

And so it was. From October to May, the sun shone every day.

From June to September, it rained for a short, predictable time each afternoon.

Irapuato felt like an icebox with the door open in December and January—cold enough to chill everything but not to freeze it. This lone frigid flaw in God's handiwork had a benefit: it provided central Mexico with a respite from flies and tourists.

The rest of the year, springtime reigned from the world's creation until July 21, 1969, when, according to the locals, the astronauts messed up the clouds en route to the moon.

I didn't know what to think. According to history and theology, the weather should have been sunny and clear during Linda's short visit to Irapuato the following spring. And when she and I headed out to attend the outdoor wedding of one of my ex-students, an *Instituto* graduate, the weather was lovely. Unfortunately, it didn't hold.

Somewhere between "Do you?" and "I do," there was a crash of thunder, a flash of lightning, and a flurry of guests scurrying to find a dry port in the storm.

There wasn't one. The homeowner had opened up his garden to his friends for their wedding, but had declared his house strictly off limits. Linda and I raced to the wedding canopy but came in second and third. The first place winner pulled down the six-by-six foot tarpaulin, wrapped himself in his trophy, and streaked to the parking lot. Linda and I huddled under a clump of trees with a few dozen other losers.

Being squeezed in together was kind of cozy until the trees began to leak. I spotted a dry patch of ground near a section of the tall stone wall surrounding the property. "Let's try over there," I suggested. When Linda and I ran for it, the rest of the herd followed. We lined up against the wall, pressing our backs against the stones. The wall blocked the drops arriving at an angle, but those on a vertical path pelted us.

A voice at my side interrupted my misery with a cheerful, *"Hola, Señora."*

I turned and saw my least favorite person in the country, Maridél. The rain mixed with my face powder, and cloudy drops cascaded from the tip of my nose and chin. Meanwhile, the raindrops slicking Maridél's creamy complexion glistened like dew. My poufy saloned coiffure had flattened like a popped balloon. My hair clung to my scalp like a skullcap and sent wet streams down the back of my neckline. Maridél's ponytail held its bounce.

I gave the gorgeous goddess a withering smile and turned my back to her, but she stepped around and positioned herself between Linda and me. "This is your daughter?" she asked in English.

There was no way out of this conversation. I nodded bleakly.

"Gee," Linda said. "Your English is great!"

"Your dear mother is an excellent teacher," my tormentor gushed. "Such a beautiful daughter you have, Mrs. Sonna. Such interesting hair."

Linda touched her drippy kinks, and her smile dissolved. Before I could concoct a consoling comment, Maridél did a quick about-face, smacking my face with her wet ponytail. "*Ay, Señora.* I am sorry," she said, though the glint in her eyes suggested otherwise.

As the heavenly onslaught continued, the guests began grumbling about the gall of the *gringos* to mess up the weather. Linda's college Spanish classes had served her too well, and she looked nervous as the Yankee-bashing intensified. "When the United States sneezes, Mexico gets a cold," a woman said.

The crowd murmured agreement with the tired cliché.

"When the United States gets a cold, Mexico gets pneumonia," her husband ad-libbed.

The crowd murmured agreement and chuckled.

"If God wanted help with the weather, He would have put a weather-man on the moon," an aging gent proclaimed.

The crowd pondered his strange comment. Lee would have appreciated his logic.

"The *gringos* shouldn't be allowed to cheat Mexicans out of a free meal," a patriotic soul declared. "I'm staying for dinner!"

"*¡Sí!*" the crowd shouted.

Maridél smirked at me. No one else seemed to notice the two gringas in the group, so I pretended not to notice us, either.

"Where did the word *gringo* come from, anyway?" Linda asked.

"Supposedly from the Alamo," I replied. "En route to the San

Antonio slaughter, Davy Crockett's white-skinned bandits belted out choruses of *Green Grow the Lilacs.* Pancho Villa's soldiers heard 'green grow' as gringo."

"Is it a racial slur, like 'honky?' "

"It depends on whether the speaker says it with a smile or a snarl."

"People are snarling," Linda said. "Let's leave."

But the guests were miserable, and misery loves company, so I was determined to stay. I thought it important to prove that Mexicans aren't the only ones who get wet when it rains in April.

The drops coalesced into sheets. At the other end of our stone wall, a gentleman offered his coat to the bride. She offered it to the groom. He took it.

Linda tsked in disgust. "What a brute," she said.

I wanted her to love Mexico enough to approve of her brothers growing up here and to return for more visits. "That coat probably isn't her size," I pointed out. "It certainly doesn't match her outfit."

To lighten everyone's mood, the oldest guest in attendance, *Don Juan* hobbled onto the lawn and did an arthritic imitation of Gene Kelly's *Singing in the Rain.*

Linda chuckled. "I wonder what he did to merit that nickname."

"*Don* is a title of respect for men of a certain age. I think it's safe to assume that Juan's seductive prowess disappeared several decades ago, if he ever had any," I replied.

In his poor peasant's attire, he looked out of place at this upscale event. But his dance lifted our spirits, and as we soaked, we joked. Given that the spikes of my high-heeled shoes were sinking into the ooze and my sneezes were triggering thoughts of pneumonia, I wasn't enjoying myself.

But I still held out hope that a wonderful something would happen and tip the Mexico-is-a-great-place-to-visit-but-you-shouldn't-be-living

-here scale in my favor. Linda had brought the good news that my divorce was now final, and the bad news that Lee's temporary custody had been made permanent.

She wanted me to return to LaGrange and battle for custody. "Then you'll have Larry and Mark legally," she said. "You can live in the U.S. And even if you stay in Mexico, you won't have to worry about getting picked up by the police each time you set foot in the U.S."

I couldn't explain to Linda that I couldn't handle being in the same state with Lee, because I couldn't even explain it to myself. Hopefully I'd be ready for a trip to Illinois by next Christmas, because I was determined to visit my mother then. But the very thought of being in the same state filled me with dread. Being in the same courtroom was out of the question. And even if I won custody, that wouldn't solve anything. The court would grant him visitation. If I didn't hand Larry and Mark over to him on schedule, I'd be back in jail and my custody would end. I'd be worse off than I was now.

Linda pointed to the wedding cake and chuckled. The weeping clouds had melted the six tiers of angel food into one and dripped off the table into a puddle. The small plastic bride and groom had slid off the icing, and the unfortunate couple was being entombed in muddy batter. There were rueful smiles all around as we stared at our ruined cake and the fallen effigies. Only the flowers laughed. Maridél narrowed her eyes at me as if to say, "This food fiasco is your fault!"

When the rain slowed to a drizzle, the caterers distributed limp paper plates. Because we guests were still lined up with our backs against the stone wall, the waiters filed by and served us refugee style. We ate damp chicken with rain gravy and watched the rolls melt right in our hands before they made it to our mouths.

When the sun finally reappeared, some guests went home to their medicine chests. Others stayed and dosed themselves with tequila to

127

fend off illness.

As I sloshed through my good-byes, Maridél approached me for the customary farewell kiss. I presented my cheek to her lips, but instead of a hearing a soft smack, she emitted a loud screech. *"¡Una araña!"* Maridél exclaimed, pointing to my face.

A spider? I glimpsed a hairy critter fall from my cheek and felt it land on my upper chest. I frantically swatted at my bosom until the creepy crawly tumbled to the ground. A small child bent down to inspect it, and then held it up for the crowd to see. It was one of my false eyelashes. Everyone found this funny and began to laugh.

I smiled like the good sport I wasn't, and my cockeyed grin struck the crowd as funnier still. The laughter grew louder. I fixed Maridél with my most menacing someday-I'll-get-you-for-this stare.

On the way home, Linda read me the riot act. "It's not good for Mark and Larry to grow up as members of a despised minority group. It will erode their self-confidence and destroy their self-esteem."

"Larry is very popular at school," I said. "Mexican kids admire classmates who make good grades, not the ones who make good kicks on the soccer field during recess. Because he's at the top of the academic heap, the kids voted him as their class president. And of course, everyone loves Mark due to his sunny disposition and sweet personality."

I didn't add that the class bullies pummeled both of Larry and Mark every time unflattering news about Mexico's Big Bad Northern Neighbor made the local news.

"Mom, you know the NASA computers that got the spaceship to the moon? Now the police are getting computers, and supposedly all the government offices will soon have them, too. When they check your passport at the border, you could be arrested for kidnapping. Dad promised to drop the charges if you go back to him."

"I'd prefer prison!" I said. "And I thought you said he had divorced me. Why would he do that if he wanted me back?"

Linda shrugged, but we both knew the answer. He'd obtained the divorce to get permanent custody of Mark and Larry so that I could be charged with criminal kidnapping. If the police ever caught up with me, I'd go to jail. Then Lee would offer to drop the charges if I returned to LaGrange and resumed my old life with him. The mere thought of being back with Lee filled me with a mind-numbing, stomach-twisting terror.

"Anyway," I said. "Doing time could be fun. I could entertain the convicts with my funny stories, and as a captive audience, they'd have to listen. And I could read to my heart's content. Just don't forget to bring a checkerboard and a bag of caramels on visiting days. We can play and pig out on sweets."

Linda was not amused. Suddenly tears swarmed her eyes. "I'm not kidding," she said.

"Nor am I." Figuring out the worst thing that could possibly happen and then worrying about it endlessly had been one of Linda's specialties since she was a tot. By giving Linda so much to worry about, I had provided opportunities for her to practice. Thanks to me, she had honed her talent for obsessing over trivia into a fine art. Too bad she hadn't inherited my talent for putting off worries until tomorrow. "It seems we are at a Mexican stand-off," I told her. "Can we agree to disagree?"

She nodded, and we hugged.

There was no point in complaining to the U.S. Weather Bureau about NASA's moon meddling, but something needed to be done to shore up Mexico/U.S. relations. A poster in the U.S. consulate in Mexico City admonished Americans to behave when traveling abroad because "All U.S. citizens are unofficial ambassadors of their country." That provided the inspiration.

On my next trip to the border, I bought a supply of clear plastic raincoats and bonnets—the kind that fold into a tiny plastic envelope—and several sets of clear plastic boots.

There wasn't a cloud in the sky when I dressed for my next Irapuato patio party, but I covered my hair-do with a clear plastic rain bonnet, my floor-length gown with a clear plastic raincoat, and my high-heeled shoes with clear plastic boots. I added a pad of paper and pencil to my purse so I could take orders for made-in-America rain gear.

As I started walking to the party, I wondered if the exceptionally hot, humid weather might actually be NASA's fault. Then I realized that being encased in plastic baggies was turning me into a terrarium. I had my own weather system. My hair and scalp were raining. I loosened the rain bonnet, and water poured down my face and neck.

A block later my perspiration streamed down the raincoat's plastic sleeves to the point that my hands were soaked. The sweat coursed down my legs into my plastic boots, to the point that I was walking in puddles. The plastic boots made loud raspberry sounds with each squishy step.

As I neared the venue, I heard giggles and someone calling my name. I turned and saw Maridél. How was it that she managed to appear at my most embarrassing moments? Her bright print sundress set off her shiny black hair, nymph-like body, and luscious golden skin.

I swiped the sweat from my soggy brow, acknowledged her and her three sisters, and steeled myself for Maridél's insults.

She looked me up and down for a long moment before launching her attack. "Oh, Señora!" she exclaimed. "I love your outfit!"

I hadn't expected her to be *that* rude! To return her tit with my tat would make me sound like an ungrateful wretch. Darn, but she was such an incredibly artful dodger!

As I turned to leave, my left foot made a loud raspberry sound.

"*¡Ay, Señora!* Are you ill?" she asked with a look of concern.

"That wasn't me!" I exclaimed. "It was my—" I couldn't think of the Spanish word for "galoshes," so I pointed helplessly to my foot.

She winked at her sisters and turned back to address me. "Don't worry, Señora," she said. "We won't tell."

As I sloshed off, their giggles suggested that the news would soon circulate through the entire town: "Have you heard? The *Instituto's* director accused her foot of committing an anal indiscretion!"

None of the patio party guests ordered a portable wetsuit, so I couldn't spread U.S. culture through commerce, Marco Polo style. Still, I hoped that my fellow partiers would add the important news to the local grapevine: When U.S. moon flights ruffle the clouds and mess up the weather, Yankee ingenuity can solve at least some of the catastrophes the *gringos* create.

CHAPTER 15

WANTED: LOIS SONNA

"In matters of conscience, the law has no place."

– *Mohandas Ghandi*

At first I was intimidated by Mexicans' philosophy of driving: might makes right.

Traffic signs served as warnings that a train, pedestrian, or another car might try to interfere with a driver's God-given right-of-way. On Mexican stoplights the green light meant "go"; red meant "go"; and yellow meant "go faster."

Drivers only heeded the small altars, large crosses, and elaborate shrines families had erected to mark the spot where a loved one had died. These memorials provided more convincing warnings about precipitous curves and hazardous intersections than the government highway signs, which were subject to personal interpretation.

There was only one hard-and-fast rule of the Mexican road: it was illegal to touch cars. The theory of driving was Darwinian, with the winner being the emotionally fittest. The road warrior strategies were mental, not metal. It was fine to bully, intimidate, or scare another driver into slowing down, speeding up, or moving over. It was against the law to rub fenders when nosing, nuzzling, or forcing a competitor's car off the road.

Fender benders and those who had their fenders bent needed to arrive at quick on-the-spot settlements. If they couldn't reconcile their problem before a policeman arrived, they had to pay him for his time and trouble. The driver with the deepest pockets got the not-guilty verdict. I assumed that having to pay the police was like paying a bribe: pure, unadulterated graft. But a police recruitment ad in the newspaper listed "cash tips from citizens" as one of the employment perks.

To survive on the roads, I learned to wield my vehicle with the-do of other drivers, and to resolve clashes from crashes like other civilized citizens. Unfortunately, my new-and-improved driving didn't work out in the barbarian nation to the north.

When I was visiting my mother in Cicero at Christmas, I drove into downtown Chicago to shop. As I was driving on the Stevenson Expressway on my way back to her house, I missed the exit. Just a few yards ahead, I spotted a break in the barrier that had been erected to keep cars off the median strip.

The heavy expressway traffic was moving fast, but since there were no warning shrines to advise against a U-turn, I swished across four lanes of traffic and then braked to await an opening in the traffic speeding toward Chicago.

When I stopped on the expressway, the car behind me stopped. Not so the next seven vehicles. After the crashing and crunching ended, the cursing began. I hadn't bent anyone's fender, nor had my fender been bent. So when I saw a break in the traffic, I completed my U-turn and left the scene of their crime.

According to the mess on an envelope from a Cook County court, a judge had sent a letter to my LaGrange address, and Lee had forwarded it to my mother. She then sent it to me, and it arrived in Irapuato about six months later.

Apparently the guilty parties had noted my license plate number, called the boys in blue, induced them to issue me a ticket, and paid bribes the American way: by giving money to a lawyer, who then sued the innocent bystander—or the innocent byparker—and the tailgaters had won! A judgment had been entered against me for a quarter of a million dollars.

I was flattered that anyone would consider me that wealthy, especially since Linda had managed to learn the terms of my divorce. I was an official food-stamps-and-welfare case, at least by U.S. standards. In addition to custody of Larry and Mark, Lee had been granted the house, bank accounts, and everything else. The only thing I got out of the divorce was me.

Anyway, my Cook County court traffic accident letter said that the judge had graciously offered to set me up on the handy installment plan. If I didn't pay up, the court would garnish my wages at the going rate of ten percent of my salary.

My official monthly *Instituto* salary totaled two hundred U.S. dollars, so my legal monthly obligation was twenty dollars, though the verdict was of course unenforceable in Mexico. Were I to pay voluntarily, I calculated that after subtracting a third for the lawyers and splitting the balance seven ways, each driver would receive almost two U.S. dollars per month.

As a goodwill gesture, I sent twenty-dollar payments for several months. Then I skipped a few months to see if anyone cared. No one contacted me, so I stopped sending checks.

Unfortunately, the court had revoked my Illinois driver's license pending payment of the final installment, which was scheduled for 1,041 years away.

On my next trip to the U.S., I obtained a Texas driver's license in the name of María Luisa González, with the help of a notary who failed to uphold the finer traditions of her seal. I chose María for my new first name, because it was the first name of almost every Mexican female. I chose Luisa as my middle name, because it was the closest Spanish equivalent of Lois. And I chose González for my surname, because it was as common and nondescript as Smith in the U.S.

Each time I crossed into the U.S., Lois Sonna, an American vacationing in Mexico, became María Luisa González, a Mexican vacationing in America. That way, the U.S. computers wouldn't connect María, an upstanding Mexican to Lois, the delinquent U.S. debtor and kidnapper.

But one glitch remained: the Mercury's title was still in the name of that U.S. criminal, Lois Sonna, and I needed the title to renew my license plates. I considered selling the car to Maria, but that would have required Lois to transfer the title. María would have to pay the tax, and Lois would be exposed to the Texas computers, which might have been linked to Illinois computers.

Luckily, Illinois 1968 plates had black letters and numbers on a white background—the exact same color scheme as Mexican plates. The camouflage worked wonderfully in Mexico, but driving in the U.S. with expired license plates was somewhat harrowing.

When Larry, Mark, and I met Linda and Bill in San Antonio, Texas, for Christmas in 1970, their bus arrived very late in the evening. The city streets were basically deserted by the time we finished dinner, so I decided to risk driving the Mercury on the freeway instead of sticking to the back roads en route to our motel.

Suddenly Linda shouted, "Mom! Check your speed! You're going to get us killed!"

I glanced at the speedometer. "I'm well under the speed limit," I reassured her.

"That's the problem! You're doing twenty in a sixty-five-mile-per-hour zone!"

"I can't risk a speeding ticket."

A heavy-handed horn, a hefty screech of brakes, and a skid of tires interrupted our conversation. On glancing in the rearview mirror, a pair of truck headlights blinded me. "These Texans are a bunch of speed demons!" I complained.

"No, you need to speed up!" Linda sputtered. "It's illegal to drive this slowly!"

I gritted my teeth. College kids thought they knew everything.

"See that sign?" Bill asked. "It says the minimum speed limit is forty."

High school dropouts also thought they knew everything.

"Just think about it, kids. People get tickets for speeding. When have you ever heard of anyone being ticketed for driving too slowly?"

At that moment red lights flashed and a siren blared. I pulled onto the expressway's shoulder, and a tall Texas officer sauntered to the window.

"Is there a problem?" he asked, shining his flashlight in each of our eyes, including those of my two little hostages.

"There's no problem here!" I answered cheerfully.

"I clocked you doing nineteen miles per hour."

"Oh? Well, you see, Officer. I'm just a bit lost."

"I need your driver's license and registration."

Oops. The names on those two documents didn't match. Could I explain why María was driving Lois' car? "Officer, I was just looking for the—um, for our motel." I craned my neck out the window. "I can't seem to find it. Perhaps you know the San Antonio Best Western. It can't be far, or maybe it can. I'm actually very lost."

"Take the next exit. I need to see your—"

"Excuse me, but I'm so confused. You say the Best Western is at the next exit? But which one is that?"

He pointed to the sign.

"Oh. Do you mean that one, right there? Imagine, children. We're that close."

"Your license and—"

"So I assume you mean that I should just continue going, let's see, straight? And I exit, um, there? But I don't see the motel."

"You will when you exit the expressway."

"Oh? Which side of the street is it on?"

"The left."

"Oh. I just go left? Let's see. That would mean I should turn, um—?"

"Left."

"And which way, exactly, is that? I know it's hard to believe, but I can't tell my right from my left. I used to keep track by my wedding ring. I wore it on the ring finger of my left hand, so I knew that my right hand was the other one. But when I divorced, I switched the ring to my other hand. As you can see, I now wear this lovely ring here, on this hand. You can imagine my confusion when what had been right for so many years became left. Or was it the other way around? Did I wear it on my right hand while married and move it to my left after the divorce? Anyway, it is Christmas Eve, we're in a strange city, and it's past my children's bedtime, I'm lost, it's almost Christmas, my two older children traveled here all the way from Illinois on the bus, and—"

The southern gentleman inside the stern lawman stepped forward. "Now, now, Little Lady. Don't worry your pretty little head about a thing. I'll take you on up to your motel. Just follow my car." He put his pen in his shirt pocket.

"Oh, that would be wonderful, Officer. Thank you so much. I would be so appreciative."

As we exited the highway about half a block later, I realized following him was not a good idea. "If the officer looks in his rearview mirror and notices the date on my license plates, there will be trouble. I need to lose him."

"WHAT?" Linda and Bill chorused.

"Hold on!"

As soon as the police car turned left (or right—I really do have trouble remembering which is which) into the motel parking lot, I floored the accelerator and took a hard right (or a left—I went the other way). Then I drove in circles around San Antonio's back roads for about twenty minutes. "Whew, that was close," I said. "It should be OK to go back to the motel now."

A stony silence emanated from the backseat.

"I can't wait to get some sleep," I added. "I'm exhausted."

No comment from the crowd.

But then I began to wonder: what if the policeman's suspicions had been aroused by behavior he might consider a bit odd? "Kids, that policeman could be waiting for us at the motel. I'm going to park the car here, and we'll walk the rest of the way."

As we started to get out of the car, I realized that if the policeman were there, he could demand my driver's license, and I'd still have a lot of explaining to do. "On second thought, we need to change motels."

"But our suitcases are already in there!" Larry reminded me.

"Right. You can go to our room and bring them out to us."

"But he's too little," Linda objected.

"Exactly. The police won't be looking for a young child."

"What if the policeman is waiting inside the room?" Linda asked.

"He would need to get a search warrant. That takes time."

"Get real!" Bill said. "Larry can't carry all our suitcases!"

"Not all at once, and they're mostly empty. I haven't started shopping yet."

"But won't that look suspicious? A little kid carrying suitcase after suitcase out of a motel room late at night?" Bill asked. "Send me."

"You're a teenager. If you got caught, they'd think you were stealing."

Silence.

"You want Larry to sneak around like a criminal. Have you thought about how that might affect him?" Linda asked.

139

Mark bristled. "Sneaking is the easiest. When we are bringing in the contrabands from Texas, we are being good helpers to Mom."

"WHAT?" Linda and Bill exclaimed in unison.

"Let's not get sidetracked, kids. Here's the room key, Larry. Bring a suitcase down and leave it by that tree. Linda, you carry the suitcase from the tree to the car, which I'll park in the shadows over there. If somebody follows Larry, walk away as if you're just out for a midnight stroll. Larry, if anybody asks any questions, say in Spanish that you don't speak English. I'll be back in ten minutes to pick you up."

Linda and Larry disappeared into the darkness, then re-emerged in the lights of the motel parking lot.

"Mom, what's up with Mark's English?" Bill asked.

"What do you mean?"

"It's totally messed up."

"Larry and I understand him. You understand him. He's only been on earth a few years and has had to learn two languages. I'm sure it will straighten out in time."

When I returned to the motel parking lot, Linda and Larry were waiting for us. The evacuation had taken place without incident. Everything was fine.

It was after midnight by the time we piled into Motel 6, which made it Christmas morning. We opened a few presents to celebrate the holiday. We were exhausted, and after so much excitement, the gift exchange was anticlimactic.

"Sorry it is only just a little scarf I am presenting to you, Mom," Mark said when I opened his present.

"I love it. Why are you sorry?"

"It was in my mind to be getting you some new identifications with all the names being the same, but I did not know of the stores that are selling them."

"Mom, did you hear that?" Bill asked. "You've got to do something about the kid's English."

"Leave to me alone!" Mark shouted. "If you are understanding to me, that is being enough! Anyway, I was not talking for your ears!"

"That's the least of Mark's problems!" Linda said. "How about being an accessory to his mother's criminality?"

"Nothing illegal happened! It's not a crime to change motels."

Nevertheless, Linda and Bill proceeded to discuss my maternal failings, just as Lee used to do. "It's Christmas," I reminded them. "Let's keep it friendly, OK?"

We turned out the lights, but I couldn't sleep. I'd tried to explain the financial realities of our situation to Linda and Bill, but doubted they could comprehend them. To teenagers, my little *Instituto* salary sounded like a fortune.

While it was true that everything cost about one-third less in Mexico than in the U.S., Mexicans at my income level didn't send their kids to private schools or own cars. This weeklong Christmas journey alone would cost three months' income, and I certainly hadn't counted on paying for two motel rooms tonight. The Mercury was on its last legs; every extra peso I could eek out went into savings.

Nevertheless, Linda and Bill's accusations gave me pause. Was my unusual sideline harming Mark and Larry in ways I couldn't see? I nudged Mark. "What do you think about what happened tonight?" I asked.

He moaned in his sleep and slurred, *"Muy divertido."*

"What? Tell me in English, Honey."

His lips curved into a faint smile as he whispered, "Much funning."

For better or worse, I agreed. Personally, I thought it was for the better.

CHAPTER 16

DANCING WITH DEATH

"If you cannot get rid of the family skeleton,
you may as well make it dance."

– *George Bernard Shaw*

Not all Mexican customs are easy to embrace.

It took me almost a week to learn to put things off till *mañana*, a year to giggle at a Mexican joke, and nearly two years to dance the samba.

Four years passed before I could eat chile without wincing (it took that long for my mouth to build up enough calluses), six years before I conquered the cockroaches (combine beer and boric acid in a mixing bowl and leave in any infested location to zap the suckers forever).

It took me a decade to decipher exactly when and whom to bribe, how much to offer to open the negotiations, and how much to pay.

But I never did learn to appreciate the Halloween, All Saints Day, and All Souls Day festivities, which Mexicans combine into *El Día de los Muertos*. Though the celebrations last for three days, the literal translation is "The Day of the Dead."

I tried to view the grisly festivities from an anthropological perspective—a Mexican's ability to celebrate anything and everything is definitely a charming cultural quirk. Still, I found The Day of the Dead festivities more eerie than quaint.

Preparations for the hideous holiday began weeks in advance. Families created special altars with deceased relatives' pictures to guide their ghostly ancestors to the right location, and topped the altars with their favorite foods and beverages to entice the relatives to stop in for a visit. Classrooms of students and civic organizations did the same, erecting altars around town to lure in the spirit of a famous historical figure or favorite movie star.

Mexican housewives cooked up colorful candy confections molded into macabre skeletons, cadaverous skulls, and assorted ghouls and demons to hawk at the local market. These devilish delights drew hundreds of people and thousands of flies.

Each year Larry, Mark, and I toured the marketplace to marvel at the cleverness (they) and audacity (me) of the ghoulish sugar sculptures, called *alfiniques*. We only looked; we never bought. I couldn't imagine that anyone would actually appreciate a gift of a candy tombstone with his or her very own name etched in black frosting.

I found the cynicism of the *alfinique* inscriptions vaguely unnerving. Tiny candied skeletons held miniature placards with Spanish sayings such as, "Here today, hell tomorrow." A skull's sign advised, "Do it now! Who knows if heaven is worth waiting for." One tiny tombstone epitaph read, "John loved Mary and her husband found out."

When Mark, Larry, and I passed a tiny dead teenaged girl candy tucked inside a doll-sized candy coffin, I shielded Larry's eyes from her little placard that proclaimed, "Do it! It's easier to ask forgiveness than permission." That was one lesson I wasn't eager for him to learn.

While some vendors sold *alfiniques* to cheer the living, others sold huge palm wreaths to lift the spirits of the dead. Men balanced the wreaths on their heads and carried brooms and flowers in their arms. Mothers and children toted picnic baskets while parading to the cemetery to pay homage to their ancestors and spiffy up their graves. At the end of the three-mile hike, everyone feasted, eating part of the repast and leaving the rest for dear departed Granddaddy Gomez or unfortunate Uncle Umberto.

Even though the pilgrims didn't betray any hints of grief or grimness, the whole affair struck my American sensibilities as gruesome, and I didn't feel inclined to participate. I certainly didn't want to dance on any of *my* relatives' graves. (Then again…)

Larry didn't share my squeamishness about these funky foreign affairs, and Mark was intrigued. After Mark started kindergarten, he developed a sudden urge the first day of November to go on a family picnic the very next day. As the celebration of death approached shortly after he turned seven, he had a solution. "Dr. Responsable's family are offering to be adopting me for this only one day," he announced.

His desire to participate in the foul festivities concerned me. As Linda and Bill had predicted, my American-Mexican son was losing touch with his cultural roots. "You may think it would be fun to walk all those long, long miles carrying those heavy, heavy decorations and weighty picnic baskets," I warned. "But that park is really a cemetery! The picnic benches are graves! The tables are tombstones! You would find the whole affair terribly upsetting."

"Why?" he asked.

"As Americans, the mere thought of a graveyard party is enough to give me gooseflesh and you nightmares. An American child would be traumatized, scarred, warped for life."

"Why?"

"Because even though Americans know death is a fact of life, we do our best to pretend it's not."

"Why?"

"Because we believe life is for the living."

"Why?"

"You can't go, and that's all there is to it! Besides, Linda would never forgive me if I let you."

"Why?"

"Because Americans believe children must be protected from the darker side of life."

"But these parties, they are being in the daytime. The sun, he will be shining."

"A cemetery is a terribly scary, spooky place."

"He has the trees and the grasses that are green," he countered, squeezing back tears.

"Who has?"

"The cemetery has these lovely stuffs."

"In English we say 'it has,' not 'he has.' "

"It has the trees and the grasses."

He had absolutely no qualms whatsoever about hanging out in a graveyard. Maybe Linda and Bill were right—living in Mexico was warping him.

Now that I thought about it, Mark should have reached the stage of irrationality long ago, but he never worried about ghosts haunting his bedroom like a normal child. Nor had he awakened from scary monster dreams. I didn't need to check with Dr. Spock, much less Dr. Linda, to know this abnormal behavior might have grave (!) consequences for his future development. I needed to straighten him out fast.

"There may be shrubs and flowers at that picnic area, Mark. But that doesn't stop it from being a cemetery. Oh! How scary!"

"Why?"

"Dead people are buried there." I shivered to get the message across. "It's filled with DEAD BODIES! Corpses of PEOPLE! Cadavers! Yuck!"

He was nonplused.

"Besides, we don't have any corpses to visit out there."

146

Mark burst into tears. "That is what is being our problem," he wailed. "This family, she is so small, we are not even having our own dead person. Margarita has ten. Rico has five. I am the only one in my school without dead peoples!"

"Sorry, fellah," I said, trying not to laugh. "Next time a friend loses a family member, I'll take you to the funeral."

He stared at me disconsolately.

"Wouldn't a funeral be fun?" I asked hopefully.

"Maybe we could be adopting a dead people from Dr. Responsable."

"No, the point is to visit your own dearly departed."

"Can I go on the celebrations if I have my own dead one in the cemetery?"

"You mean a relative? Yes, I suppose so."

The faucet of tears flipped off. "Mom, do we need Larry being here all of the times? He is such a bratty one."

"You would suggest fratricide just to wrangle a party invitation? I'm ashamed of you!"

"Well, I know it is bad to kill a people …"

"It's called murder. And yes, it's a terrible crime," I said severely. Maybe I'd ask Linda to have a long-distance chat with him after all.

"What is feeling wrong with you?" Mark asked. "You look like you are having a little bit of sickness all of a suddenly."

"I've just got a lot of worries. It's not easy being a mother."

"What did the doctor tell to you when you are seeing to him?"

I detected the hopeful note in his voice. "I've been over Montezuma's Revenge for months! Not only do I feel fine, but I plan to find the key to eternal youth! If you want to celebrate The Day of the Dead, I'll make you a peanut butter and tortillawich, and you can have a pretend party on the patio. Use your imagination. Pretend that Abe Lincoln or JFK is a distant relative. If you're good, I'll take you into town and buy you a sugar tombstone with your name on it. No, that doesn't sound right. I mean if you're bad I'll buy you one. Oh, that sounds worse."

"An alfinique will be very fine for presenting to me," Mark said. He walked toward the door but was dragging his feet, still hoping I'd change my mind. Or hoping I'd keel over.

"I would do almost anything to make you happy, but there are limits to my martyrdom. Run along now."

But he wasn't giving up. "I will say to Linda and Bill about this. They understand to me better than you."

"Fine. Now go play!"

But it wasn't fine. If he told Linda and Bill that his heartfelt wish was to spend a day partying in a graveyard, they'd insist I return him to the States for a proper American upbringing. And if they told Lee, he might agree that both boys needed the good old U.S. of A. and try to take them. I needed to explain the situation to Linda and Bill before Mark did.

I sat down to write them each a letter. But what to say? How to convince them that Mark's attitudes might be strange by American standards, but weren't bad. Better still, I needed to think of a benefit. Well, at least Mark wasn't terrified of losing a parent like so many children; he yearned for my demise! And as for death being a cause for celebration rather than mourning, well, maybe Mexicans did have a better idea.

Suddenly I had a better idea, too. What I wanted most was to have all four kids with me again, and perhaps this issue could be the bait.

Linda had finished her bachelor's degree in education and was planning to study psychology in graduate school. She could come down to investigate the Mexican attitude toward death and use her research to help Americans improve theirs.

If Bill could grasp the economic implications of adding another religious holiday to the U.S. calendar, perhaps he would come to Mexico, and together we could work together to export the Day of the

Dead holiday to the States.

Bill had relayed the news that Lee was about to remarry and move out of state, so hopefully Bill's gypsy days were about to end. He'd said that Lee was marrying a Mexican woman from California. I had shivered when I'd heard his choice of brides. Given Lee's extreme bigotry, that seemed like a convoluted way to hold onto me. I nevertheless predicted a rosy future for Lee and the new Mrs. Sonna, because Bill said she didn't speak any English. Since Lee didn't speak a word of Spanish, they could walk off into the Los Angeles smog to live silently ever after.

Before Bill's hippie days, he had been a committed capitalist—so much so that he'd gotten in serious trouble for selling candy bars to his junior high school classmates. The administration hadn't objected to his business per se but to his outrageous prices. The principal had called me in for a meeting to inform me of Bill's grievous crime, had shut down his operation, and had threatened to expel him if he engaged in any more price gouging.

If a bit of materialism still lingered in Bill's flower-child heart, we could work together to make a new line of wreaths, candy cadavers, and greeting cards. Larry and Mark could do the illustrations. I was so excited at the prospect of a family business, I began jotting notes:

We could create Happy Condolence cards: "Congratulations on having added another skeleton to your closet."

We could make party invitations: "Join us for a graveyard gathering."

We could do bumper stickers: "Here today; ghost tomorrow."

There was nothing like a holiday to spark the kind of religious fervor that kept the U.S. economy rolling. We could make a fortune.

To prepare America for the new holiday, Dr. Linda and I could co-author a book about the Mexican way of death. All we needed was a great title. Most Americans were even less enthusiastic about their ancestors than about their families. Apparently parents were now viewed as toxic, siblings as rivals, and spouses as dysfunctional. Suggesting that they honor their forefathers and foremothers wouldn't work.

Money was still popular, and get-rich-quick books were perennial favorites.

Suddenly inspiration struck. To ensure our book would become a runaway New York Times best seller, we would call it *Dying for Fun and Profit.*

CHAPTER 17

THE GALLOPING GRINGA GOURMET

*"I don't even butter my bread;
I consider that cooking."*

— *Katherine Cebrian*

Larry and Mark chatted about school at the table while I fixed lunch. "From now on, I am doing all the homeworks every one of the nights. Even calification," Mark announced.

"What's calification?" I asked.

"Spelling," Larry said. "In Spanish it's *calificación.*"

"I will even be doing the spelling homeworks," Mark said.

I nodded, glad that he was finally going to apply himself to his schoolwork.

"You shouldn't do homework just to do it, Mark," Larry said in a professorial tone. "You need to use your pea brain."

"*¡Pendejo!*" Mark exclaimed.

"I don't care *why* Mark does his school work," I said. "If he'll just do it, he'll learn."

Mark shook his head. "No, the teacher does not say for us to be learning, just to be doing all of the homeworks all of the days. If we do, she will be presenting to us a candy bar on the Fridays." He paused, considering. "*¡Ay!* If the whole class is doing all of the homeworks, the teacher will be presenting sixty candy bars. That is very much chocolate!"

Larry humphed. "Anything worth doing is worth doing well, Mark."

"Larry is bugging my mind again, Mom," Mark whined. "Make for him to stop!"

I sighed as I set lunch on the table. I wished the loving, caring, affectionate way Mexican siblings treated one another would rub off on my boys. How did Mexican parents get their kids to relate as life-long caregivers, helpmates, and cherished friends. Maybe it was because American religious types pointed to the Cain and Abel story as proof that sibling rivalry was innate and personally nurtured by God. Perhaps Mexican Catholics took the fratricidal legend as a warning rather than an inevitability. But what was their secret? How did they get their kids to be so very kind toward one another?

"Enough, boys!" I said. "Eat your lunch before it gets cold."

Larry's face was glum as he stared at his plate. "It was cold before you served it."

"Then hurry up before it hits room temperature! Think of the millions of starving—"

"Children in China," Larry and Mark intoned together.

"I was going to say, um, children in Mexico. The hungry multitudes are languishing outside our door as we speak."

Larry leapt up, plate in hand. "They can have it!"

"Sit down, young man, and count your blessings."

Larry bowed his head. "Thank you, God, for Chef Boy-R-Dee ravioli. For Old El Paso refried beans. For Doritos tortilla chips and peanut butter. For bottled Coke."

"Yes!" I said. "Thank God or thank me for this exquisite medley of imported Italian, Mexican, and American cuisine. A gourmet international feast. You are such lucky children."

Larry gagged. "Boy, do I ever feel lucky."

"Larry, how about thanking to God for the mother who is buying for you the foods?" Mark said.

Sometimes sibling rivalry did have benefits. "Thanks, Mark. But why don't you eat your meal?"

"I guess my stomach is not having much hunger," my little diplomat said.

Despite all the changes in our lives since moving to Mexico, Larry continued his LaGrange campaign to improve my culinary capabilities. Once I managed to convince him that pot roast and stew ingredients weren't available south of the border, he began extolling the virtues of homemade tacos over the heat-and-serve variety.

"What happened to that cooking book Linda was presenting to you for the Christmas, Mom?" Mark asked.

I cringed, remembering. In college Linda had discovered that she alone savored the cafeteria's fried spam balls, rainbow beef, and soy burgers. Her classmates' yearning for home-cooked meals led her to believe that she had been deprived of a normal childhood. For Christmas she had given me the *I Hate to Cook Book*—an attempt, I assumed, to save her brothers from a similar fate.

"Get real, Mark," Larry said. "You think Mom would read a cookbook?"

"As a matter of fact, smarty-pants," I said, "I did read the preface. It said, 'faster is better.' I'm already the fastest cook on either side of the border, so I didn't need to read the rest."

Larry lifted a minuscule portion of El Paso refried beans to his lips and made a face. "You'd have more energy and feel better, Mom, if you'd include more low-cholesterol, low-sodium foods in your diet."

"Include WHAT? Any kid who can say THAT and know what he's talking about is old enough to fix his own peanut butter tortillawiches!"

That silenced my future physician, but I knew I hadn't dampened his hope that by regulating my blood sugar and shaping up fatty acids, I'd have more energy for domestic pursuits. And I knew who was poisoning his mind: Mrs. Kocmoud's Mexican counterpart, Señora Responsable.

If my grasp of the domestic arts had been poor compared to my U.S. neighbors, in Mexico they were the pits. I contended that keeping up with two point five children (Bill lived with us about half of the time) would be too much for any mother. But my argument lost force when my kids became aware of what went on in the Responsable household next door.

Señora Responsable was the perfect example of domesticity run amok. Her two babies rarely cried. Her three toddlers were tidy. Her five elementary school-aged children did their homework. Her four teenagers were polite. To make matters worse, her husband's shirts were always pressed, her windows sparkled, and her garden bloomed. To add insult to incongruity, she looked relaxed and happy.

As if reading my thoughts, Mark said, "Señora Responsable does not need to be reading that hating the cooking book."

"Why not?" I asked.

"Señora Responsable loves to be doing always the cooking." As Mark spoke, he had the dreamy-eyed look of a love-smitten lad.

"But haven't you noticed?" I asked. "Señora Responsable is so busy feeding and caring for her children, husband, and house, she has no time left for herself."

Mark nodded vaguely.

Not so Larry. "But Mom, if Señora Responsable wasted time combing her hair and shaving her legs, she couldn't cook such great meals."

I sighed. Señora Responsable's meals were becoming a major thorn in my pride.

A few days later Mark asked about the odors creeping into our apartment from under the Responsables' door.

"It's called lunch," Larry answered.

"Lunch?" Mark stared bleakly at his peanut butter and tortillawich.

TORTILLAS & PEANUT BUTTER

"You're so dumb," answered Larry. "You can't expect a cold sandwich to smell. Haven't you smelled warmed up Franco American spaghetti? The heat releases some molecules into the air. As I see it, there are two kinds of moms in this world: cookers and heater-uppers."

"Oh," Mark said, nodding as if he understood.

But he obviously didn't. "Americans have different customs, Mark," I explained. "We believe that mothers should retain positions of equality in relation to their families. We try not to be slaves to our children's digestive systems."

"We are reading about the slaves in our school," Mark said. "America was in a war with itself, and Lincoln said to the slaves 'now you are being free.' "

"Yes. And then a famous feminist, Gloria Steinem, freed the American moms," I said.

"I know!" Larry said. "Maybe Señora Responsable could teach us to cook."

"But there are other issues to consider. Americans believe in free enterprise. If I cooked great meals at home, we might not want Whataburgers, and I wouldn't stock up on canned goods when we go to the U.S. If American mothers acted like Señora Responsable, Ronald McDonald would be stuck with a zillion spoiled hamburgers! Wendy, Denny, and the Burger King would be bankrupt."

"And then all the American kids, they will be being sad," said Mark.

"Yes!" I nodded emphatically. "They would."

"Only until they tasted *real* food," Larry said.

And then they would be spoiled, as Linda had been spoiled by that college cafeteria food. At least her palate was her problem now. "Larry, did you know that packaged food costs twice as much as food cooked from scratch? If American mothers cooked food from scratch, they could trigger an economic crisis. Have you ever heard of the Great Depression?"

Larry looked impressed. "Yes. It was in *Volume D* of the encyclopedia. No wonder Mexico is so poor!"

"Yes! There are too many Señora Responsables making home cooked meals in this country. Anyway, your big brother and sister want you brought up as Americans, and I don't want you to lose touch with your compatriots. Eat up."

A few minutes later I glanced at the clock. "It's time to return to school. Let's hold our breaths and run through the hallway so we don't smell the Señora's lunch and change our minds about quickie meals."

After lunch, my guilt rose faster than yeast in a hot oven, or as fast as yeast on a warm counter. I don't know which temperature yeast prefers.

To add zest to the boys' lunch the next day, I stirred Nestle Quik chocolate into their milk, substituted crunchy for smooth peanut butter, and added a dab of grape jelly to their tortillawiches. We were sitting down to eat when the doorbell rang. It was Señora Responsable.

"*Buenas tardes,*" I said. Our conversation proceeded in Spanish.

"I hope I am not interrupting your—your dinner?" Her expression didn't change as she surveyed our table, but her faint shake of the head said it all.

"Americans eat the main meal in the evening," I explained.

Mark added, "America had a big war against itself, and the president was making all the slaves to be free, and then the moms got to be free. So now they are making the childrens to be eating the peanut butter sandwiches for the lunches."

Señora Responsable looked confused.

"The President Lincoln," Mark continued, "he was cutting the chains from the mothers to their stoves."

I said, "Mark means that when Lincoln freed the peanut-picking slaves, the price of a jar of Skippy went through the roof. Still, I sacrifice to keep my boys supplied with a name-brand spread."

The Señora nodded uncertainly, patted her rumpled hair, and shifted her unshaven legs.

"It's for national defense, too," Larry said. "Food in cans, jars, and plastic keeps American capitalism strong."

"*Ay*, your Larry is such a smart one," the Señora said. "Are you still planning to become a doctor?"

"Yes, but Mom says I should stick to the laboratory and stay away from people. I'm going to be a medical researcher."

"That's wonderful. Pardon me, Señora Sonna, but I cannot stay long. I came to invite your family for supper tonight. I'm serving *pozole a la Veracruzana*."

Mark's face lit up, but I was more cautious. The stubborn streak that made me refuse to eat any Mexican dish I couldn't readily identify had saved me from eating unborn baby eels, stuffed calves' intestines, octopus tentacles, and cow tongue.

Señora Responsable explained that *pozole a la Veracruzana* took two days to prepare. After she husked and shucked and blanched the corn, she hand-peeled the kernels before cooking them for a full day. The embryonic meal, now nearing its final evolutionary stage, would be ready at eight p.m.

"Well, I appreciate the offer, but…" How could I explain that one of her meals might ruin my sons' taste buds for life?

"Can we, Mom?" begged skinny Larry and little Mark.

I was fighting the temptation to run next door and devour the *pozole a la whatever* at that very moment, so I agreed.

"If you like it, I'll be glad to give you the recipe. But I don't suppose you'd want to go to all that trouble," she said, eyeing our box of imported Hostess Ding Dongs.

"Well, I never can tell when a domestic impulse might arise and propel me into the kitchen," I said.

After we squeezed around the massive lemon-oiled and hand-waxed table with the Responsable clan, the Señora treated us to a fuller description of her labor of love. She had shopped all over town to find the freshest ingredients, and had plucked, gutted, skinned, and boiled the chicken.

The simmering bowl placed before me looked and smelled suspiciously like chicken soup.

The Señora instructed me to add handfuls of chopped cabbage, sliced radishes, slivered onions, and some homegrown oregano. That didn't sound appealing, but as my mother had said when I complained about mashed potatoes defiling my peas, "It all ends up in the same place, anyway." And serving soup and salad in one bowl would save on dishwashing, so perhaps there was a method to this Mexican madness.

Dr. Responsable, Señora Responsable, their fourteen children, and my two boys watched me stir the veggies into my broth and raise the spoon to my mouth. I paused and insisted that everyone be served so they'd stop staring at me. Then I hurriedly wrapped my lips around the spoon and tasted...hominy! Hominy in chicken broth!

"Ay, Señora Responsable," Mark said. "This is the most richness I am ever tasting."

"Goodness, what an agreeable thing to say," she tittered.

"I am speaking the truth to you!"

She gave his arm an affectionate squeeze.

"It is so wonderful, I don't know how to express it," Mark enthused.

I squeezed Mark's other arm and whispered in English, "If you don't alienate the hand that usually feeds you, you may live to remember this wonderful meal for many years!"

Mark was too busy casting admiring glances at Señora Responsable to grasp that he was treading on thin ice.

"Mark!" I said sharply. "It's not polite to smack your lips."

"I'm sorry. This is such deliciousness, the smacks just happen." He cast winsome smiles at his culinary heroine. She smiled back and pinched his darling cheek. The rest of us ate in silence and watched them worm their way into one another's hearts.

Then Larry tried to gain admittance to their club. "Mark says this is the greatest, but he doesn't know what he's talking about."

Señora Responsable coughed, her husband fidgeted with his napkin, the teenaged Responsables looked as though they might pummel the guest who, rumor had it, was a blood relative of mine. They obviously weren't accustomed to American-style sibling sarcasm, sassiness, and slights.

"Larry," I hissed in English, "At least Mark has the courtesy to thank his hostess—even if he is overdoing it."

Our little intra-family spat continued in English.

"I'm not being an overdoer!" Mark protested.

Larry looked perplexed. "I just meant," he said, "that Mark is too young to remember Grandma's cooking. He can only compare this to the garbage you serve."

"Thanks a lot, Larry," I said

He looked mystified. "What's wrong? Why are you mad?"

This was why I thought Larry should avoid a career that involved interacting with John Q. Public and should stick with microbes, which were harder to insult.

As we departed Señora Responsable issued the standard *"Mi casa es tu casa"* line.

"Oh?" Larry asked hopefully.

"Thank you, thank you, thank you!" Mark exclaimed. "My mom hates cooking so much, Linda was never tasting real food until she is being at college."

The Señora looked horrified by this report of maternal neglect.

"My boys have an American sense of humor," I said quickly. "Mexicans rarely get our jokes, and vice versa."

The next time we crossed into the U.S., I went straight to the A&P. Entering an American supermarket after a long absence always came as a shock. Now that I had developed a high tolerance to native market smells, the sanitized, deodorized, floor wax, and ammonia cleanser odor of American grocery stores seemed forbiddingly foreign. Having stickers and signs communicate the prices made shopping a boring, impersonal chore. I missed the challenge of trying to uncover the bottom price of an item as a new vendor acquaintance or long-term friend strove to conceal it.

The whole system made no sense to me. Mexico's custom of charging according to a shopper's personal means, need, and bargaining ability seemed compellingly capitalistic. People charged what the market would bear. The U.S.'s one-price-for-everybody seemed like communism.

Along with my usual assortment of junk food staples, I bought some cans of hominy and Swanson's cooked chicken, bouillon cubes, a packet of oregano, a box of green Jell-O, and a container of Dream Whip artificial non-dairy creamer. At the checkout stand, the clerk began punching the cash register without so much as a scripted "Welcome to the A&P."

"Excuse me, Miss," I said. "I'd like a discount."

"A what?" she asked.

"A price reduction."

"For what?"

"Well, perhaps for shopping here instead of Kroger? Because I can't afford retail?"

She laughed as if I had told a joke and continued ringing up my purchases. When she announced the total, I gasped. A native market was absolutely worth the olfactory assault! I ransomed my groceries and drove to McDonalds to help the economy—mine!

Larry gobbled his Big Mac, but Mark picked at his meal. The catsup was too sugary and bland; he wanted hot sauce. The bun was tasteless and squishy; he wanted a *bolillo*. The mayonnaise was too sweet; he wanted sour cream. The ice in the Coke froze his throat, the sugar made his teeth ache, the carbonation had too many bubbles, and the artificial lemon tasted like chemicals.

On arriving in Irapuato, I picked up cabbage, radishes, cilantro, and onions at the market. At home I knocked on the Responsables' door, gestured to our suitcases, announced that we had just arrived from our one thousand five hundred mile round-trip journey, and invited the entire family to dinner in twenty minutes.

While I warmed chicken soup and mixed in the hominy, Mark gathered dried needles from under the patio fir tree and mixed them into the oregano on a plate. The spice looked just like Señora Responsable's homegrown variety! I plopped canned jalapeños into a bowl in case someone preferred their *pozole a la Yanqui* spicy.

Our guests arrived as I was burying the empty cans and bags in the trash. Everyone found a place to perch, and I served.

"It is quite good," said Señora Responsable.

"A bit salty, but tasty," said the good doctor.

The fourteen Responsable children ate without comment.

My boys declared my *pozole* superior to Armor Beef Stew and had second helpings.

As a side dish, I served imported Doritos with Skippy peanut butter. The Responsables ate only one each, but I understood. Tortilla chips and peanut butter is an acquired taste.

I offered the Señora my *pozole* recipe.

"Thanks, but it is too much work. All those hours driving to Laredo to shop! Americans make things so difficult."

"Mom," Larry said in English, "tell her how packaged groceries and fast food help the economy."

"And tell to her about the great depression she could have for being too busy to be quitting the disgusting hair from her legs," Mark added.

I was afraid that one of the Responsable kids might know enough English to have understood him. But on glancing nervously about, I became distracted by the sight of Dr. Responsable holding his wife's hand. The unexpected glimpse of husbandly affection caught me off guard. How could she feel more romantic than resentful after spending hours peeling and simmering his corn kernels? Would his passion survive if she served him macaroni casseroles?

Suddenly I felt uncertain about the point of my *pozole a la Yanqui* meal. Had I set out to prove that her labor of love was a waste of time? That an indifferent homemaker could be a loveable wife? That an incompetent cook could be a good mom? Had I been trying to prove something to the Responsables? To my kids? To myself? Was I still trying to prove myself to Lee?

Suddenly I felt like my joke was on me. I wished I could pull a batch of Toll House cookies from the oven or Rice Krispy treats from the fridge. All I could do was hold my head high and pretend to like my icky quickie desert.

"OK, who wants Cool Whip on their Jell-O?" Larry asked as he spooned jiggling glutinous green globs onto plates.

Mark smacked his lips as he savored his sugar and chemical treat. "If the students at my school are to be doing all of the homeworks, the teacher should be presenting to them this deliciousness on the Fridays," he enthused.

One of the Responsable children asked me to give the recipe to his mother.

Mark shook his head. "Only a special mother can be traveling so far to be buying this for her children."

"Such a loving child," the Señora cooed to Mark.

Larry squared his shoulders. "A working mom made this meal," he said proudly. "And she's also a teacher, a school principal, and the school director, in addition to giving private English lessons. And she sells school uniforms, textbooks, and contraband on the side. Pretty amazing, huh?"

I knew Larry was just trying to upstage Mark for the Most Loving Child award, but I nevertheless appreciated his affirmation. It's supposed to be the thought, not the gift that counts. But sometimes the thought behind a gift is the pits, but the gift is wonderful. This was definitely one of those times.

CHAPTER 18

THE WITCH OF IRAPUATO

"Actions lie louder than words."

— *Carolyn Wells*

Whether the U.S. space program was to blame was unclear, but the spring and summer of 1973 had been exceptionally rainy. When the army unexpectedly marched into Irapuato in August, rumors hurtled up and down the town grapevine. Was a war about to break out? What was going on?

Finally the government made an announcement on the radio about a local plumbing problem: Irapuato's water reservoir couldn't cope with the pressure of so much rainwater, and the dam had developed a crack. The reservoir was located on a mountaintop outside of our valley town. If the dam suddenly gave way, we'd be up to our sombreros in water.

My Mexican friends and neighbors weren't worried. They speculated about how the politicians would benefit from a story about a looming liquid disaster. Did the *políticos* hope to snare federal emergency relief funds to spiff up their mansions? Had the city fathers waylaid a shipment of life preservers and cooked up the flood story to sell them? Had the mayor bought shares in a boat manufacturing company?

I decided to follow the radio's emergency directives. I directed Ricardo, the *Instituto's* new school secretary, to move all the furniture up to the second floor.

"That is not a good idea, Señora," he said. "You shouldn't give in to political scare tactics." He explained that governments of third-world countries commonly spread news of upcoming disasters so that citizens will run out and buy the commodities in which some politicians have a vested interest. The subsequent run on toilet paper, sugar, cooking oil, batteries, and other essentials causes the predicted shortage, which drives up the prices. That way, the politicians line their pockets and turn the governments' lies about upcoming shortages into truths, even though no disaster happened.

Ricardo's chest puffed with pride. "But Mexicans know our officials are liars, so we citizens ignore their warnings," he said.

From his explanation I gleaned that not buying the government's recommended emergency items creates a surplus, which would cause prices to decline, thereby exposing the lie driven by officials' greed.

"You really believe that someone on the elected ladder, or a relative on one of the steps will profit from spreading news of an upcoming flood?" I asked.

"Not if we do not panic and act."

I nevertheless insisted that Ricardo carry all movable items to the second floor. Then I had him come to my home to move my living room furniture upstairs. It was worn and shabby, but I'd tangled with my landlord over past apartment purchases and lost. If anything needed to be repaired or replaced, I would have to bear the expense.

The radio kept us up to date on the reservoir's status. The Mexican equivalent of the U.S. Army Corps of Engineers was tirelessly toiling to figure out what to do about *La Presa del Conejo*, Rabbit Dam.

Then an announcement declared that a repair wasn't possible. To

TORTILLAS & PEANUT BUTTER

prevent the dam from unexpectedly cracking wide open and flooding the town, the troops would reduce the pressure by drilling a few holes to release some water.

The army would drill the little holes at night. That way, a gentle rivulet of water would trickle into town while we slept and drain into the earth by the time we awakened. We wouldn't even get our tootsies wet.

When the six-foot wall of water swept into town in the dead of night on August 18, the flood killed untold numbers, completely washed away forty thousand adobe homes, left three hundred thousand valley residents homeless, and according to the press reports, wiped out sixty percent of Irapuato's buildings.

Some locals blamed the army, maintaining that its drill bits had proved too puny to penetrate the dam's massive concrete wall. No one could find the next best solution, a jackhammer. The troops had resorted to dynamite, which had blasted the entire wall of the dam to smithereens. As a consequence, the little holes ended up a tad larger than expected.

The army's spokesman denied that charge (no pun intended), insisting that the engineers had just made a few small holes.

I believed the army, because I knew about a small hole (pun intended) in the Mexican educational system. Students weren't required to read the story about the little Dutch boy who pulled his thumb out of the dyke. The army engineers therefore didn't know what a few million cubic tons of water pressure do to a crack and a thumb-sized hole in a concrete dam.

Because I was one of the few residents to survive the flood unscathed, my reputation as a witch who could foretell the future spread faster than the ensuing cholera epidemic. Only Ricardo knew the truth—or so I thought.

"I do not understand, Señora. If you're not a witch, how did you know the officials would ruin the dam and flood the town just to line their own pockets?"

"Oh? How did the officials benefit?"

"By selling off the army's old uniforms. Haven't you noticed the troops' new clothes?"

Yes, I had noticed. The uniformed troops had marched into town en route to the dam repair project. After the flood, they sloshed around town clad in University of California sweatshirts and God Bless America baseball caps. The clothes had been donated by Irapuato's U.S. sister city and benefactor, La Jolla, California. Having to rescue our soggy city's residents apparently qualified the troops as victims of the flood.

"I'm not a witch, Ricardo." I insisted. "I read The Little Dutch Boy in school. And I've had a lot of experience with Mexican plumbing. But there are some important lessons to be learned from this," I informed him. "Number One, I trust your government, and you should too."

He looked skeptical. "And Number Two?"

"As the Mexican saying goes, 'He who loses it carelessly didn't deserve it in the first place!'"

Ricardo shook his head sadly. "No, Señora. You didn't deserve to lose it," he said.

"Lose what?"

"Your reputation. Now everyone who suspected you were a witch, knows that you are."

CHAPTER 19

MY DARKEST HOURS

"Weather forecast for tonight: dark."

– George Carlin

I admit that I'm an electric junkie. I can be turned on, tuned in, and ticked off with a flip of a switch, twist of a dial, or push of a button. Cut my wires, and I lose my three most important senses: sight, common, and horse. Or so I discovered when a series of mysterious citywide blackouts forced me into sudden withdrawal.

In asking what was going on, some people suspected that communists had sabotaged our power tower. Most guessed that a simple fuse had gone bad and the city electricians were too lazy to replace it. Finally, the truth emerged: Irapuato was in the midst of a labor strike.

It turned out that the city's electrical workers had begun demonstrating for more pay by staging a work slow-down several weeks prior to the blackouts. Because government workers do so little, no one had noticed anything unusual.

Next, the workers had tried to advertise their grievances by pulling the city plug. They had shut off the TVs, radios, and presses, which thwarted the workers' attempt to air their grievances. *Juan Q. Público* was too accustomed to power outages to suspect foul play.

When the news of the strike finally got out, the mayor hired a skeleton crew of scab electricians, divided Irapuato into four time zones, and scheduled rotating blackouts to ensure equality of deprivation.

Our Zone Four apartment was doomed to gloom each day from six p.m. until midnight—my favorite time for seeing!

My friends couldn't understand my upset over being cut off from the television, clock radio, record player, and reading. They suggested I relax, but I knew that too dangerous. If I succeeded, I might lose my ability to relate to my eternally busy, nervous compatriots. Although I didn't have plans to return to the U.S., I wanted to keep my options open.

Being stuck in the dark seven evenings each week without the customary sources of entertainment and distraction made Larry, Mark and me cranky. We tried telling ghost stories, but neither boy produced any good ones. Mark's affinity for playing in the puddles of melted candle wax grated on my nerves.

As the sibling squabbles intensified, Mark complained that Larry was "pulling the air through his nose that way just to be bugging my mind."

"Enough!" I said. "Larry has my permission to breathe in as well as out!" But without TV or books to distract me, Larry's snuffling inhales and whistling exhales were "bugging my mind," too.

During the second week of the strike, even Larry's constant reading and studying bothered me. He could manage with an Abe Lincoln candle, but my aging eyes needed more than a flickering flame.

At least all the family togetherness erased my working-mom guilt about not spending enough time with my kids. When Mark begged me to join his Saturday morning craft-kit candle-making project, I declined with a clear conscience.

"But you are not doing the anything," Mark said. "It will be much fun."

From the comfort of the couch, I replied, "No, I'm busy staring at the living room wall. I love being able to sit here and actually see it. If you want to make candles, you're on your own."

"I can be making the candles by my only self?" he asked.

"Sure."

"But the directions, they are saying to use a big knife for cutting the end."

"Cutting the what?"

"Cutting the *para fin.*"

I looked at the craft box. "It says 'paraffin.' That's another word for wax. You have to cut it with a large knife. Permission granted."

"And the directions, they are saying to do the wax-melting on the stove and then to be pouring her into a mold."

"Permission granted."

"I cannot be wax-pouring by my only self!"

"What does the box say?"

"'A project the whole family can enjoy.'"

"Not that! Look at the top right-hand corner."

"For children age eight to adult."

"If the manufacturer says you can do it, you can! Well, I guess I should cut the wax, but that's it! To answer your other questions in advance, I have no preferences for candle colors, sizes, shapes, or fragrances. I'll like whatever you choose."

After chopping the wax, only three precious hours of light remained to fulfill my darkest fantasies: to watch TV, read my junk novel during the commercial breaks, and munch potato chips that I could see as well taste.

A few minutes later, the smell of wax wafted into the living room. I looked up in time to see a giant bolt of orange lightning leap from the kitchen and retreat. A second later, a bomb boomed. Mark half flew, half blew into the living room.

I leapt to my feet. "Oh, no!" I cried. "Not my new stove!" I raced into the kitchen.

When I stepped inside, my feet slid out from under me. From my position flat on my back on the floor, I saw the ceiling. Except for a blackened mess above the stove, the rest was covered in a red film. I managed to rise and slip-slide across the waxy floor. Every square inch of every cabinet and appliance was also coated.

Mark was white-faced and shaking. "It was the most terriblest, Mom. The wax, she was boiling her big, happy bubbles. A tiny drop dripped herself on the stove. Then the fire, he was all over the everywhere! I was fast pouring the water onto him, but he kept on getting bigger."

"Just look at this mess! How could you!"

Mark's face darkened. He put his hands on his hips and shouted, "I was being exploded into the living room floor. But are you asking, 'Mark, are you hurt or OK'? No! You are only asking, 'My stove, is she hurt or OK!' " He started to sob. "The stove is more importanter to you than I am being!"

Oops. "You were my first concern," I hastened to reassure him. "But you flew into the living room so fast, I knew you were OK. Injured kids don't fly and land. They slither and sink."

Mark didn't look convinced. He would likely detail yet another of my maternal missteps in a letter to Linda, Bill, or both.

"How about this?" I asked. "Help me clean the kitchen, and I'll keep you in my will."

The power company didn't black out our zone that night. Perhaps the workers feared the Zone Four candle bomb had been intended for them.

I spent my first lamp-lit evening scrubbing black smoke and red wax from the kitchen.

And I spent the next week of evenings scrubbing.

And the next month.

Francesca put in hundreds of hours during the day.

The only effective solvent was a mixture of boiling water, elbow grease, and tears.

When my electric bill arrived, it was bigger than ever. Due to the drastically decreased consumption during our forced abstinence, the power company had raised the rates. Nevertheless, I was grateful to be able to see at night again, even if what I saw was a mess. Facing the fiasco with flickering fluorescent fixtures was easier than grappling with ghost stories in the gloom.

CHAPTER 20

KIDNAPPED!

*"It's far easier to forgive an enemy after
you've gotten even with him."*

— *Olin Miller*

Under my charming ministrations, the *Instituto's* initial planting of thirty young seedlings had quickly become root bound.

I had already transplanted my burgeoning bouquet to a bigger pot once. Since then, our esteemed institution of higher education had continued to flourish. With over two hundred students, our school needed a roomy garden to call its own.

After an intensive search, I settled on the *Casa de La Inquisición*, "House of the Inquisition." Originally constructed in 1764, the historic baroque building's name and reputation promised to set the perfect disciplinary tone for our students, some of whom were mimicking the mouthy teens on American TV sitcoms. I decided to save the architectural relic for posterity to stand as a time-honored memorial to adults charged with ushering infidels onto the proper behavioral path.

I spent over a year pouring over blueprints and supervising the renovation of the crumbling interior to restore the house of torture to its original glory. In addition, I had workers tuck modern conveniences like water pipes and electric wiring into the three-foot-thick rose granite walls.

Cost overruns prevented me from adding some finishing touches. I had to forgo the replication and installation of the traditional racks, thumbscrews, and Spanish donkeys I had planned for Maridél.

Yet for all the *Instituto's* success, and despite my brisk business in school uniforms, textbooks, and contraband, my personal income wasn't keeping up with the outgo.

According to the reports in the government-controlled news outlets, inflation was running at thirty percent. Everyone knew that figure to be ridiculous. The cost of essentials, like tortillas, cooking oil, and milk, had doubled in a month. To further complicate my bank balance, the car needed repairs.

And then Guillermo, who had so loved his U.S. toilet seats, offered to let us live in his country house rent-free. The price was right, but the rural placement was all wrong.

Being both born and bred a city girl, I felt comfy in concrete jungles, surrounded by the familiar smell of smog and the hustling bustle of a rush hour. I liked the cultural advantages of nearby stores and fine-dining restaurants to feast on goat steak, which I had come to love.

Like most city dwellers, I harbored some romantic notions about trading alarm clocks for roosters and TV twinkles for starlit nights, and bowls of Fruit Loops for vine-ripened berries with cream.

But I wasn't fooled by the down-home hype. I knew bugs and blight ran through those fields of amber grain. I had seen cows and chickens up close and knew their smell. I'd never had an urge to pickle a cucumber, raise a prize pig, or crochet a doily.

"I don't know much about agriculture, but I once grew a lawn," I told Guillermo. I didn't add that after Lee nixed my Astroturf solution, I ignored bits of Kentucky Blue and watered the crab grass.

"My ranch hands tend the crops," Guillermo reassured me. "I just need someone to live in the house to deter squatters and thieves. I'd rent it if I could, but no one wants to live in the middle of nowhere."

Larry and Mark certainly didn't.

They whined through my five-minute pep talk about the joys of country living.

They were unmoved by my five-minute sob story about the trials of single motherhood.

My five-minute lecture about the plight of orphans abandoned by impoverished city parents got their attention.

They agreed to accompany me.

The clouds released an unseasonable torrent of rain as followed Guillermo's cocktail napkin map to the outskirts of town.

After even the boonies had faded into the distance, we neared our destination: the middle of nowhere.

Near a row of sagging shacks, the muddy dirt lane forked. When I stopped to search the napkin for the correct prong, a dozen ragged ranch hands lined up in front of their hovels. Several men cradled rifles in their thick, work-hardened arms. The grim group formed a formidable unwelcoming committee.

We looked embarrassingly ostentatious next to their poverty. In a country where white means wealth, we were gaudily overdressed in our light skin, eyes, and hair. I waved and called out a cheery *"buenas tardes"* to let them know that I related to other races and socioeconomic groups as equals.

Without a lip twitch that might betray an urge to smile, they stood staring at us like stone statues.

I was tempted to ask our new neighbors where we should go but doubted I would like their answer. So I made a quick eeny-meeny-miny-moe decision and chose the mud trail to the left.

"That must be the house," Larry said, squinting through the car's mud-splattered windshield.

I inched along the rutted, strawberry-lined path until the puddles merged into a small pond. When I tried to drive around it, the back tires slid over and dove in, dragging the rest of the car with it. We were up to our axles in mud.

From behind us came a chorus of laughter. I rolled down the window, and about twenty ragamuffins trotted over. They pounded on the hood, and then jumped on it. I overcame my terror of unruly savages, ordered a trampolinist off the roof, and sent him to find help.

A few minutes later a tractor puttered up. A small, dark, middle-aged man dressed in rags jerked us out of the doldrums onto higher, drier ground.

"My name is Lois," I said brightly in Spanish.

He nodded. "I'm Estanislado."

"Is this the road to the farmhouse?"

He paused and scratched his head as if hesitant to share the secret with the new kid on the block. "Sí," he finally admitted.

"The car won't make it down this muddy road."

He paused again and then said, "Sí."

"Is the house far?"

Another pause. "Sí."

"We can't carry our stuff through the mud by ourselves."

"Sí," he answered. Then he restarted the tractor and puttered off.

Larry, Mark, and I began walking. A few steps later, we were up to our ankles in mud. When I lifted my foot, my shoe stayed behind. I balanced like a flamingo on one leg, leaned over, and gingerly fingered the ooze. I extricated my shoe but couldn't bring myself to insert my foot into the gooey mess. That meant I could hop to the house on one foot, which was ridiculous, or drive the car, which was impossible. I opted for the ridiculous.

A small adobe structure sagged in a clearing. With its lopsided roof, cracked windows, and tattered tile entryway, the house was as unwelcoming as our neighbors.

On entering we startled the current residents from their nests in the foyer. The little rodents disappeared under the hall closet door.

The living room doubled as a garbage dump for dozens of liquor bottles, beer cans, and cigarette butts.

The three bedrooms contained enough cobwebs to be the setting for a horror movie.

I donned my best cheerleader smile and pointed out the clothes washer that might work and the stove that might be fixable.

I silenced Mark's and Larry's threats to move in with Linda by promising to seize the domestic reigns ASAP, which I did by hiring Francesca to help. After a week of hauling, scrubbing, buffing, polishing, and fumigating, she transformed our Hell House into a habitable home.

Mark and Larry settled in quickly. As soon as the electricity was on, Larry poured over the encyclopedias with as much gusto as in town. Mark was rosy-cheeked from playing outside with the farmworkers' children.

I had a harder time adjusting. I missed the finer things of life—a TV, a telephone, and neighborly neighbors. Working long hours entertained me during the day, but I suffered acute sensory deprivation after school and on weekends. In the city my mind zipped like a record player set at seventy-eight rpm; in the country my thoughts lazed along at thirty-three rpm.

Amid the dawdling interior drone, I found myself pondering the imponderables. Did the boys share my love of Mexico? I'd always assumed that as long as I was happy, my kids would be, too, but Larry and Mark kept threatening to move in with Linda. Would they go if I gave them permission? And would Bill find a life path he could believe in and follow?

And why did I tremble when a stray memory of Lee wandered into my mind so long after I'd left LaGrange? Perhaps because in that one terrible moment as I confronted the broken vacuum, I had finally faced that I was powerless to interrupt Lee's ire. By turning up the charm I could instantly warm his skin, but nothing I did or said ever defrosted his icy heart or melted his frozen mind. That was the moment when the most terrible lesson I'd never wanted to learn had sunk in: there was a person walking the earth who didn't consider me awesomely alluring, delightfully ditzy, fabulously funny, or even wonderfully winsome.

That shocking knowledge had undone me at the time. The fear that there might be another like him in the world whose path I might someday cross had dimmed but never fully faded.

Would I ever want to marry again? If I did, would I ever have the courage to commit? What did the future have in store for me?

The canopy of twinkles in the sky outside my bedroom window promised answers to every human question. But they refused to answer mine.

Even sleeping was difficult for me on the farm. I tossed and turned among the unfamiliar sounds of animal murmurs and plant whispers, longing for the comfort of traffic noises and people sounds.

Then, in the pre-dawn darkness during our third week on the farm, I heard a people-sound somewhere inside the house. An adrenaline-driven spurt of fear quickly turned into tingles of excitement, and I leapt out of bed to explore.

As I tiptoed by the kitchen door, a movement above the sink caught my eye. I squinted in the darkness and saw a hand reaching in from the open window above the sink.

A set of fingers tip-toed across the ledge, walked down the wall, stopped on the counter top, and grasped a teacup. Then the fingers retraced their path, inching back up the wall, across the ledge, and out the window, until the hand, the fingers, and my cup disappeared. A moment later the fingers reappeared, again walked down to my counter top, and grasped a glass.

I ran to the window and called out to the woman crouched in the shadows below, "Stop, thief! *¡Ladrona!*"

I returned to the bedroom, threw a robe over my jammies, and hurried outside but arrived too late to confront the culprit. But then my eyes detected someone picking strawberries in a field near our house—or picking something. In the darkness, it was hard to tell.

The woman didn't look up when I approached her. She acted as if it were perfectly normal to pick strawberries in the middle of the night and to collect them in her apron instead of a wooden crate. As my eyes adjusted to the darkness, I noticed that she'd converted her *rebozo* from a shawl into a makeshift backpack. Whatever she had inside was large and bulky. I heard suspicious clinks every time she moved.

"*Buenas noches,*" I said.

"*Buenas noches, Señora,*" she replied.

I recognized her voice. "SOMEONE has been stealing my dishes, Lupita," I said severely.

She continued plucking and plopping whatevers into her apron.

"SOMEONE had better put them back before I get home from school later today, or I will report SOMEONE to the police."

After feasting on the tantalizing turmoil at school the next day, I returned home to find that my dishes were still missing. And all of the ranch hands had mysteriously disappeared as well.

Francesca suggested we go to Lupita's house and steal back my kitchenware.

In Lupita's front yard, a lone, skinny turkey pecked hopefully at the barren ground. When I tried to knock on the ragged sheet serving as the front door, a dozen flies awakened. They buzzed half-heartedly for a moment before settling back onto the fabric. I pushed the sheet aside.

The poverty inside was more abject than I had imagined possible. The furniture totaled two rickety wooden chairs, a little lopsided table, and a tower of straw-stuffed sleeping mats. A candle stub attested to the lack of electricity; a metal water bucket confirmed the lack of running water. Yet the fresh broom marks on the dirt floor showed Lupita to be a careful housekeeper—she had swept before she and her husband set out for their twelve-hour shift in the fields.

"Never mind," I told Francesca. "My dishes aren't there. And Lupita needs them more than I. I'm ready to forget the whole thing."

"But Señora, if you let someone steal your dishes today, tomorrow the workers will rob your pots and pans. The next day they'll take your phonograph and records. Soon you will be as poor as they are. Why not take that turkey hostage? If Lupita has nothing to cook, she won't need dishes. If she doesn't return them, you can eat the turkey."

Without further ado, Francesca took off after the feather-flapping fowl. In a matter of seconds she held its long neck with one hand, its skinny feet with the other, and its gyrating body under her armpit. She was clearly an experienced gobbler grabber.

Our little farmhouse wasn't designed for an avian hostage. After the turkey stopped pecking at the speckles on the linoleum floor, it started in on me. Soon there were welts on my ankles and trails of small brown turds on the floor.

I imprisoned the foul fowl in the bathroom. When I was forced to answer nature's call, the jailbird caught me in my most vulnerable position and attacked. I learned then and there that it is easier to be a hostage than a turkeynapper.

After school the next day, I delayed going home as long as possible. Larry, Mark, and I stopped off to visit friends and use their bathroom. We overstayed our welcome, but the delay didn't help. My worries intensified as we neared the farm. What if no one ransomed the bird? What if the ranch hands retaliated against my retaliation? What if I had to use the bathroom during the night?

We arrived after dark. Despite the moonless night, not a candle flickered in the ranch hands' huts. They all looked to be deserted. Apparently everyone had gone into hiding. As we neared our house, my headlights haloed a short brown man holding a very long rifle in his muscular arms. I recognized my tractor friend, Estanislado.

He held up a hand, signaling me to halt.

I feigned ignorance of universal sign language by waving back and flooring the accelerator.

After skidding to a stop, I prepared the boys. "Ready to make a run for it? On your marks, get set, GO!"

We dashed to the front door. I unlocked it and pushed the boys inside. Suddenly a long rifle descended across the doorframe and prevented me from following them.

"*Buenas noches, Estanislado,*" I said in Spanish. "*¿Cómo estás?*"

"*Bien. Gracias, Señora. ¿Y usted?*" His courteousness was contradicted by his metal barricade.

"*Bien. Gracias. ¡Adios!*" I said cheerfully.

I tried to step into the house, but the gun didn't budge. Our conversation continued in Spanish.

"*Por favor, Señora.* I must speak with you."

"Another time. I have to fix dinner for my children, and—"

"Lupita said you have our turkey. We want it back!" he said.

As I stared at the long-barreled barricade, I regretted having stolen his turkey. I regretted moving to the farm. As my life flashed before my eyes, I regretted leaving Lee, moving to Mexico, and every other life decision. If I died with Jesus' name on my lips, would He accept a last-minute convert? I asked St. Peter to erase any trespasses he might have recorded in his holy ledger.

My knees continued quaking, but the adrenaline rush had lubricated my sluggish country brain. It leapt into high gear. "But, Estanislado," I said. "What makes you think that I have your turkey?"

My ungrateful hostage unleashed a torrent of gobble-gobbles, punctuated by Mark's screams. "He is chasing to me! He is trying for to eat me! *¡Ayúdame!* Help!"

The gobble-gobbles grew louder.

"Quick! Jump up on the bed!" Larry yelled. "It can't follow you there!"

The subsequent spate of feather flaps and kid shrieks suggested it could.

"*¡Animal desgraciado, ven!*" Francesca yelled, commanding the wretched animal to come.

"Gobble, gobble, flap, flap," the turkey replied.

Estanislado readjusted his rifle. "I need my turkey, Señora."

To deal a blow to his wife's dignity with a direct accusation would violate Mexico's strict anti-defamation laws. I didn't want to justify my death. "Maybe one of the ranch workers has seen your turkey. Ask them. And while you're at it, ask if they have seen my dishes."

Lupita emerged from the inky night and stepped into the glimmers gushing from a window. "I already asked," she said. "One of the ranch hands stole your dishes."

She slipped her hand into the folds of her voluminous rebozo backpack and plucked out three cups, five saucers, two glasses, and ten pieces of silverware like a magician pulling rabbits from a *sombrero*. "Be careful, Señora," she said as she handed them to me. "Some of the farmworkers are thieves."

"Thanks," I called as she retreated into the shadows. "Good night,

Estanislado."

"Wait!" he said. "My turkey!"

From the screeches and shrieks, it sounded like the turkey had the upper claw and was holding the boys hostage. "I will ask around," I said. "I heard that some of the ranch hands are thieves. You might ask them."

Estanislado nodded. "Francesca can put my turkey in the barnyard."

My relations with all of my neighbors improved dramatically the next day. The caste system prevented true friendship, but we began trading regular grins, greetings, and gossip. They brought me fresh tomatoes and homemade tortillas; I bought treats and shoes for the children.

I gave Lupita and Estanislado a set of plastic dishes for Christmas but declined their dinner invitation when I heard the menu. I couldn't eat a gobbler that might still hold a grudge.

Country living made me a better person. I became more tolerant of barnyard smells and the sound of wind whooshing through a fruited field. I began pausing to smell the strawberries.

Depositing rent money into a bank instead of giving it to a landlord sent me on a new economic trajectory. With accounts paying thirty percent interest, my small financial cushion would quickly grow into a giant sofa. And it helped that Guillermo and I had become an item. When we went to dinner and a movie, he picked up the tab.

But when I experienced an urge to knit and can tomatoes, I decided to move back to town while Mark, Larry, and I could still appreciate a bustling crowd and crush of traffic. So back we went.

CHAPTER 21

BEASTLY BUREAUCRATIC SNAFUS

"A lizard is a perfect pet…"

— *Abbey Lee Kershaw*

Living in a land where siblings are friends hadn't rubbed off on Mark and Larry. Still, I hoped to reap other benefits from having my boys away from the scourges that wreak havoc on American families.

I was seven hundred miles from the nearest child-rearing book.

The nearest parent/child relationship class required a twelve-hour trip to the border.

My kids didn't pressure me to keep up with a Jones family located half a hemisphere away.

I was delighted to discover that there wasn't a word for "teenager" in Spanish. Mexicans didn't know that adolescents were supposed to be moody, uppity, defiant, and driven by hormone surges. Lacking the vocabulary with which to forge a teenaged identity, Mexican children sailed across the life transitions from little (*chico*) to young (*joven*) to married (*casado*). Those that didn't get *casado* stayed *joven*, no matter that they had been bachelors or spinsters for half a century.

Because Mexican children weren't expected to leave home at age eighteen, they didn't have to collect evidence against their parents to establish grounds for a family divorce.

Booze was available to anyone old enough to walk into a cantina and tall enough to set pesos on the bar, so tequila was useless for proving teens' temerity. Drugs were too valuable as a Yankee export commodity to waste on local consumption.

And Mexican *mamacitas* had solved the teenaged sex problem. They simply sent a sibling to serve as their personal ambassador to co-ed activities. Moms didn't have to glean clues from a daughter's tousled hair and smudged lipstick to figure out what she had been up to. The chaperone happily detailed every real and imagined offense so as not to have to spend more time hanging out with his sister and her dorky date.

Besides protecting my children from teenage blight, I decided that Mexico was paradise when I discovered that so few people had pets, there wasn't even a word for pet in Spanish.

But my time in heaven didn't last long. One day Mark noticed some street urchins peddling iguanas to gullible American tourists, and he began longing for a lizard to call his own.

My reasons for nixing a lizard could have filled a book. I needed to remember my past traumas—what had happened when I'd let my kids turn my "no" into a "yes." A book would take years to write, so I made a short list:

Linda's white kitten: It grew up and produced thirty more.

Linda's Siamese cat: It hid in the basement for six months until I announced she would have to take over the poop-scooping job.

Linda's albino bunny: We renamed Snow King a litter later. He became she, Snow Queen.

Linda's mice: Linda and her friend Diane moved two white mice into our basement for their science project. It took me five months, one hundred fifty-one babies, forty escapees, zero experiments, no hope for a Nobel Prize or passing grade to unmask their research subjects as pets and oust them.

Bill's dog: It was the product of our neighbor's female terrier and a male that snuck into the yard one heated night. We called him Spot because he left so many on the carpet.

Bill's alligator: He spent his own allowance to buy baby Ali during a Florida family vacation, but I paid the price. At first Ali would not eat—he was starving! I force-fed him lunchmeat bits on a toothpick. Then he ate—then he was growing! To restore our ability to use the bathtub, I donated him to the Brookfield zoo.

Larry's canary: It never learned to talk.

The kids' goldfish: We'd had enough dead ones to restock Lake Michigan's smelly shoreline.

Turtles, gerbils, lightning bugs, frogs, crickets, etc.: The list was endless.

"No, you can't have an iguana, Mark," I said. "Mexican animals are for work, not for play. There isn't even a word for 'pet' in the dictionary.

The closest translation is *animal domesticado.*"

"How about a horse? Please say yes!" Larry begged. "It can trim and fertilize the lawn."

If I didn't keep the upper hand, I'd relive the nightmare of setting up a shoebox coffin for Carlos the Chameleon or catching insects for Tomás the Turtle.

"You've already had an authentic pet-owners' experience with the turkey. One pet per childhood is more than sufficient."

"If I'd known the turkey was a pet, we could have trained it!" Larry said. "Chickens can learn to play the piano, you know, with classical conditioning techniques."

"Have you forgotten already? Even when we ignored the turkey, it followed us around and kept attacking us."

"But—"

"No! You may NOT bring home a beast to burden your mother," I said a bit too loudly. "Mexico has freed me from the parent trap. I'm on a straight and narrow childrearing road. And if there's a pet on that road, I'll run over it!"

Mark looked horrified. Larry blanched. My vehemence shocked me, too, but I didn't recant my terrible threat. I'd neutered my last cat and punched my last hole in a jelly jar lid.

Or so I hoped.

As we hurried outside our apartment a few mornings later so as not to be late to school, we found a burro sitting on our front porch. American stereotypes notwithstanding, this is about as likely as finding a cow on the third floor balcony of a Chicago condominium.

I couldn't fathom the how, what, or why of our strange guest, but I knew it was Dr. Responable's fault.

After leaving the farmhouse, I had rented one of his small cinderblock rental houses in the new *Ciudad de los Olivos* development at the edge of town. I hadn't liked the green paint—it was a shade that burros might find appealing, but it reminded me of the icky color of American school lockers. The homebuilders had enclosed the yard with a cinderblock fence except for a space for a gate. Dr. Responsable had agreed to install one but had been dragging his feet. The space was just the right size for a burro.

My best guess was that the beast had wandered into the neighborhood during the night, walked into our weedy yard through the missing gate, followed the scent of last night's leftover salad, and paused to rest.

What concerned me most about the burro was that he was sitting instead of standing. He appeared to be planning to stay.

"Oh, Mom," said Mark, eyes aglow. "Just what I was so much wanting for a present! Thank you!"

"No! He's probably lost. I'm sure he'll find his way home before we get back for lunch."

"If no one claims him, can we keep him?" Larry asked.

"No way, José! In a week I'll be bailing his dinner and mucking up afterwards."

"I will be caring for José, I am promising to you, Mom!" Mark vowed, crossing his heart and hoping to die. "I only have need for the objects for giving to José the food and for taking away his *caca*."

Larry's face shone with excitement. "Just think, Mom. Free transportation when the car breaks down. No need to buy a lawn mower. I promise to keep him outside during the day and out of your bedroom at night." Larry, too, crossed his heart.

I needed to end the discussion before their arguments killed my resolve. "Let's go now or we'll be late for school."

When we returned that evening, the burro was lying down on our front porch, his eyes closed, his swollen tongue protruding from his mouth.

"*¡Caray!* He is staying ours!" exclaimed Mark, the prophet.

We were the not-so-proud owners of a dead burro, though in death he seemed larger than life. Perhaps he was the result of a donkey's infatuation with a horse. "What am I going to do?" I whimpered.

Mark looked worried. "Why are those so many flies?" he asked. "Why is José not moving down and up his eye tops? Why is his tongue being so fat and out of his mouth?"

I tried to soften the blow. "José's soul has moved on to greener pastures. The flies will keep him company on his long trot to the sky. His eyes are open so he can see the pearly gates. His tongue is hanging out because—because he's ready to give St. Peter a big donkey kiss."

Larry gave the unembellished translation. "José is dead," he said. "Mom, can I autopsy him? I need a project for the science fair."

"Better you should flunk!" I told my hopelessly nerdy son.

"But—"

"No! You'll have to content yourself with mangling frogs in biology class like everyone else. Inside now, boys. Don't trip. Don't touch. Don't even look. I'm going to find help."

What I found was the word I hate most in any language: the bureaucracy.

The maintenance man sent me to the leasing office, where the teenaged secretary was applying polish to her long, carefully manicured fingernails. When she finally finished, I explained my dilemma.

She wet a cotton ball with nail polish remover and dabbed at her cuticles. "*Mañana,*" she said.

I insisted that I needed José gone today. Getting me to grovel seemed to be her goal, so I groveled away. At my insistence, she began filling out a work order, fastidiously fashioning a little heart over each small "I." Since her slow-motion form-filling seemed designed to upset me, I thought it best to let her know she had succeeded. I shifted my weight, tapped my foot, and sighed to show my impatience.

When I handed the document to the maintenance man, he shook his head. The shake looked all too much like "no." I asked him what the *problema* was.

He explained that burro burying wasn't his job. Worse, he said it with a straight face.

I hurried back to the office. "Your maintenance man refused!"

The secretary blew on her fingernails to dry yet another coat of polish. "It's not his job."

I contained the urge to smudge one of her glistening nails. "Call the manager," I rasped through clenched teeth.

"He left for the day."

"The assistant manager, then."

"He's out of the office."

"The owner."

"I can't disturb the doctor at home."

I picked up the bottle of polish remover, unscrewed the cap, and held the bottle over her nails.

"You wouldn't!" she screamed.

I tipped the bottle toward an orange pinky.

She dialed the phone.

I took the receiver from her fingers. "This is Lois, Dr. Responsable." I explained that my broken lawn mower and leftover salad had inadvertently lured a starving burro to my doorstep.

"You cannot have a domesticated animal living on the premises," he replied. "Your lease forbids this."

My composure was slipping away. "He's not living; he's dead!"

"Excuse me, but if he hadn't been living, he wouldn't have died."

"Dr. Responsable," I said with as much calm as I could muster. "YOU had better do something about YOUR problem before YOUR other tenants get wind of José."

"Remove your carcass by midnight, Señora Sonna, and I won't evict YOU!"

Then he hung up on me! I was stunned. I glared at the secretary, but she now had the upper hand. She had hidden her polish remover and kept her hands in her lap.

Not knowing what else to do, I went to Irapuato's department in charge of health, education, and the welfare. A smiling, balding administrator shook my hand and invited me into his office.

I gave him a good education about the health hazards of dead burros and how to ensure the public's welfare.

He smiled continuously while alternately listening and talking in circles for half an hour. Then it sank in that he wasn't going to file my report of a dead burro that was about to unleash a pestilence into the town.

"What am I supposed to do?" I asked.

"Since you are a foreigner on a tourist visa, perhaps visit the *Departmento de Turismo,*" he said.

"Would they care about a dead burro?"

Still smiling pleasantly, he replied, "No."

I asked the secretary the location of the tourism office. She didn't think Irapuato had one, and directed me to the Office of Business Development.

On arriving, I informed the bureaucrat in charge that a senior official at the Department of Health, Education, and Welfare had recommended I talk to him about developing a new tourist attraction.

The middle manager regretfully informed me that the fiscal year 1972 budget was spoken for, fiscal 1973's would be tight, and he doubted a statue of a burro would make money. To gain approval, I would need to figure out how to cover the cost of José's bronzing and taxidermy.

Reason had failed, so I tried passion. "Unless you get that animal off my porch, I'll publish an exposé in the *LaGrange Citizen* newspaper. It will ruin Irapuato's reputation. Your tourist trade will dry up and disappear!"

"If Irapuato had tourism, that would be the concern of another department," he replied evenly.

"Which one?"

He shrugged.

"Couldn't you use José in another statue?" I pleaded. "As the mount of some war hero, perhaps?"

He shot me a look of haughty disdain. When I threatened to cry, he was nicer. "Well, perhaps, if José had historical value. For example, if he had been in a war…"

I had the perfect solution, but he doubted the city fathers would want to memorialize battles with the Mexican bureaucracy.

When I arrived home, Larry and Mark were dickering over how to divvy up the profits from their little carnival. The boys had covered José with my mother's lace tablecloth and doled out peeks to the *barrio* kids at fifty centavos each. And that business development bureaucrat had scoffed at my plan for José!

Crying usually solves nothing, but I shooed the kids inside, sat down next to José on the porch, and sobbed. My self-piteous party was interrupted by a battered pick-up truck sputtering down the street.

I hurled myself in its path. "Please," I said in Spanish. "I am in desperate need of someone to haul away my carcass."

"Climb in," he said.

"No! I mean THAT carcass." I pointed to the porch.

He shook his head. "I haul strawberries."

"But your truck is empty."

"My truck is very small. Your burro is very big," he said.

I offered him fifty pesos to reconsider the relative sizes.

"For one hundred pesos it might fit," he said finally.

As he headed off into the sunset with José, I blessed the worlds' small businessmen, those resourceful entrepreneurs who can quickly adapt to the ever-changing needs of consumers.

I thought my bureaucratic struggles were over, but the red tape rolled on.

The next day, I saw a gray-suited man stepping onto our porch. With his clipboard at his side, he looked alarmingly official. Before I could tell Mark not to answer the door, he had opened it.

"I need to speak to the Lois Sonna," the man said.

Before I could deny knowing her, Mark nodded and claimed I was his mother.

The man handed me a document. "I am from the Department of Agriculture. I have here a warrant for your arrest."

I was too tired to quibble with another government official. I opened my wallet and asked, "What's the charge?"

"You have been charged by the Department of Health for failing to have your burro vaccinated for encephalitis, by the Department of Agriculture for failing to notify them of the contracted illness within seventy-two hours, by the Department of Transportation for abandoning a dead animal on a federal highway, and by Señora Flores for causing her so much pain and suffering."

"Señora who?"

"Your animal was blocking her driveway."

"MY animal? Do I look like the kind of woman who would keep a burro?"

The inspector pointed to a telltale pile on the porch.

"That's just circumstantial evidence!"

Mark tugged on my arm and asked in Spanish, "Mom! Does this mean we can have our burro back?"

"Ah-ha!" said the G-man.

"Señor, you're not going to believe this, but it all started with some leftover lettuce—"

Before I could grease his palm with a twenty-peso note, Larry leapt into the conversation. "But Señor, how do you know the burro died of encephalitis? It could have been typhoid, hepatitis, hoof-and-mouth disease, or a combination of infections. My mom doesn't understand the hazards of dumping a dead animal by the side of the road. Birds and flies can pick at the carcass and carry the contagion far and wide. All of Mexico could be infected in a matter of weeks. I will gladly help do an autopsy to determine the cause of death."

"I give up! You might as well arrest me," I said.

The bureaucrat bilked me for a bigger bribe instead.

After he departed, I turned to Larry and Mark. "This mad mama hereby issues the following admonishment: No mangy beasts are ever again to be considered 'ours!' Do you hear me?"

Mark's lower lip trembled. "You are always saying to me that the Sonnas are not liking the animals at their houses. But Linda is with a dog in her house. A really cute one."

"Remember that I told you that Linda had finished her bachelor's degree and married her boyfriend, Tom? She took his last name, so she's no longer a full-fledged Sonna."

"If I am living at their house, I can be playing with the dog."

"I've exceeded my weekly bribery budget, and I'm not into blackmail. You're free to move in with them. I'll help you pack."

He looked down, and I sensed the wheels turning. "So," he said after a pause. "I must be using my own allowance to be buying an iguana."

"First you'll have to buy a bus ticket to Linda and Tom's. But since Linda has gone to the dogs, maybe she'll fund your lizard. You'd better write to her right now. I need to be alone."

I munched a peanut butter tortillawich while pondering the beastly burdens I had borne. Sometimes life seemed too hard. I yearned for easy street — a soft white bread sandwich in America the beautiful.

But then I remembered how things actually were up north:

Citizens get stuck in red tape because bureaucrats are blind to the beauty of bribes.

People's missteps are typed into computers with indelible memories.

Parents are overpowered by peer and kiddy pressures.

Moms repetitively vacuum cat hair, spilled gerbil pellets, scoop putrid poop, clean foul fishbowls, and force feed anorexic alligators.

That's when the realization sank in: It's not only in Mexico that people are bedeviled by bizarre bureaucratic and pet problems. It's part of life and part of motherhood, wherever they may be.

CHAPTER 22

PIÑATA PERILS

*"A freeloader is a confirmed guest. He is the man
who is always willing to come to dinner."*

– Damon Runyon

Instead of celebrating birthdays, Mexicans celebrated the day dedicated to the Catholic saint after whom they had been named. Often the two coincided, because parents liked to name their children after the saint who was in charge of the day on which their little ones were born. Thus, boys born on St. James' Day were likely to be named Jaime; girls born on St. Anne's Day were likely to be named Ana.

As Americans, we celebrated birthdays, but as Mark's Saint's Day approached, my increasingly Catholic boy decided he wanted a San Marcos' Day party. After chopping his proposed guest list from fifty down to eight, I agreed.

I assumed that inviting eight eight-year-olds to share cake and games from four p.m. to six p.m. meant that eight children would arrive at four o'clock and leave at six. Unfortunately, I didn't understand Mexican party etiquette.

Every Mexican guest is automatically entitled to extend a party invitation to his or her family, friends, and acquaintances. Those guests may in turn extend the party invitation to their family, friends, and acquaintances. And so on to infinity. This raised the possibility of the entire country showing up for a single shebang.

Etiquette further dictated that the host suggests the party's start time but has no say in when the festivities end. The guests arrive whenever and decide when, if ever, the party stops. Like at an opera, the party isn't over till the fat lady sings. If she doesn't, it can theoretically last forever.

Being ignorant of these customs, I didn't know how to comfort Mark when four o'clock came and went and no guests arrived. At four-fifteen we went outside to wait by the curb in case our partiers were having trouble finding us.

When Señora Del Campo arrived at four twenty-five, I smiled, and Mark stopped fretting.

I was still smiling when I told her to come back at six o'clock to pick up her child.

And I smiled on when I agreed to let Javier use our phone so he could call home for a ride when he decided he was ready to be picked up.

I wiped that silly grin off my face when her station wagon doors flew open and Javier along and six siblings, cousins, or friends climbed out of the car and hit the pavement running.

"Have fun," Señora Del Campo called in Spanish as Javier, David, Armando, Mariana, María Elena, Luz, and Miguel disappeared into our apartment.

A few minutes later, Carlos, Ricardo, Esteban, and Pancho arrived. I think Mark had invited Carlos. Carlos' mother also requested a phone call so she could retrieve her children.

"That's not necessary," I advised her. "The party will end at exactly six p.m."

She looked confused but nodded vaguely before driving off.

The same scene was replayed until the headcount hit thirty. There wasn't space for such a large crowd to wreak havoc in our little living room, but the sunny weather made it possible for part of the mob to trample my patio flowers.

To get all of the pushing and shoving to proceed in a more controlled fashion, I blew an umpire's whistle and announced the start of musical chairs. No one wanted to play.

I carried the chairs back to the table and hung up the pin the tail on the burro sheet. No one wanted to play

"Mothers should supervise, not organize," Javier informed me.

An hour later Javier reminded me that moms were also supposed to serve food. I suddenly realized that eight party hats, eight party favors, eight small sodas, and a medium-size cake would not feed the multitude.

Following the Biblical example, I said a quick prayer, tossed the hats and favors into the air, and let the children scramble for them.

After wiping tears from the faces of the youngest losers, my faith was too shaken to expect a miracle of cake multiplication. I sprinted to the corner store and bought Fanta soft drinks, several bags of potato chips, and all the *Gansitos* the shopkeeper had in stock.

On returning home I arranged the *Gansitos* snack cakes on napkins, and stuck a candle in each one. I put some candles on the larger, homemade cake so Mark could make his wish and blow them out.

He blew out the candles but wouldn't eat his piece of cake. "I want a *Gansito*," he whined.

"Does anyone want to trade their small, stale, chemical-filled pastry for a big piece of homemade cake fresh from the oven?" I asked in Spanish.

No one did.

"It is being my party, and I must be eating this terriblest cake," Mark said, his lower lip quivering. Soon every child with a slice of Duncan Hines cake was echoing Mark's "I-want-a-*Gansito*" theme.

I ended the food feud by announcing that it was time to play break-the-piñata. I had heard about this Mexican custom back in the U.S. and looked forward to seeing the game in action. It is like blind man's bluff, pin the tail on the donkey, and an Easter egg hunt all rolled into one.

A brightly painted papier maché figure dangles from the ceiling by a rope. One by one the children are blindfolded, spun, handed a baseball bat, and given three swings while the rest chant in Spanish, "Hit it, hit it, hit it. Don't lose your good judgment. Because if you lose it, you lose the route. You hit it once! You hit it twice! You hit it thrice! Your turn is over."

When someone breaks the piñata, its penny-candy stuffing falls out, and the children scramble to fill their mouths and pockets.

Our piñata was a purple and yellow fish with orange crepe paper streamers attached to the fins. I had named him Carlos the Tuna. After some lively discussion about who would go first, the biggest child won. Larry blindfolded Javier, spun him, and handed him the bat.

Javier's first swing broke a lamp. The warm-up to his second swing removed a framed picture from its hook. I managed to grab the bat before his third swing connected with a little girl's head.

Faced with the reality of what happens when a dizzy, blindfolded child is handed a bat and given three swings, I took charge.

"I can see how anxious all of you are to fulfill the true purpose of this game, which is to get the candy out of the piñata. So I will help this game along," I said as I arm-wrestled the bat from Javier, who was swinging wildly while stumbling toward my étagère.

I aimed, swung, and broke the piñata. No candy rained down upon the circle of expectant faces.

"Where is it?" I asked. I dealt the fish two more hefty blows.

The mutilated fish rocked back and forth on its string, but only small pieces of crepe paper and papier maché floated to the ground. After four more blows, Carlos the Tuna lay in pieces at my feet without having disgorged a single chocolate kiss or peppermint stick.

"What a rip-off! I guess the factory workers ate the candy or forgot to put it inside," I said.

"No, Señora. The mom has to buy candy," Javier informed me. "That way she can stuff it with her kid's favorite kinds."

"What an ugly party," an ungrateful guest stage-whispered to a friend.

Mark's lower lip quivered.

"Oh," I said. "Of course…the moms put the candy in," I said. "I knew that. This was just a trick. I mean a joke. Get it?"

No one smiled.

"I mean, not a joke. It was a warm-up. A practice session for the real thing."

Mark looked at me hopefully.

I ran to the kitchen, grabbed a bag of lemon drops—Mark's favorite—and found a box of Chiclets. I dumped the candy and gum into a large paper grocery bag, drew a large smiley face on the bag with a magic marker, tied the top with a string, and ran back into the living room.

"And here, children, is the real thing. An American piñata!" I tied the bag to the piñata's rope.

Now I just needed to make sure that Mark would win. "The American custom is for the Saint's Day child to go first," I announced.

While Larry blindfolded Mark, I explained the other differences between the American and Mexican versions of the game. "In America, a mother stands behind the batter and puts her hands over his to help direct his swing. See?"

Mark hit a home run on his first try. The candy and gum rained to the ground. In the ensuing scramble for lemon drops and Chiclets, only one small chair was overturned. In seconds, every piece of candy and a bit of grit or lint had vanished inside a child's mouth or pocket.

Mark removed his blindfold. "What happened?" he asked.

"You broke the piñata. Congratulations! You won!"

"Where is being the candy?" he asked.

"The kids picked it up off the floor and ate it."

His lower lip quivered once again. "The every piece?"

"Think how much joy you have brought to your friends," I admonished.

Tears oozed from his eyes. "This is the most terriblest Saint's Day party I am ever being at!"

"I agree! When it's over, I'll buy you a bag of lemon drops all your own."

I felt relieved as the hands of my watch inched toward my six o'clock salvation.

When the hands reached six-fifteen, I grew concerned.

At six-thirty, I still hadn't given up hope.

By seven o'clock, I was alarmed.

At seven-thirty I offered the kids a choice: call your mothers, or I will drive you to the orphanage.

Less than five seconds later, the children lined up to use the phone.

When Señora Del Campo turned onto my street at seven-fifty, I was waiting by the curb. I ran inside to separate her batch of children and their guests from the fray and I personally escorted them to her car.

While helping them into the backseat, I thought I heard Javier asking his mother to let them stay a little longer. I thought I saw Señora Del Campo look at her watch as if deciding whether to let him!

Before she could make the mistake of my life, I called to the children on the porch, "The monsters inhabiting our garden are due to come out for dinner any minute now!"

The other children quickly exited my house. When Javier jumped into the car, Mark tried to follow him. Even after the last guest was gone, Mark lingered on the curb. "Come inside now," I told him.

"But the monsters are being hungry," he protested.

"I was just making a little joke. Even if we did have monsters, they would be friendly family pets."

"Pets?" he asked. "Mom, that bicycle you are presenting to me is very nice. But the only one thing I was wanting to receive on my Saint's Day is a dog." His lower lip trembled, and the tears began. "Linda is telling to me that in the United States, all of the children are having a pet at their houses. She said that if I am living with her and Tom, I can be having a cat."

Linda was actively encouraging him to live with her!

I was too tired to do more than compromise. "Tell you what, Mark. If you're good every day for the next three hundred sixty-four days, you can have another Saint's Day party next year. You can invite all your friends, their brothers and sisters, their friends, and the friends of their friends. I'll make an American piñata in the shape of a dog, stuff it with your favorite candy, and have Larry bash it to pieces so you can pick the linty candy off the floor and eat it. How does that sound?"

He nodded bleakly.

"In the meantime, I want you and Larry to invite everyone you know to Javier's sister's *quinceañera* party. She's turning sweet fifteen next week. Tell them the festivities start at four p.m. and last all night."

Mark may have not felt better, but I did. Yes, my upcoming vengeance would be incredibly sweet.

CHAPTER 23

THE WATER HEATER CAPER

"Show me a sane man and I will cure him for you."

— C. G. Jung

I knew I should count my lucky stars and quit the contraband biz after delivering Guillermo's toilet seats to him, but I continued. I couldn't bear to let a lowly border guard control my financial destiny. My smuggling business was limited by the size of the trunk, so I began experimenting with the gas tank and seat linings.

When we window-shopped for a new car during a trip to Dallas, Mark interrupted my conversation with the salesman. "See over to this way, Mom! The red one, he is the perfect!"

The salesman chuckled and winked at me. "Sure, Sonny," he drawled in a heavy Texas twang. "Kids love the big red convertibles. But that's probably not what yer ma here had in mind."

Mark looked confused. "No, we are always only buying the white cars. The policemans are not so much noticing white."

The salesman frowned. "Police?" he asked.

"My son has such an imagination," I said quickly. "Too much TV, I suspect."

"But Mom—"

"Show me the car."

"He is the car you always are saying is of your dreams!" Mark pointed to a white Ford Tornado.

Larry was peering inside the trunk. "Look, Mom!" he said. He removed the mat and exposed the spare tire.

Mark was grinning from ear to ear. "Just let this tire be staying at home, and we can be carrying many more contrabands!"

The salesman's eyes grew large and round.

"My son has such an active imagination. No more Kojak for you, Mark. From now on, it's just *Sesame Street and Mr. Rogers' Neighborhood.*"

"But the customs officials won't be finding our stuffs in here!"

"Really, Mark."

He looked frustrated. "You are always saying to me that your dream for your life is a trunk with a bottom that is not true."

"False, Mark. The word is false."

"A trunk with a bottom that is a false."

"A false-bottom trunk, or a trunk with a false bottom."

"You know what I am meaning, however I am saying it to you!"

The salesman's eyes were popping out of his head.

"Mark, there are many things to take into account when making such a major purchase. Travel through the Sonoran desert without a spare? I don't think so. Still, it's a lovely car, even if it is *expensive.*"

The monetary reference refocused the salesman's attention. I waited patiently in the fluorescent glare while he described the vehicle's other features. Then we dickered over the price for a few minutes. He agreed to toss in a can of fix-a-flat, and I bought it.

Deciding whether to have the title made out to María Luisa González to match my driver's license or Lois Sonna to match my tourist visa was tougher. As I waffled, the salesman again became nervous.

I suspected this purchase wouldn't happen, so I decided to give him the rest of the upsetting news. "I'm going to pay in cash," I said.

Surprisingly, that calmed him down. I pulled a giant stack of bills from my purse, and he happily took them. He had either missed or decided to overlook the fact that such very large cash transactions typically involve money laundering.

On checking the title two days later, I saw that it was in Lois Sonna's name. Had that been my decision? I still couldn't decide which of us would be a better owner.

Guess what I found on sale at the Brownsville Sears the very next morning? Exactly what I simply had to have: an automatic water heater. This may seem strange to soft Americans who are accustomed to having hot water flow at the turn of a knob. To fully appreciate "automatic" requires some experience turning on the gas, lighting the pilot manually, hearing the mighty wump, and doctoring singed eyebrows with a make-up pencil until the hairs grow out.

The water heater wouldn't fit in the trunk.

"Just return it," Larry said.

"Where there is a will, there is a way. And my will is steel!" I told him. That was because I couldn't master the art of predicting my hot water needs twenty minutes in advance. Time and again I ended up with cold water when I wanted to wash dishes, cold water when I wanted to shampoo my hair, and cold water when I wanted a hot bath. Maybe I also wanted the challenge of sneaking the water heater past Sancho Panza without penalty or prison.

"The water heater will have to ride in the backseat, Larry. You'll need to sit up front."

Larry had hung in there through my penny ante days, but he balked about moving up to big-ticket items. "You tried hiding that mascara in plain sight. Remember how that turned out."

Mark, who usually understood my deeper motivations, also objected. "It would be great for you to be putting that border guard into his place with smuggling a big something under his nose hairs. But what if he is catching to us! How do you pay the so much taxes or the big bribes for keeping yourself from the jail? The *aduana* will be stealing the water heater and keeping it for himself. And that is the that."

"Forget it, Mark," Larry said. "Nothing will stop her. Mom, lend me a dime. When the police take you to jail and us to a children's shelter, I'll need to call Linda to come get us."

I was too smug a smuggler to believe even the craftiest customs official could outwit me. I gave Larry a dime.

Mark couldn't fit next to or on top of the hot water heater, so I had him scrunch onto the back window ledge. I covered the water heater with a tablecloth I had purchased for a friend.

When I stopped near the border to don my wide-brimmed hat, sunglasses, and dark face make-up, Larry exited the car. "Where do you think you are going?" I asked.

"I'm not blowing my chances for medical school with a felony conspiracy conviction just so you don't have to think before you bathe."

I gave him his passport and money for a visa, and he started walking toward the inspection point.

When the customs official peered inside my car, his astonished look said it all: I had made a grievous error. I tilted the rearview mirror and saw that the tablecloth had slipped to the floor.

The official cackled and began filling out a tax form without even offering me a chance to pay a bribe. When he invited a fellow official to check out the backseat, I knew I was up to my neck in hot water. When Sancho himself waddled over, my hands went clammy and butterflies pummeled the inside of my stomach.

"*¿Qué es esto?* (What's this?)" asked Border Guard Number One.

"*¿Qué tiene aquí?* (What does she have here?)" asked Sancho.

"*Les voy a explicar* (I can explain)," I said.

Both officials turned to look at me.

"I thought you'd never been to Mexico before," said Border Guard

Number One.

"What?"

"You speak Spanish."

"I studied to prepare for my weekend holiday in Mexico."

They stared at me, incredulous.

"How exciting that you understood me! We've been studying a phrase book in the car. The book has one hundred common expressions and guarantees readers a safe, happy trip south." I babbled on, employing my usual tactic, which Larry had succinctly described to Linda: "When she can't dazzle them with data, she babbles 'til they're bonkers."

"Book?" asked Sancho. He reached through the open window for one of my contraband-filled books. I'd spent hours removing the centers of the pages to create a well.

"No!" I screamed, grabbing my book with fifty tubes of eyeliner before he could hear them rattle. "You can't see the book–because it isn't here. I threw it away. Because I'd already learned it all."

"Right," said Border Guard Number One. "Let me see your driver's license and tourist visa."

My hands were shaking so violently, I had a hard time pulling the documents out of my wallet.

Sancho squinted at my driver's license. "Who, may I ask, is María Luisa González?"

"I am," I said.

"And who is that?" he asked, gesturing at the body crammed on the rear window ledge.

"My son, Mark Sonna."

"Your son?" He studied my visa. "And who is Lois Sonna?"

"I am."

"What?"

"Oh!" I exclaimed, realizing I had given him the wrong driver's license. "No, I made a mistake. I'm not Luisa. I am Lois Sonna. Lois, like it says on my tourist visa."

"Then who is María Luisa?"

"It's a long story."

Sancho stroked his eyebrows. "Why do you have a fake I.D.?"

"It's not phony! It belongs to—to my mother. No, I mean my sister. My maternal grandfather was Mexican, and my mother very sentimental. She named her first daughter María Luisa. María married a Mexican man, a Mr. González. I've got Maria's driver's license because—because she died. In the car. On the way down here. It was awful—such a tragedy. I am taking her effects to her husband. He lives in Mexico City. That's where I'm going. This is not a happy holiday for us."

He pointed to the water heater. "And what, pray tell, is that?"

I heard the cell doors clanging shut behind me. I saw myself wasting away in a Mexican jail. I heard Linda and Bill refusing to play checkers with me or bring caramels on visiting day to punish me for having endangered their brothers. I was so upset, I started to cry real tears.

"Oh, kind señors, please let me be on my way. You see, that thing in the backseat, well, it may look like a water heater. You're probably thinking it is a hot water heater. But it's not. It's a present for my mother. For my sick, dying mother. Yes, she's dying actually. Of arthritis. I mean she has arthritis, but she's dying of something else."

I knew my story sounded as phony as my I.D., and my sobs were intensifying. "So this present is for my mother," I continued. "For our mother. From her daughters, Lois and dear departed María Luisa. To fulfill our mother's dying wish for a water agitator. She'll die anyway, but the doctor said a Jacuzzi-type bathtub massage would help. Help with the pain, that is. It would comfort Mom in her last days. But I've got to hurry! I must get to Mexico City before Mom dies. Which should be in a day or two. You wouldn't want my mother to die in pain without saying farewell to her last living daughter now that María has passed away, would you?"

After I paid my way out of this mess, would I have enough money left for gas?

"Come," said Sancho, snuffling into his sleeve and swiping at his tears. "I'm off duty in an hour. I will leave now and escort you to Mexico City."

As if Sancho had pushed a button, my tears suddenly stopped. "You've got to be kidding!" I said. "That's seven hundred miles away."

"I, too, lost my mother. I know the pain you suffer. But you must not drive when you are so upset." He started walking toward a squad car.

"I'm not really very upset. Look, I'm smiling!" I called.

He climbed into the car, leaned out the window, and signaled me to follow. "¡Vamos!"

Too confused by this strange turn of events to make sense of what was happening, I followed the official's vehicle for about five dazed minutes. When my mind cleared, I remembered Larry!

"Mark, I forgot your brother. We have to go back for him. I need to lose this guy. Hold on." I pulled a hard left and swung through the streets of Nuevo Laredo, Steve McQueen style, just like in that San Antonio Christmas Eve debacle. Why did officers keep leading me to destinations I needed to conceal?

Larry was waiting at the appointed place. He climbed in and settled onto the top of my contraband-filled books. "Congratulations, Mom. I never thought you'd pull it off."

"You doubted your *mamacita?*" I asked. I glared at Mark in the rearview mirror to silence any snide remarks he might be tempted to interject.

"It was being so much exciting!" Mark said. "You should have heard to our mom talking to those *aduanas*. Their heads were turning in a big spin."

Mark applauded most everything I said or did, just as he booed most everything Larry said or did. I shouldn't have doubted him.

Mark opened a bag of chips and continued, "If Linda was hearing to our mom, she would not be wondering, 'Should I be giving to Dad her address?' "

"WHAT? LINDA IS THINKING ABOUT GIVING LEE OUR ADDRESS?"

"That is what she was telling to me in her letter."

Now my head began "turning in a big spin." Linda had spent her youth quaking in fear of Lee's sudden explosions of violent rage. In fact, she had even expressed regret that our separation came too late to save her childhood. Yet she would conspire with Lee to force her brothers and me back into his clutches? Did Linda now consider him the better parent? Even if she did, this was between Lee and me. It wasn't any of her business!

Though realistically, what did it matter if Lee showed up in Irapuato with U.S. court documents showing that he had custody of Larry and Mark? Lee didn't speak Spanish. He wouldn't be able to negotiate the above-board Mexican legal system, much less the under-the-table deals needed to get a favorable ruling. The issue was whether I could keep a roof over our heads and tacos on the table without him.

The hot water caper turned out to be a bit too exciting for my taste, but it had provided a stimulating test of my derring-do, and I had passed with flying colors.

Best of all, I knew how to secure our financial future. On the long ride back to Irapuato, I mapped out ideas for transporting a freezer to a feverish uncle, a stove to a starving aunt, and a hideaway bed to an invalid cousin.

I considered selling the automatic water heater, but decided there was more to life than money, so I kept it. And it definitely enhanced the quality of my life. Whenever I had a sudden urge for a soak, within minutes I was luxuriating in two inches of steaming bath water.

Life was good.

CHAPTER 24

MY BORDELLO BROUHAHA

"When ideas fail, words come in very handy."

— *Goethe*

From the time I began my contraband sideline, Linda had expressed her opinion about it through not-so-subtle frowns, humphs, and tsks interspersed with occasional lectures. But now that she was studying psychology in graduate school, the soon-to-be Dr. Linda had new ammunition. She dedicated herself to convincing me that my little business would wreak lifelong havoc on Mark's mental health.

"Smuggling will compromise his sanity as an adult," she insisted during yet another of her long-distance reprimands.

"But he's got my genes," I pointed out. Won't they protect him?"

"Sure, if you consider criminals sane. Either way, genes are only part of the story. The effects of environment are powerful! What do you think he's been learning during your smuggling transactions?"

I shifted the phone to my other ear. "He's learned to deflect questions from a probing official faster than you can say 'import tax.' How to distract and hold the attention of an immigration official faster than you can say 'bribe.' He can charm the *pantalones* off a customs official faster than you can say 'import tax.' He's learned to remove tags, toss cash register receipts, and hide instruction booklets and warrantees to make new merchandise look used faster than you can say 'customs.' And he can then reassemble each item to look like new faster than you can say 'customer satisfaction.' "

"Valuable skills for a future criminal!"

"No, Honey," I explained in a soothing voice. "He's going to be a ballet dancer."

That silenced her for several seconds. "What? He's taking ballet lessons? Doesn't he have flat feet?"

"No lessons or arches, but he's got a strong can-do attitude. That's another effect of his experiences watching me outwit customs officials."

None of Dr. Linda's objections to my little smuggling sideline had ever moved me, but she got my attention when she insisted that Mark would turn against me if he ever ended up living in the U.S. She said that re-casting quirky parents as dysfunctional and severing ties with them had become the norm.

"I've put the fun in dysfunctional. But it doesn't matter. Like all good Mexican kids, Mark knows that mothers are Madonnas. In the local Catholic scheme, Mary trumps her Son. That means I'm second in the heavenly hierarchy, right below God but above Jesus."

Despite my confidence, I wondered if there might be a more traditional way to supplement my meager salary. Then Guillermo, whom I had dated for a time, offered me a job. "I need someone to cover the night shift at my motel," he said. "You would earn a percentage of the profits."

Visions of peso signs danced in my head but were quickly replaced by images of shifty-eyed señores pawing shady women while waiting their twenty-minute turn for a room. "Thanks, but I don't know anything about the motel business," I told Guillermo.

"What's to know? If there's a vacant room, rent it. If not, ask the clients to wait a few minutes." He cleared his throat. "At least, that was the policy in the past. Now we charge by the night instead of by the hour."

"You are polishing your, um...I mean the motel's image?"

"Both."

Guillermo's foray into the hospitality business had made him a *persona non grata* in Irapuato. After his motel opened, too many husbands began "working late" on weekend nights. Too many wives suspected the worst. Guillermo was excluded from social gatherings for fear the when, who, and with whom might escape his tequila-loosened lips.

"It's easy work, Lois, and the motel is in great shape. The plumbing usually works, there's often hot water, and eleven of the twelve rooms have made-in-America toilet seats."

He explained that the decent motels were booked solid for the upcoming Strawberry Fair. He expected the overflow to swallow their scruples and seek lodging at his place. If greeted by a respectable school teacher-clerk who makes sure there was no hanky-panky so that guests could actually sleep, word would spread.

"It sounds tempting."

His voice became wistful. "My son wants to get married, but the bride's family disapproves because of the motel. My son loves that girl, Lois. As it is, he's hardly spoken to me since high school. He'll never forgive me if her parents nix the match."

It seemed that both of us were being pressured by children to clean up our acts. "As a school teacher and director, I can't be involved in a sleazy operation. I'd lose my job," I warned. "Frankly, I'm surprised that my contraband hasn't raised any parental eyebrows."

"Why would anyone object to smuggling?"

If only Linda could hear him say that!

I signed on Guillermo's dotted line and became his official partner.

My first night on the job, I rented all twelve rooms in less than an hour. I was about to retire when Señor Rivera from Room Six entered

217

the office.

The fit, middle-aged man must have used a ruler when ironing his gray business suit, so precise were its creases. He'd pasted every neatly trimmed hair on his shiny black pate into position. Even the smile lines at the sides of his mouth were perfectly matched, which made him look more like a mannequin than a person. A very distinguished gentleman, this. Just the kind the motel wanted as a repeat customer. I smiled graciously.

Señor Rivera chuckled and pointed to the makeshift "No Vacancy" sign I had hung over the "20 Minute Wait" poster. "Even *this* motel is full? For the whole night?" His chuckle sounded neat and tidy, too.

"Yes. This motel has a new character."

"You're new?" he asked. His question sounded like an insult, but before I could analyze the grammar point, he continued, "I often come to Irapuato on business, so I am aware of this establishment's reputation. Unfortunately, with the fair going on, I had no other choice."

"In the future I hope this motel will be your first choice rather than your last resort."

He didn't pause to analyze the grammar point, either. "I have to go to San Luis Potosí to take care of a family emergency and won't be back until morning. I'll need my room when I return, so I'd like to pay for the extra night now."

"No problem," I said. I accepted his money and handed him a receipt.

"I'd like to leave my luggage in my room."

"I won't even let the maid inside," I told him.

I locked the front door behind him. The "No Vacancy" sign looked overly harsh, so I added a hearts-and-flowers border.

A moment later there was a knock on the office window. I shook my head at the three young women outside and pointed to the sign. They clasped their hands in a gesture of prayer, and I lip-read the words, "*¡Por favor!*"

I opened the door a smidgeon.

"*¡Ay!*" they cried in unison.

"*¿Qué pasa?*" I asked. I opened the door a bit more, and they poured into the office.

"Oh, Señora, we have a terrible problem."

"Terrible, just terrible," the other two chorused.

"Every hotel in town is full! The clerk at the Camino Real said you'd undoubtedly have a room open up tonight. We wouldn't usually come to this kind of motel, but we're desperate."

"We no longer rent by the hour. We're full for the weekend."

"You're a mother, no?" the shortest girl asked. She looked like a young teen. "You have a daughter?"

I nodded.

"If your young daughter had been stranded in a strange city with two young girlfriends, would you, like the innkeeper what's-his-name, look the Virgin Mary herself in the face and just say no?"

Her girlfriends moaned on cue.

Quite the con artists, these. Still, I shivered at the thought of Linda and her best friend, Diane, stranded in a strange city as teenagers. "If I had a stable, I'd gladly let you use it," I said earnestly.

"How about that rug?" one of the girls asked.

"What? It isn't mine. Besides, this motel has a reputation to consider. We can't have guests sleeping on the office floor."

"We don't mind," the chubby one replied.

"But passersby can see you through the windows. It's dangerous," I told them.

"How so?" they asked.

"Someone could come in and—" How naive were they, anyway?

They looked at me blankly. "Come in and what?"

That naive. "And step on you."

"But you can't turn us away!"

I couldn't, but I wasn't about to make the supreme sacrifice and give them my own bed, either. "The man who rented Room Six is leaving for the night. I suppose you could—"

"*¡Gracias, Señora!* Come on, Nacha, Isabel. If we change clothes *pronto*, we can visit the fair."

"I don't know when Señor Rivera will return tomorrow. I'll wake you up at six-thirty in the morning. Promise me you'll be out right away."

"Sure. Don't worry about a thing!"

But I did! I imagined them rifling through Señor Rivera's things. I imagined being unable to pry them out of bed in the morning. I imagined being convicted of theft for giving away the room he had paid for. I imagined my under-the-eye bags sagging to my chin from lack of sleep.

After tossing and turning for a while, I got up and revised my window sign to read, "ABSOLUTELY NO VACANCIES." I covered the hearts and flowers with the black magic marker to make a sterner impression.

At about two o'clock in the morning a car raced into the parking lot and screeched to a stop, its radio blasting mariachi music. I pulled on my bathrobe and fuzzy slippers, topped my curlers with a bandanna, and ran outside to silence the noisemakers.

To my horror, it was Señor Rivera. Instead of tidy, he was rumpled. In the glow of the courtyard light, I saw his mussed hair, wrinkled shirt, and his tie slung up over his shoulder. "*Hola, Señora,*" he slurred. His voice was rumpled, too.

"You're supposed to be in San Luis Potosí!"

"I went to the fair. I'll leave for San Luis in the morning."

Then he asked for his room key!

"I can't give you the key, because…" I searched my imagination for a believable story.

His bleary eyes narrowed. "You rented my room again!"

It looked like my only option was the truth. "Shortly after you left, three little homeless girls strayed into the office, and—"

"Are they in the room now?"

"I saw them go out."

His face reddened. "You took my money and gave away the room. Before I call the police, give me the key!" he demanded.

"I would if I could, but—"

"They took it with them!" he roared. "And you don't have a copy!"

"It's my first night to work here. The fair attracts unseemly elements, and these poor waifs are too innocent and naive to fend for themselves. So, to save them from the dregs of society, to defend their virginity and the honor of Mexico's youth, I, well…. This motel doesn't have a stable, and if the innkeeper what's-his-name had turned Mary and Joseph away, where would the world be today?"

"I'll give you five minutes to straighten this out."

"Perhaps you can share with Señor Arrieta. His room has a queen-sized bed. I'll wake him up and ask him to do us this one small favor." I crossed the patio to Room Ten.

"No!" Señor Rivera yelled after me as I knocked on Señor Arrieta's door. "That solution would not be—"

Before he could finish, another car zoomed into the courtyard and halted, with a little help from the curb. Its radio blared the same mariachi song Señor Rivera had been listening to. When I hurried over to hush the intruders, a chubby face poked through the window. "¡Hola!" the girl slurred.

An arm emerged from the back window and extended a Tecate beer toward me. "Join the party, Señora!"

Three giggling, giddy, gaudy girls tumbled from the car. Attired in scanty sequined bikinis, black mesh stockings, spiked heels, and waist-length blond wigs, my three innocents looked like hoochie koochie dancers. As they wiggled and jiggled around me, I felt doomed and dowdy. Doomed because Señor Rivera would kill me. Dowdy because of my bathrobe and bandanna.

Señor Rivera's bleary eyes were popping out of his face.

"Señoritas!" I admonished. "You shouldn't be undressed like that in public. Get back in the car and lower that radio!"

"You didn't have to wait up for us, Señora," one of them said.

"Señor Rivera has returned unexpectedly. You can sleep on the floor in—"

"As you said, Señora," Señor Rivera said. "We must make sacrifices to protect the youth of Mexico. The señoritas are welcome to share my room."

I shook my head. "No, I—"

"It won't be an imposition, I assure you."

Señor Arrieta of Room Ten suddenly emerged from the shadows. "The señoritas are welcome to share my room. In times of crisis, it's the neighborly thing to do."

"Oh, no you don't!" yelled Señor Rivera. "It's too late to move luggage at this hour. Everything is PERFECT the way the Señora arranged it."

"ARRANGED IT?" I gasped.

"Be reasonable, Man," Señor Arrieta said. "At your age, you can't possibly handle all three. Let me have at least one."

"What's it worth to you?"

"¡Por favor!" I said. "I cannot permit this. There is more at stake here than simple morality. The motel's reputation—"

"Leave this to us," Señor Rivera snarled. "We can work this out by ourselves, can't we, girls?"

They tittered and took his arm.

"Señoritas," I pleaded, "The rug in the office is available."

Two of the girls were too busy nibbling Señor Rivera's earlobe to answer. The chubby one was already sashaying with Señor Arrieta toward his room.

"I'm warning you," I said. "If you men put extra people in your rooms, I'll—I'll—"

The men glared at me and said together, "You'll what?"

"I'll charge!"

The men pulled out their wallets. Their debate over who got to pay for whom escalated into a shouting match. Other sleepy-eyed guests came out to see what was happening. I forged a compromise: each man paid for himself and three guests.

When I returned to the office, all I could do was pray. "Dear God, please don't let anyone in town find out what went on here, especially Guillermo. And don't let Linda or Bill get wind of this, either. Amen."

Guillermo phoned early the next morning. "I heard there was some big excitement at the motel last night."

So much for my lip-zipping prayer. "You need to replace me as soon as possible. With these giant circles under my eyes, people are going to mistake me for a raccoon."

"You signed an agreement. I'm holding you to it, Partner."

"Huh?"

"Your concept is brilliant! From now on we cater strictly to swingers. Instead of charging by the room, we charge by the head. We put a couple in a single bed, two couples in a queen. A couple of king-sized orgies, and we'll be wealthy!"

"But what about your reputation? Your son? I thought you wanted to be accepted by Irapuato society."

"The word has spread that you organized the parties and are running the show. But I do need to ask you something. Did you receive the invitation to my son's wedding yet?"

"It arrived yesterday."

"Do me a favor, Lois. Don't come."

CHAPTER 25

THE CLAIROL COUNSELOR

"Put all your eggs in one basket—and then
watch the basket."

– Mark Twain

I felt a surge of relief as I descended the steps of the *Instituto.*

Another day of forcing English into the heads of giggling girls was over. I was ready to go home, chill out, have supper, and curl up with another of the dozens of psychology self-help books Linda had sent me.

The American pop psychology titles and covers promised solutions for every problem except the one I faced after work each day: what to do about supper. Bill (when he was living with us), and Larry and Mark (all the time) were increasingly resistant to quickie meals like peanut butter and tortillawiches, heat-and-serve canned goods, and pour-and-stir powder packets. Tacos, enchiladas, and the like had hijacked their taste buds.

So far, the most interesting thing about the books Linda sent was that so many people spent their time reading them, since they didn't seem to have much content. All the how-to-save-your-marriage books did little more than satisfy my desire to consume English words.

The next book in my stack was called *Creative Divorce*. I doubted the author had a more creative solution to the spouse-dumping problem than mine: flee the country and don't look back. But that was OK. I didn't want to anything heavy tonight. Fluff was fine.

As I walked to my car, a throaty voice croaked, "*¡Ay, Señora Sonna! ¡Por favor!*"

It was my dish thief from Guillermo's ranch. What was she doing in town? "*¿Qué pasa, Lupita?*" I asked.

"Forgive me for disturbing such a great lady as yourself," she replied in the broken Spanish of the rural poor.

I couldn't figure out how to say, 'A friend in need is a friend, indeed,' so I said, "A friend is a friend."

"Because there are so many people asking God for a miracle, the line is very long. My problem is urgent," she wailed. "I hope you can be the angel to help me."

I patted my hair. I couldn't feel a halo, but perhaps it was an aura and not an actuality.

Lupita smote her chest. "I'm doomed, Señora…" Her voice dissolved into a tubercular cough. "It's my husband, Estanislado," she croaked.

"Is he ill?"

"In the head. He is loco! I'm losing him to other women!"

"That's impossible. Who else would work her fingers to nubs to support him like you do?"

"It's true! He's reaping his wild oats!"

"You mean sowing his wild oats."

"No, he was always sowing them. Now he is trying to harvest one!"

I had just read an entire book on that subject! Maybe I had learned more than I'd realized. "Men his age go through what psychologists call the 'middle-aged crazies.' He'll get over it, so—"

"The woman is a bad one, Señora. She is out to get everything he's got!"

226

I remembered their hovel. "All Estanislado has is dirty clothes for you to wash, a big appetite for you to feed, and a little manhood. Who would want those?"

"Me!" She began to cry. "I do!"

I gave her a hug and cooed, "There, there, Lupita."

"He doesn't look at me anymore," she sobbed. "He told me some blonde puta winked at him the other day. *¡Ay, Señora!* How can I compete with a blonde?"

I patted my golden tresses. "They do say blondes have more fun, but I personally know a few who are bored to death." That sounded more intense than I had intended. I hadn't thought of myself as lonely for male companionship. But was I?

"Maybe where you come from, Señora, but in Mexico, blonde is beautiful! Every blonde I ever knew was carrying a baby as soon as she became a woman. If I were blonde, Estanislado would come back to me in a minute."

"Blonde is available at every drug store, Lupita. But surely you wouldn't bleach your beautiful black hair."

"I'm losing my husband! Look at me. What do you see?"

With her voluminous *rebozo* covering her head, shoulders, and short, plump body, Lupita resembled a tent topped with a cabbage. Her snaggletooth smile usually dominated her dark face. Tonight her smile was gone, and her long, brown tooth poked out at an odd angle from beneath her upper lip.

Like other *ranchera* women who spent decades baking in Irapuato's strawberry fields when they weren't bearing babies, at age forty Lupita looked to be sixty-five. Nevertheless, something in her serious, coal-black eyes reflected exactly what she was: a faithful, hardworking wife and a devoted mother to her eleven children. She might not have had much laughter in her life, but she had dignity.

"*¡Por favor, Señora!* Turn me into a blonde like all the women in your country."

"There are ways to keep a husband at home that don't need a touch-up every three weeks," I said, remembering a book I'd read the previous month entitled *How to Win Back the One You Love*. Linda had recommended it highly. I hadn't been impressed but now realized it contained invaluable information.

Lupita looked at me hopefully.

"After cooking Estanislado's favorite dinner, put the kids to bed early. Then put some romantic music on the record player and light some candles. I'm sure you can imagine what happens next!"

She nodded. "Estanislado falls asleep. We do not have electricity, so I cannot play the music. I burn a candle every night, when I have the money to buy one."

I considered the other things I'd learned in all those marriage manuals. "Then I bet a marriage encounter would help. Many American churches offer special workshops to help couples improve their relationships. Perhaps Mexican churches offer them, too."

Lupita shook her head. "We wanted to marry in a church, but the priest is so expensive."

And then there was that book on divorce I was going to start tonight. "Maybe this is your chance to find a better husband," I said gently.

"Better than the father of my children?" She looked confused, as if I'd switched to speaking in Chinese.

"Well, many couples in my country improve their relationship by sharing their innermost thoughts. When was the last time you two discussed your goals? Shared the secrets of your heart?"

"Yesterday. I told Estanislado my goal is to keep him away from that blonde *puta*. I told him what was in my secret heart: 'Stop seeing her or I will cut off your eggs!' "

"Good heavens! What you need is training in fair fighting! You must argue correctly, or you'll kill the relationship."

"Good idea, Señora! I will kill that blonde, and the relationship will die!"

My words seemed to be losing too much in the translation, and I felt like I was in over my head. What would Dr. Linda advise? "I think you and Estanislado need a professional marriage counselor."

"What is this?"

"A person who will teach you two to communicate."

Lupita nodded. "We do need that. ¡Sí! When I yell at Estanislado, he doesn't answer me anymore. When I hit him, he goes to the cantina."

Maybe American psychology didn't have answers for my Mexican friend. Maybe American commerce did. "Becoming a blonde is easy enough. Leave it to me."

Her upper lip curved up and revealed more of her long tooth. "You are an angel! A saint!"

And so it came to pass. At seven o'clock that evening, I anointed Lupita's waist-length mane to convert her from an obese, aging peasant wife to the alluring flaxen-haired waif of her dreams—and hopefully of Estanislado's.

"Wash out the bleach in forty-five minutes," I said. "Blonde is just a matter of purchase, precision, peroxide, and patience."

I shouldn't have said "patience."

Long after the boys had feasted on fiery enchiladas and I had enjoyed a hamburger at Enrique's Restaurant, I was awakened by a loud knock at the front door. I quickly disentangled myself from a dream in which I was saving marriages by distributing bottles of peroxide to the poor. I tossed the *Creative Divorce* book onto the end table—it had proved to be a powerful hypnotic—and hurried to the door.

Lupita's hair was still wrapped in my towel.

"*Perdóneme, Señora*. Should I wash it now?" she asked.

I looked at my watch. "I said forty-five minutes! It's been five hours!"

Her head drooped with shame. "There are no clocks on the ranch," she said. "And I didn't learn numbers."

"Hurry home and wash your hair! Now!"

Lupita fled into the night.

Several weeks went by before I saw Lupita again. When I did, I was horrified. Instead of a black beauty or a blonde bombshell, the poor woman looked like a flaming fuzzy floozy. Her orange hair looked like a miracle wrought by an avenging angel or a novice saint.

I would have run, hid, and pleaded the Fifth if it hadn't been for Lupita's broad smile. There was a bit of a swagger in her walk, a certain giddiness in her demeanor that was alien to peasant women who had only known hard work, too many babies, and grinding poverty.

"*¿Cómo estás?*" I asked fearfully.

"*¡Fantástico!*" she exclaimed. "Estanislado fell back in love with me. And now he loves me so much, he is *celoso!*"

I frowned. A ride down the slide from in love to love to "jealous" sounded like trouble to me, though I knew that for most Mexicans, jealousy didn't signal deep-seated insecurity and an over-the-top need to control. After dealing with Lee's possessiveness for seventeen years, it was hard to believe that jealousy could be positive. Did Mexican psychologists know how to keep jealous mates from turning into tyrants? If so, an expert needed to write a self-help book for the U.S. market.

"Well, I'm glad your relationship is going well," I said.

"It's excellent!" she said, her eyes shining. "One of the farmworkers gave me an apple. Estanislado was going to kill him, but he ate the apple instead." She giggled like a besotted schoolgirl.

"I guess blondes do have more fun. Or perhaps I should say, um, redheads?" Her cap of smooth, inch-long black roots with the frizzy orange border looked like a clown's wig.

"And there was another miracle." Her voice dropped to a conspiratorial whisper. "God has put a child in my belly!"

I gave her a sly wink. "No, I think Estanislado put the baby there."

Lupita laughed. "No, he is not that clever. Only God can make a baby. But thanks to you, my hair got His attention, and then He heard my prayer."

I stared in open-mouthed amazement. She didn't know about man's contribution to babies? I certainly hadn't considered that red hair could aid conception. I felt like a traitor to Planned Parenthood, zero population growth, and women's liberation—not to mention to poor Lupita.

But she was delighted. "Can you teach me how to make a miracle, Señora? My sister only has eight children. She prays for more."

Obviously my intrusion into a foreign culture was turning it topsy-turvy. "Sorry, Lupita. I don't have a license to be a marriage counselor or a beautician. And I can't accept responsibility for anything that has happened between you and Estanislado. As you said, only God can work a miracle. I'm just a lowly saint." I brushed my hand through my hair but felt nothing. If I'd ever had a halo, it was gone.

"If I can do anything to repay you for this most wonderful gift, just ask."

"Wonderful? How can you say that? You can't afford another child!"

"Afford? *No comprendo.* My children make me rich!" Suddenly her smile dissolved and her brow creased. "I am sad for you, Señora, with only four children, and two so far away. I pray for God to send you more."

"No!" I said a bit too loudly. "I mean, I'm sure you have more important things to pray for."

"More important?" She looked confused. "What could be more important than a child?"

Her question opened an album of images in my mind. I saw myself cuddling the miracle of my firstborn baby girl, bursting with pride when Bill took his first tremulous step, loving Larry so much I thought my heart might break, hearing Mark call me "Batman" for the first time.

Certainly the richest moments of my life had been helping wee ones discover the wonders of flowers, eensy-weensy spiders, and Winnie the Pooh. If motherhood wasn't always fulfilling, it was because I forgot what mattered most. Instead of resenting having to cater to my kids' cravings for Mexican cuisine, I should be glad my kids had hearty appetites.

I had been terribly wrong to consider Lupita's new baby as just another mouth to feed. It would be a little person to love.

I hugged Lupita. "You have already repaid me," I said. "I am glad Estanislado is reaping his oats at home again. Pray for me if you wish, Lupita. We'll leave it to God to decide whether to take pity on a poverty-stricken American and make me as rich as you."

CHAPTER 26

THE SEDUCTION

"When you're in love it's the most glorious two
and a half days of your life."

— *Richard Lewis*

When I first arrived in Mexico, the never-ending stream of leers, stares, and catcalls from macho males set my teeth on edge. I wished I could walk through a city crowd cloaked in anonymity. But as a *güera*, a light-skinned, light-haired female, I was always on stage, and the curtain was always up.

After about a year, my picture of myself as a dowdy housewife had faded, and I began to appreciate the lusty male attention. With the onset of cellulite, the low whistles helped edit out my mental picture of my sagging *chi-chis*. As I settled into middle age, I found the men's admiration admirable. How could I fault the opposite sex for seeing beyond my figure's flaws and appreciating me for the person I wanted to be—beautiful?

Eventually the Don Juan syndrome proved irresistible. When a passing señor didn't express admiration, I worried about my failure to appeal to man's baser instincts.

It has been said that American men are led by their purse strings and Mexican men by their heartstrings. I found this an apt stereotype. A Mexican male might not be *macho*—a good provider, involved father, or faithful husband. But all men were unabashedly in love with love.

Though I often cursed the maddening machismo that deterred men from treating me like an intelligent, competent businesswoman by day, my irritation disappeared whenever an antagonist stood beneath my balcony, *sombrero* in hand, and offered up a midnight serenade. The chemistry of scented flowers and sweet love songs wafting into my bedroom on a starlit night created an opiate powerful enough to dissolve my daytime grudges. After a few strums on a mandolin, I forgot I was intelligent, competent, or in business. I was an alluring, sensual female, and that was enough.

But when I rose and tried to shine at work, the endless verbal jousts and one-up-womanship cast a heavy cloud. When I was in a bad mood, the battle of the sexes made me downright cranky.

Late one afternoon, my latest tangle with my least favorite pupil, Maridél, the *Instituto's* renowned student from hell, had left me especially out of sorts. She'd had to re-take so many failed courses and had been expelled so often, it looked like it would take her at least six years to finish the three-year program. Her parents didn't seem to mind. They could easily afford the tuition. I supposed it was cheaper than a shotgun wedding.

On this particular day, another teacher had sent Maridél to my office for an unspecified classroom offense. When I insisted that Maridél confess whatever heinous crime she had committed, she climbed on top of my desk and began shimmying.

It turned out that when the teacher had asked her to translate the

234

verb "to shake," Maridél had walked to the front of the classroom, climbed onto the teacher's desk, and proceeded to wiggle her hips instead of her lips.

As I sat on my chair gazing up at my dancer, I had an overly clear view of the undies inside her miniskirt. The ample purple and blue striped cotton briefs took me by surprise. I would have expected a racier design, like bikini cut and red lace.

And as bad luck would have it, as I was watching Maridél reenact her desktop crime and contemplating her incongruous underpants, a passing pedestrian pair glanced in the window and saw her. They stopped in mid stride gaped in horror at *me*. It occurred to me that they might be mistaking me for a voyeuristic pedophile. I ran outside to catch them and explain what they had witnessed so they wouldn't jump to the obvious conclusion. But by the time I got to the street, the couple had disappeared.

As I hurried through my paperwork to put the dastardly day behind me, an ancient man appeared at my office door and demanded to see the director. If Cary Grant had wanted to speak with me at that dismal moment, I probably would have told him to come back another day.

And this old geezer was definitely not Cary. I didn't know or care whether his frayed coat, torn shirt, and scuffed shoes reflected poverty or poor grooming. I just wanted him to go away.

"Where is the director? Call him immediately, Señorita," he commanded in English overlaid with a heavy Spanish accent. His slurred vowels, dropped syllables, and verb conjugation errors revealed his lack of schooling and missing teeth. Still, in the Mexican pecking order, man was superior to woman, and older was superior to younger. As a mere forty-six-year-old female, I was supposed to obey.

"I'm the director," I said curtly. "How can I help you?"

"YOU? A pretty little señorita?" He hobbled to my desk, took my hand in his arthritic one, and didn't let go. "What kind of directing do you do? Ah, but it must be beautiful, your directing."

As his lips curved into a salacious grin, the leer struck me as vaguely familiar.

"But," he said, patting my hand, "my business is important. Go tell your boss Señor Juan Gonzales de Paz is here."

Now I remembered him. He had danced in the rain during the soggy wedding party that Linda and I had attended several years back. He had been vocal when carrying on about the evils of the American space program.

I extricated my hand from his. "I am the only director here," I snapped. "How can I help you?"

Not that I needed to ask. Strangers often came for help with U.S. insurance claims, tax notices, and love letters. I charged the equivalent of one U.S. dollar per page for translations and tossed in advice to the lovelorn for free.

The old codger proceeded to undress me with his rheumy eyes. I waited for him to complete the ritual so he could ask for assistance from a lowly woman. "So, *güerita*. You do translations?" He looked over his shoulder as if the real director were lurking nearby.

It didn't seem that his stiff knees would make the journey from my side of the desk to the chair at the other side, but he shuffled over in just under two minutes. A two-minute meter. At this rate, I'd be here all night.

"Here is my *problema*. For fifty-three years, I work and live in the United States of North America. Then I come home to Mexico. Every month for twenty years, your government sends to me the pension check. The life is good. And then this terrible letter arrives!"

"What does it say?" I asked.

"I do not read *English!*" He spat the word as if it were the devil's tongue. "A letter from your country is always bad news."

He'd spent half a century in the U.S. without learning to read English!

And he had the gall to disparage the country that had supported him. Was his blasphemy driven by senility?

I took his letter, and immediately recognized the U.S. Social Security Administration stationary. Juan's name and address were followed by the greeting, "Dear 337-23-8790."

I pointed to the salutation. "My government addresses you by your very own social security number. Uncle Sam cares! You might show some respect." I squelched the urge to sing *The Star Spangled Banner.*

The letter explained that if Juan continued living outside the United States, his retirement payments would be reduced by one-third. To receive full benefits, he would have to move back to the U.S. The letter concluded, "To appeal this decision, you must appear in person at the nearest Social Security office." That was about seven hundred miles north, as the burro trots.

"Such devilish news!" Juan said, shaking his head. "How to tell my wife? Ever since we marry, the bad news comes and comes."

I felt a sudden surge of compassion. "That must be—what? Fifty or sixty years of bad tidings?"

He shook his head. "Three years."

"Oh. Well, your translation is finished, so—"

"I do not marry the first pretty face the life presents to me. I wait a little longer than most of the billy goats, and then I choose a young one." He puffed with pride. "She is only seventy-six."

"You robbed the cradle." My sarcasm rolled off of him like rain from a cactus. At least, I assumed that rain rolled off cacti rather than soaking in. On my drives through the Sonoran desert storms, I hadn't noticed.

"*Sí.* But I meet many pretty young ladies before my wife."

I had lost the thread of his boring conversation and lacked the energy to pick it up. "Well, your translation is finished, so—"

"When I live north of the Rio Grande, I meet many pretty North

American girls. One very beautiful one, almost as beautiful as you. All North Americans look pretty much the same, but this one girl is special. We could be a pair, maybe, but she hears of my woman and six children in Mexico. I'm not even married, and she gets jealous! North American girls are so particular."

I was not impressed by a fertile wanna-be cheat. "If you'll excuse me—"

"But it is the fine life in Texas. I pick the cotton from the rise of the sun to the dark, waiting for the Sunday afternoons. That is when the *compadres* ride in the back of a truck to Harlingen. You know this fine city?"

I pointed to the wall clock, but he ignored me.

"We go to Harlingen to see the North American girls. We see but we do not touch these beautiful *güeritas*. So white, their fine skin. So shiny, their blonde hair!" He sighed heavily and closed his eyes. "Such a pretty picture! I hold this picture through all my years in the United States."

Protest was useless. He was going to drag me through his stroll down memory lane until the bitter end.

"When I return to Mexico, I carry this same picture all of the years since I arrive, right here." He tapped his heart.

I had to admit his sentimentality was a bit touching.

"Every Sunday for fifty-three years, I go to watch the *güeritas* like they are at a museum. I hear them chatter like sweet little birds. I smell their scent like sweet flowers, but *¡Ay!*" he exclaimed, as if in pain. "Do they feel so wonderful as they look? As they sound? As they smell? I never know." He shook his head sadly. "How can a man so humble hope for God to answer his only prayer in the life: to touch the beautiful white skin. Now I am old. Soon it is too late."

How sad to die without fulfilling his one lifelong wish. Such a con artist.

Juan swallowed hard and lifted his hand to his heart. "As this ticking clock slows, I treasure one special picture most of all."

His voice had faded to a faint whisper, and I found myself leaning closer to hear.

"My most special picture is of one young *norteamericana*, the most beautiful girl of all. Every night for these many long years, I hold her in my mind that I may dream of her."

Was the shiny drop at the corner of his eye a tear?

"When I wake up, I keep looking, thinking, wondering, is my picture of a real girl? Will I find her not only in my dreams, but also in my days?" He paused and squinted at me. "And then I come here, and what do I see before me? My picture! She is here! It is you!"

I was mesmerized. Juan's words or some sentiment they embodied had caught me in their web.

Our eyes locked, and then I squirmed under his admiring gaze like a besotted schoolgirl. His story was so amazing! He had admired hundreds, perhaps thousands of American women in his long life, but every night he hugged the most beautiful one of them all. Me!

It made no sense, but I wanted to laugh at his patently transparent attempt to seduce me and hurl myself into his arms all at the same time.

How could a geriatric ex-cotton picker seem so hauntingly attractive? Did I harbor a predilection for great-grandfatherly types? Or was it that he had let me peek inside his mental diary? I certainly had to respect a man whose aging heart beat faster in the presence of a beautiful blonde. I was only forty-six, after all.

I forced myself back to the business at hand. "Juan, shouldn't we discuss your Social Security problem?"

"*¡Caramba!* Under all that pretty blonde hair is a head for business. I must add that to my picture. It is hard to change her after so many years, but her business mind will make her even more beautiful."

"I hope so," I tittered. "I mean… I'm not sure what I mean."

"Perhaps you can advise me?" he asked. "I am sure you can! I am sure this pretty blond *norteamericana* thinks as good as she looks! And as good as she sounds! And as good as she smells!"

"Oh, Juan," I blushed. "Be serious." But when I looked into his eyes, I saw that he was.

Suddenly eager to impress him, I cleared my throat. "Some calculations may help," I said. "If you move to the U.S., you will receive three hundred dollars per month. If you stay in Mexico, you will only receive two hundred dollars per month. You will lose one thousand two hundred dollars every year. In ten years, that's twelve thousand dollars!"

"Terrible," he muttered.

"If you move back to Harlingen and live frugally, in ten years you can retire to Mexico a wealthy man."

"Then I am rich?"

I nodded.

"As a poor man, I cannot hope. But, when I am rich, perhaps you—?"

Our gazes locked, and I was transported to that magical place where a fantasy, however foolish, becomes a sacred dream.

"Perhaps I go back to Harlingen," he said slowly, breaking the silence but not the spell. "My beautiful picture will be better company now that I know she is real. In ten years, I return to Mexico for my girl?" He gave me a meaningful wink.

I felt as giddy as when Johnny Leznikowski spilled lemonade on the front of my dress in sixth grade. "Goodness, Juan! Won't you ever act your age?"

"God willing, no," he said, rising to leave.

I also hoped he wouldn't.

After Juan left my thinking cleared. He was so old and feeble, he couldn't possibly live much longer. How ridiculous of me to suggest that he spend ten long years in the U.S. to save money. If he did last that long, what would he do with money then? It would be terrible for him to go for American gold instead of staying put to enjoy Mexican gusto!

As I pondered my strange mental lapse, it dawned on me that I had also forgotten to collect my twelve-peso fifty-centavo (one dollar) fee. That was completely out of character for me. How had Juan jangled my heartstrings to the point that I lost sight of my precious purse strings?

I never unraveled the mystery of how hoots and howls from handsome Latino males triggered dreams of undying love that were every bit as enchanting as arthritic Juan's appreciative gaze. All I know is that they were so very enchanting, that even these many years later, I hold Juan's picture of me in my mind, and I am beautiful.

CHAPTER 27

TRAFFIC COURT TRIAL

*"Two wrongs don't make a right,
but they make a good excuse."*

– Thomas Szasz

In my many contraband runs from Irapuato to the border and back, I expertly coped with all the hazards of a long drive through Mexico, except for one.

The seven-hour stretch of straight-as-an-arrow highway that sliced through the cactus-filled Sonora desert was so monotonous, even the buzzards looked bored.

On each trip I waged desperate battles with highway hypnosis. Larry passed the time in the car reading, so it was Mark's job was to keep me awake.

We played spelling games, he told me endless knock-knock jokes, and he read aloud to me from *The Book of Lists*. But on one return trip, none of those exciting activities was working.

"Mom! Wake up yourself!" Mark yelled for the fifth time in about as many minutes.

"Thanks," I said, shaking my head to try to restore thought circulation.

When the mental numbness ebbed, I realized that the twelve-year-old passenger in the backseat wasn't pulling his weight.

"Larry, are you tall enough to see over the steering wheel and touch the gas pedal at the same time?" I asked.

"Cool! You're going to let me drive?"

"What would Linda and Bill be saying to you, Mom?" Mark asked.

"They would say it's better to have a twelve-year-old behind the wheel than a snoozing adult.'"

Larry couldn't see over the steering wheel, but by slouching he could see between its spokes.

"Just press the accelerator, Son. There are no curves, bends, or intersections for the next hundred miles, so don't move the steering wheel."

Highway Marker Number 402, according to Mark, was where Larry's driving lesson began.

Highway Marker Number 403, according to Mark, was when I began trembling, sweating, and hyperventilating.

Highway Marker Number 422, according to Mark, was where Larry's driving lesson ended.

Although Larry hadn't so much as bent a cactus or dented a burro, I had discovered the absolute antidote for highway hypnosis: turn the steering wheel over to a child.

But less than ten minutes after having the sleepiness scared out of me, I was again drifting off behind the wheel. My heavy eyelids didn't lighten until I was safely ensnared in the stimulating Guanajuato gridlock, just a little over an hour from Irapuato.

And then it happened. Right in the middle of a rush hour jam of traffic, my car stalled and someone else's rear-ended us. To make matters worse, a policeman standing on the sidewalk saw the accident. He hurried over to collect his bribe before the other driver and I could settle up and disappear.

Luckily, the macho witnesses and policeman took one look at my blue mini-skirt and declared the other woman had been "racing like a *loca* without looking where she was going." Only the road signs declaring that parking, stopping, and standing were forbidden were on her side.

Even though my opponent spoke Spanish like the native she was and kept reciting the facts of the case to the policeman and growing crowd of onlookers, nothing could alter the fact that she had exercised extremely poor judgment. On leaving her home that morning, she had donned baggy-kneed stretch pants and purple gym shoes, and she hadn't removed the pink hair curlers. Apparently she hadn't anticipated making a public appearance.

Her dowdy attire overcame a half-century of Mexican traffic law. The policeman was about to award an on-the-spot verdict in my favor when the guilty woman demanded we reconstruct the crime, crunch-by-crunch, to see whether I deserved to pay a fine, too.

"All right. What do you think happened?" the policeman asked the baggy-kneed one.

The crowd of mostly male onlookers booed and hissed, drowning out her answer.

"And what is your story?" the policeman asked. The crowd cheered briefly before falling silent to listen. I did my best to look frightened and innocent.

"Oh, Señor," I said, hoping he'd notice my American accent. "I don't know, exactly. Here I was, visiting your fine country, when my car stopped in the middle of this through street. That woman raced up in her car and hit mine. Just look at that dented fender and chipped paint. Whatever will I do?"

With a lecherous smile, he whispered, "Don't worry, Honey. I'm sure I can help."

The male on-lookers nodded vigorously to let me know they were willing to help me, too.

The condemned woman shrieked, "Why don't you ask why she was

245

parked in the middle of a through street?"

"Honey, were you parked in the middle of a through street?" the policeman asked.

"Oh no, Señor. Well, not quite. I didn't park, stand, or stop, so I haven't broken any laws. My car paused. I thought she would go around me. But she didn't."

The crowd applauded.

The officer turned to the reckless driver. "Why didn't you go around her?" he demanded.

At that point, the crazy lady demanded we go to the police station!

The crowd gasped, I was horrified, and even the policeman's mouth fell open in shock. Involving more officials meant paying more bribes.

But then the policeman closed his mouth and smiled. "How do you feel about a trip to the station, Baby?" he asked me.

"Well, Officer—"

"Ignacio. Nacho to my friends."

"My name is Lois. Lois, to my friends. I'd love to accept your kind invitation, Nacho, but I'm in a hurry to get to Irapuato. Couldn't we please take care of this while all these nice witnesses are here to help?"

"Sure, Honey—" he began.

"NO!" the other driver shrieked.

The crowd booed. We were pretty fed up with this hysterical woman.

"Unfortunately, it is her right to decline," Nacho sighed, "though I'm sure there are better ways you and I could spend our time."

"Oh, Nacho," I cooed, "If she'd just say she was sorry, I'd be willing to forget the whole incident."

But she wouldn't so I couldn't.

"Perhaps your son could drive your car home," Nacho suggested. "You can ride with me to the station, Lois, and I'll drive you home when you finish."

"My son is only twelve."

"Oh? But he looks tall enough."

"Please, Mom?" Larry begged.

"No. But you can ride in Nacho's squad car to the station."

I asked Nacho for directions in case we became separated. Which was good, because I never did see Nacho's car.

Apparently the other driver got lost, because thirty minutes later she still hadn't finished the five-minute drive. I wanted to leave and go home, but Nacho insisted on returning to the scene of her crime to find her. After he left, I sent Mark and Larry to wait for me at a restaurant across the street from the police station.

While waiting for Nacho and my adversary, I described the accident to the police chief, judge, and jury, Rodrigo Vásquez. The case was almost closed with my acceptance of Rodrigo's dinner invitation when Officer Nacho and the guilty party arrived.

"Why did you do it?" Rodrigo asked when she walked in. "Don't you know that when a car is parked in the middle of the street, you should go around? In the United States, that's called defensive driving. The idea is to defend other drivers at all times!"

Then the woman's lawyer arrived. I guess his dark-tinted glasses prevented him from appreciating the hue of a blue mini-skirt. He took his job so seriously, he asked to see my visa and driver's license!

The last thing I needed was to try to explain the María Luisa González versus Lois Sonna story in front of someone else's lawyer. "Oh, Señor," I apologized. "I seem to have forgotten them. But you can be sure I have both."

Judge Rodrigo rose to my defense. "The driver's license is irrelevant. She obviously knows how to drive."

"Where's her car permit?" asked the lawyer.

"You do have one, don't you, Dear?" asked Rodrigo.

"Of course. I'm very law abiding, but also very forgetful. I left everything in my car—I mean, at the hotel. I'm a tourist, and touring by

car is such fun. Guanajuato is such a handsome, progressive city, as I
can tell from its very handsome, progressive police force."

"Thanks, Señorita," Rodrigo said. "Or is it Señora?"

"Señora. But my dear husband is no longer in my world to protect
me from life's difficulties," I confided.

He shook his head sadly. "My wife died two years ago, so I know how
it is. Living alone, eating alone, sleeping alone—"

"Stop!" screamed the other woman. "This is disgusting! She has a
foreign accent, but haven't you noticed she speaks Spanish fluently?
She knows you men better than you know yourselves! I demand that we
move ahead with the case."

"I suppose we'd better continue," Rodrigo said apologetically. "Do
you want a lawyer, too, Honey? Or is there a friend you'd like to call?"

Then the situation became a bit confusing. I asked my new friend,
Rodrigo, to serve as my attorney, but the lawyer objected. I objected to
his objection on the grounds that Rodrigo was the only friend in town
of whom I could ask such a favor. Judge Rodrigo reluctantly sustained
the lawyer's objection and overruled mine.

Friend Rodrigo then suggested that Officer Nacho represent me.
Nacho agreed, but Her Ugliness' lawyer objected. I objected to his
objection on the grounds that Nacho was the only other friend in town
of whom I could ask such a favor. Judge Rodrigo reluctantly sustained
the lawyer's objection and overruled mine.

I called my friend Guillermo in Irapuato. After living in his farmhouse
and building up his motel business, he had become the special man in
my life. He agreed to rescue his damsel in distress.

While waiting for my knight to arrive, I entertained Judge Rodrigo
and Officer Nacho as best I could, accepting their flirtatious advances
while trying to hold their overly affectionate hands at bay. When things
got to be a bit too intense, I excused myself and went outside to wait.

When Guillermo arrived, I breathed a sigh of relief. He was tall, light skinned, and light haired, hence a hunk by Mexican standards, and very charming by anybody's standards.

He studied the damaged cars. "Not good," he whispered in Spanish.

He read the accident report, which mentioned the "No Parking, No Standing, No Stopping" sign, and my lack of a driver's license, tourist visa, and car permit. "Not good," he whispered.

When Judge Rodrigo emerged from a back room, Guillermo's face broke into a grin. *"Hola, amigo!"* he said. "When did you enter the law-and-order business? I haven't seen you since…how long has it been?"

"Since the wedding of my brother's oldest child."

"And a wonderful wedding it was!" Guillermo said. "Let's settle this little matter, compadre, and then I'll buy you a tequila."

I smiled when he said *compadre.* That literally meant "co-father," technically meant "godfather," metaphorically meant "you're like family to me," and to me personally meant, "Lois wins."

As they hugged, Her Nastiness ripped up the accident report, flung the pieces into the trash, and stamped out of the station.

"She didn't offer to pay to repair my car!" I whispered to Guillermo.

He shot me a don't-you-dare-say-a-word look.

Guillermo postponed his drink with Rodrigo to accompany me back to Irapuato. No sooner had the boys and I piled into the car than Guillermo began asking irritating questions. "Why in the name of *la Virgen María* and all the saints were you parked next to a No-Parking-No-Stopping-No-Standing sign?"

"I didn't park the car, it just paused," I said as we drove off.

"Paused?"

"Yes. I'm not sure why. I was going to have the car serviced in Texas, but K-Mart had blue-light specials, turtleneck sweaters at three for ten dollars, so there wasn't time. And we have a saying in English, 'If it ain't broke, don't fix it,' and my car wasn't broken, so I was hesitant to let a mechanic change the spark plugs, oil, filters, and all the rest. Anyway,

I was right here, by this No-Parking-No-Standing-No-Stopping sign, when suddenly—"

Then it happened again. At the very same spot, my car paused, and there was a sudden jolt from behind.

"Gee, Mom," Larry said. "When we're done at the police station, maybe I should drive us back to Irapuato."

"No thank you, Son. You're too young."

"I drove Officer Nacho's squad car to the police station."

"What! I can't believe he let you do that! What if there had been an accident? You're not even insured."

"Well, you didn't call the insurance company about your accident."

"Good point. OK, I'll start letting you drive, but first we'll have to buy you a mini-skirt. I'll pick one up for you the next time we go to the U.S."

"What? Why?"

"Auto insurance companies won't cover under-aged kids, so I'll have to get you non-standard coverage. It's available in the women's section of most clothing stores."

CHAPTER 28

HUMAN TRAFFICKING HICCUP

"Until you walk a mile in another man's moccasins,
you can't imagine the smell."

— Robert Byrne

As I placed a diploma in Patricia's hand, I was suddenly overcome by sentimental nostalgia. I turned my head away from the microphone to avoid broadcasting my snuffles to the audience of proud parents and restless children.

Patricia's English was excellent, her shorthand fast and flowing. Her term paper on Dialing International Telephone Calls had set a new standard for academic excellence at the *Instituto*. Any executive worth his pinstripes would gladly put her on his company's payroll, but she had accepted my invitation to join the *Instituto's* staff as our secretary. With our current enrollment of three hundred sixty students, she would certainly have her work cut out for her.

When Maridél sashayed toward the podium, my gastric juices bubbled into heartburn. Between expulsions, she dedicated herself to creating classroom chaos and rousing the student rabble. The previous week I had found Terry Aldredt huddled in the bathroom, sobbing while scribbling her resignation letter on a paper towel.

"What's wrong?" I'd asked.

"Maridél," she'd blubbered.

And that one-word answer had said it all. None of the classroom teachers could quite pinpoint or describe how every interaction with our Chiquita Banana left us feeling like her blackened peels.

We'd allowed her to remain in school in deference to her parents, who had been desperate to keep her out of the baby-making business until she reached a properly marriageable age. She'd set a record for taking the most years to complete the three-year program.

Maridél's term paper on office fashions had featured pictures of young secretaries clad in dresses with long slits and plunging necklines. Her research would prepare her to achieve her career goal: to snag an executive groom and then to retire to Irapuato's country club to spend her days yukking it up with like-minded high society wives.

I was so delighted that Maridél was leaving, my smile was genuine when I handed her a diploma. However, at the last possible second, instead of taking it she withdrew her hand. As the diploma drifted downward, I tried to grab it, but a breeze nudged the sheepskin sideways, and my flailing fingers batted it further away. My subsequent attempts to catch the paper included several more misses and a stumble before Maridél snatched it from the air and clutched it to her chest, as if protecting it from me.

The audience laughed and applauded; Maridél bowed, winked, and blew kisses to her admiring crowd.

Her dramatic breach of graduation etiquette and my klutzy display would surely live on in *Instituto* history. All I could do was toss up a silent prayer that God would grace her with a miserable future in the form of a philandering husband, a bunch of bratty kids, and an excess of belly fat.

As I walked home after the ceremony, a young mother was sitting on a newspaper on the sidewalk with a baby peeking from her *rebozo*. The mother stretched out her hand, and I paused to give her a coin. My heart ached, and I wished I could do more. Without a net of social services to catch the crippled, the elderly, and the unemployed, financial falls often proved fatal.

At least my *Instituto* graduates were protected. If they fell on hard times, they could use their diplomas to get good jobs. Not that many would ever work—most were from wealthy families and just needed a supervised place to hang out for a few years.

But my scholarship students did use their degrees as bootstraps to pull themselves and their families out of poverty. The scholarship program was the most satisfying part of my job. The poorest students were all exceptionally bright and motivated. Their achievements would ripple to future generations.

I was unlocking the front door of the apartment when my nose detected an unpleasant eau de barnyard perfume. As I looked around, two figures emerged from the shadows.

"*Buenas noches, Señora,*" the woman said. "It's me, Lupita. And Estanislado, my husband. Do you remember us?"

"Of course!" I said. Lupita was unchanged, except that her smooth black roots had grown about a foot since last I'd seen her, and were longer than most of her ragged orange fringe.

Estanislado wore the same threadbare shirt, raggedy pants, *huarache* sandals, and barnyard odor I remembered from Guillermo's farm. Bathing and washing clothes in the river on Guillermo's property removed the grime, but eradicating the smell required soap. Apparently even the cheap brown bars were now beyond their means.

"*Ay, Señora,* we have come to ask a great favor," Lupita said.

"What is it?"

"Don Guillermo told Estanislado that soon you go to the United States of North America."

"Larry, Mark, and I leave tomorrow morning at dawn."

"Could you take something to the United States of North America?"

I frowned. If they'd been growing marijuana in the back fields and thought I would sneak it into the U.S. for them, they had another think coming. I had strict smuggling scruples: no drugs or guns. "What do you want me to take?"

"Estanislado."

"Across the border?"

"*Sí.* He must work."

"Did he lose his job on the farm?"

"No, but the wages, they are very small. And our children, they are many." She swallowed hard. "They cry from hunger, Señora."

"Smuggling people is complicated, Lupita."

"*Perdóneme, Señora.* But it is simple."

"How's that?"

"Estanislado climbs into the trunk, you close the lid, and—"

"I'd go to jail if I got caught! Anyway, he should stay here. Your children need their father."

A tear rolled down Lupita's brown cheek. "They need tortillas more."

I turned to Estanislado. "You'll live in constant fear of being caught by the U.S. police. At best you'll do back-breaking labor for terribly poor pay. The U.S. isn't the land of milk and honey like many foreigners think."

He looked up shyly. "Your country has the only thing a man wants, Señora."

"What's that?"

"A chance."

Estanislado's odor seemed to exude not just from his pits and pants, but from his very pores. Could I survive his B.O. for ten hours in the car? Of course. Did I want to? No! Could I refuse to help them? No. What I needed was an out. "Have you ever traveled anywhere outside of Irapuato?"

"Just to Don Guillermo's ranch."

"What makes you think you could handle a foreign country? You don't even speak English."

He shrugged.

No money for soap meant no money for a bus ticket. "OK, I'll make you a deal. Prove that you can manage a big trip by getting yourself to Nuevo Laredo. I'll meet you in the central plaza at one o'clock tomorrow afternoon. If you can travel that far that fast, I'll see if I can help you."

Lupita was all smiles. "*¡Muchísimas gracias, Señora!*"

"Don't thank me yet! He will have to hitchhike eleven hundred kilometers in less than fifteen hours. And if he somehow gets to the plaza in time, I don't know that I can help him cross the border."

All three of us were happy when we parted company. He wouldn't ride in my car to the border or across with me into the U.S. When I returned to Irapuato, I'd take them a big bag of groceries, a bucket of detergent, and would do something to make their lives less difficult.

It was nearing one o'clock as I whisked toward Nuevo Laredo's International Bridge. "What about Estanislado?" Larry asked.

"He couldn't possibly—. Well, I suppose I should swing by the plaza just in case."

A few minutes later, Mark pointed and exclaimed, "I am seeing to him!"

The country bumpkin stuck out from the city crowd like a pimple on a debutante's nose. Passing pedestrians did double takes and gave him wide berth, looking as surprised as if they had seen a dead burro on a porch—or had smelled one.

I arranged some small plastic bags on the passenger seat so the fabric wouldn't absorb Estanislado's odor.

A few blocks before the International Bridge, I pulled into a restaurant parking lot. "Here are your tourist visas, passports, and some money," I told Larry and Mark. "Get something to eat here while I try to get Estanislado across the border. If I fail, I'll be back in an hour to pick you up. If I don't return in an hour, walk through immigration and meet me at the U.S. end of the bridge. If I'm not there, call Linda. Do you have her phone number?"

"MOM!" they howled in unison.

"Nothing bad is going to happen! If there's any sort of mix-up, Linda can be our contact person. I won't risk jail for Estanislado."

"I am knowing you, Mom," Mark said. "You are liking too much the riskiness."

"No. I like challenges, though I don't like the smell of this one." I turned off the air conditioning and rolled down my window.

"Sure, Mom," Larry said, his voice dripping with sarcasm. "Twenty years to life would be a challenge."

"Actually, smarty pants, the maximum penalty is only ten years."

"Listen carefully," I told Estanislado as we approached the bridge. "No matter what happens, let me do the talking. To explain your silence, I will say that you are my deaf, mute husband. To explain the disparity in our outfits, and your lack of a U.S. birth certificate, passport, and visa, I will say that you were robbed during our Acapulco vacation. Don't say a word. Now let's practice."

"*Sí, Señora.*"

I pulled into the line of traffic leading to the immigration office. "No, Estanislado. You can't hear a word I say or make a sound. From this moment on, you're my deaf and dumb husband."

"*Sí, Señora,*" he said.

"You're not supposed to answer!" I admonished. "Pretend you can't hear me."

He nodded.

Our lane was moving quickly. "Don't nod, either. Let's practice. I'm going to pretend I am a border guard, and I'm going to ask you a question. Don't answer. What is your name?"

"Estanislado."

Plan A was down the tubes. Too bad I didn't have a Plan B.

The uniformed official outside of the U.S. immigration booth was waving every car on through without checking anyone's documents. It seemed too good to be true, and it was. The official signaled me to stop, pointed to Estanislado, and announced, "I need to see his visa."

"Visa?" The official had assumed that Estanislado was Mexican because of his dark skin and Indian features. This was not the moment to comment on the evils of racial stereotyping, so I graced him with a sweet smile. "Actually," I said, "this is my husband. He doesn't have his U.S. passport, because—"

"Don't tell me," the official said. "The dog ate it."

This wasn't the moment to comment on the evils of sarcasm, either. Instead, I shook my head, tsked, and forced another smile. "Someone already gave the my-dog-ate-my-homework excuse?"

He nodded. "Many someones."

"It's terrible to subject an intelligent, hard-working man to such a simplistic, unoriginal lie."

He sighed. "It comes with the job."

"You'll undoubtedly find my husband's tale of woe more interesting: he dropped his visa in the mud, and before he could retrieve it, a stampeding herd of wild burros trampled it."

He laughed. "But your U.S. birth certificate or passport survived the rampage?"

"Yes."

"You can take your, um, spouse to the U.S. consulate in Nuevo Laredo. If you pass the background checks, the office will issue a single-use document, granting him entry to the U.S. If you don't pass, your hubby will have to stay in Mexico while you enjoy free transportation to a lovely U.S. federal facility, where you will receive free bed and board for up to ten years."

"I'd be punished just for trying to get hubby here into the U.S., even though I failed? Don't you think that's a bit harsh?"

"I don't think about it."

I decided not to comment on the evils of mindless bureaucrats. "By the way, where can a Mexican citizen apply for a U.S. visa?"

The official gestured to a nearby building.

I worked out Plan B as I backed up the car and turned into the U.S. immigration office. "Do you have any identification?" I asked Estanislado. "A birth certificate? A voter's card? Any official document with your name on it?"

"No, Señora. I was born at home. A few years ago some PRI party officials gave me a free lunch and a voting card, but after I voted they took it back."

"This time I am Mexican, and you are my deaf, mute Mexican husband. Nod your head if you must, but don't speak!"

He nodded and pursed his lips. Progress!

I took Estanislado's arm, and we entered the packed room. The jostling crowd picked up Estanislado's scent, parted, and stared. To create better couple credibility, I should have borrowed Lupita's tire-tread sandals and *rebozo*. Our disparate clothes and coloring made us as conspicuous as the dandruff on the U.S. immigration official's navy collar.

"You're in the wrong place, Lady," he said when we arrived at the head of the line. "This office is for Mexican nationals seeking U.S. visas."

Plenty of Mexicans had light skin and hair, but this wasn't the moment to lecture him about racist stereotypes. "I am Mexican. This is my husband."

"Your husband?" he asked, reaching under his carpet of black hair to scratch. Some white flecks joined their brothers on his shirt; others floated onto the counter.

"We look like an odd couple, don't we?" I said lightly. "That's because his clothes were stolen by a robber. A passing peasant found my husband huddled in a clump of bushes and kindly gave him this outfit. It's awful, though obviously better than the alternative."

"Alternative?"

"To remain naked."

The bureaucrat reddened and hastily addressed Estanislado. "Your identification, please."

Estanislado pursed his lips.

"My husband hasn't spoken since that very traumatic robbery. The robber also ran off with my husband's wallet, which contained his documents. But don't worry. He doesn't need an entire visa, just a day pass."

The bureaucrat's expression was inscrutable. "Your identification, please."

I placed Maria Luisa González' driver's license on the counter.

"This was issued in Texas. I need a Mexican I.D. A Mexican driver's license is sufficient."

"I don't drive in Mexico. When I cross into the U.S., I use Avis for my shopping excursions. I'm one of those shop-till-you-drop types. Or one of those shop-till-my-day-pass-expires types. I would never out-shop my visa!"

"Your birth certificate, then," he said.

"I was born at home in 1929. Back in those days—"

"Or your voter's credential."

"Honestly now, why would I vote? The PRI and PAN parties are two sides of the same corrupt coin."

"Then I'm afraid—"

"Listen here! I don't appreciate being interrogated! I would have brought identification, but we didn't plan an international shopping expedition when we left home this morning. It came to us when I couldn't eat my *huevos rancheros* and toast in a café because my husband's smell was ruining my appetite. I had my U.S. driver's license with me, so we made a spur-of-the-moment decision to go to the U.S. to buy him new clothes."

Our itchy-headed bureaucrat regarded me suspiciously. "You had toast with *huevos rancheros?*"

Oops. "My mother, an American, met Dad, a Mexican, when she was vacationing in Acapulco. As you can see, I inherited Mom's genes, not a single chromosome from dear old dad. Anyway, Mom cooked American food at home, so I never acquired a taste for tortillas. I attended an American school and spoke English at home, so I never fully mastered Spanish. I'm a multicultural mess. I'm so American that I blame my mother for my problems. But because I did grow up in Mexico, I pray for forgiveness. And as a bi-cultural child, I pray that my mother will never find out."

"Find out what?" he asked.

"That all my problems are her fault."

He raised a flaked eyebrow. I hadn't known that facial hair could also harbor dandruff. The skin under his arm hair seemed to be fine.

"And this man is your husband?" he asked. Another cranial skull scratch, which implied at best skepticism and at worst doubt, sent a white cloud onto his shirtfront and typewriter.

"I don't like your tone, young man!" I snapped. "Bigotry, bigotry. I shouldn't have to explain our relationship to total strangers, but here I go again. I'm sure you've heard that opposites attract? That's how it was for my husband and me. From our first chance barnyard encounter, an intense animal magnetism drew us together with such force, my parents needed a tractor to pull us apart. Our aromatic—I mean our *romantic* entanglement is not unique. Have you seen *My Fair Lady?*"

He nodded.

"Then just imagine that Professor Higgins and Liza Doolittle had undergone sex-change operations. You'd then have the story of a distinguished female professor falling in love with a poor, uneducated man while teaching him to pronounce rain, Spain, and plain properly."

The official stared at me blankly.

"Are you too sexist to imagine that?"

He looked a bit flustered, so I upped my ire. "Are you prejudiced against inter-economic marriages?" I pounded the counter. "I know your type! Some of your best friends are tomato pickers, you just don't want your daughter mixing juices with one. But that doesn't stop you from drinking V-8, now does it? Does it?"

The man scratched his head again. "If you don't have a Mexican I.D., you'll have to swear out an affidavit of citizenship."

"Oh!" I smiled sweetly. "No problemo."

"You mean *problema.*"

"*Gracias, Señor.* I wish we'd had instructors like you at my American school."

"Which school?" he asked.

"What?"

"Which school?"

"The one around the corner and down a few blocks."

The creases in his flecked forehead deepened, but he rolled a form into his typewriter. "Place of birth?" he asked.

"Right here."

"Right here where?"

"Right here's where."

"I thought you were from Mexico."

Was I in Laredo, Texas? I didn't remember crossing the center of the bridge. I quickly glanced around. Everyone in the room had brown skin, black hair, *mestizo* features, and was speaking Spanish. My bureaucrat's nametag said Roberto Bañales. He was speaking English but had a heavy Mexican accent and tortilla breath.

"Sorry," I said. "I was born on the Mexican side of this bridge, in Nuevo Laredo."

"I thought you said Acapulco?"

"No, I said I was conceived there. By the time I tunneled into the world, my parents had set up housekeeping here. I mean over there. In Nuevo Laredo."

He typed on his form and asked, "Which state?"

"State?" If I'd ever known, I couldn't remember. "You don't know the Mexican state located just a few hundred feet from where you work? The deficiencies in the U.S. educational system are no secret, but your geographical ignorance is shocking. You seem like an intelligent man, so perhaps you didn't apply yourself in school. I'll bet you nevertheless absorbed a lot of information. Go ahead and guess. No, wait. I'll make it easier. Just fill in the verbal blank: the Mexican state that borders Laredo, Texas, is called…"

"Nuevo León," he said.

"Very good. You pass."

"Step out of line, Señora. You too, Señor."

My left ankle buckled, and I nearly fell off my spiked heel. When an immigration official cuts a lone tourist from the herd, it means he or she has been marked for slaughter. I hadn't committed a crime by trying to smuggle myself into my own country, had I? Thank heavens I hadn't given my real name or signed any documents.

The official reached for the telephone. I banged on the counter and called out, "Young man! If you're going to be that way, you can forget it! Just forget the whole thing!"

The buzzing crowd behind me fell silent. The official put his hand over the receiver and looked at me.

I whipped my voice into a shriek of righteous indignation and waggled my finger at him. "You can't fool me! I know what you're up to!"

The official glanced at the curious crowd, and his dark complexion deepened as blood rushed to his face. "What?" he asked.

"You Yankee immigration Nazis are all alike! You're dragging this out, purposely delaying us so we won't have much time to shop!"

He started to say something, so I held up my hand and continued, "Don't pretend you're just doing your duty, trying to protect the U.S. from illegals. If you don't want me to shop in the U.S., you should say so instead of wasting my time!"

"No, I–"

"Never mind! I forgive you! I will just drive to downtown Nuevo Laredo, and my husband and I will shop there. I mean we'll walk downtown. I don't drive in Mexico."

"But–"

I took Estanislado's arm. "Come, Dear. Who says made-in-America products are better and cheaper? Not me! I'm proud to buy Mexican." I reached my other arm across the counter and plucked the form from the official's typewriter. "The cost to buy our son an Atari game in Mexico is prohibitive, so we can't give him one for his birthday as we'd planned. But that's OK. What he wants most is an iguana."

"No luck, huh Mom?" Larry asked when Estanislado and I arrived at the restaurant.

"Not with Plan A or B."

"So what's next?"

"Plan C."

CHAPTER 29

GUILTY AS CHARGED!

"Don't worry if plan A fails, there are
25 more letters in the alphabet."

– Anonymous

I opened the trunk of the car and gestured to Estanislado to get in. "Whatever happens, don't thump, bump, or die!" I said.

He pursed his lips. At last he had mastered mute.

As he folded himself around the suitcases, I reminded him, "And remember not to speak or gesture."

He nodded.

I'd need to upgrade his hearing from decidedly deaf to impaired.

"Mom! I can't believe you're doing this!" Larry exclaimed as I started the engine and circled back toward the International Bridge.

"Now, kids, if a border official asks you a potentially problematic question, don't lie. Nod to show that you understand the question and smile to show that you are happy to cooperate. Then make up a question in your mind and answer it aloud."

"Won't the guard just ask the first question again?" Larry asked.

"Probably. In which case you should think of a second question and answer it aloud as well. If you're asked the same question a third time, which occasionally happens, I'll try to answer for you. If the guard insists on hearing from you instead of me, you should answer truthfully."

"The guard will think we're crazy," Larry said.

"Not at all. I'll show you. Ask me a question."

"OK." He chuckled. "What's your name?"

I gave Larry a quick sideways smile and a nod. "Gee, Officer, this heat wave is over the top. We must be setting new temperature records. Rain would help, but there's not a cloud in sight."

Larry paused to consider. "What question did you answer, Mom?"

Mark threw up his hands in frustration. "You are always saying you are being the smartest of the family, Larry."

"Because I am," Larry answered. "This harebrained idea is too stupid for an intelligent person to make sense of."

"No, it is not being hairy. It is—how do you say it? Slippery?"

"Slick," I said.

"It is being slick. It was sounding like a normal conversation to my ears."

"Larry, my question was, 'How do you like the weather?' "

"But I asked your name."

"Yes. I didn't want to answer that question, so I answered one I liked better."

"But—"

"Trust me, Larry, this strategy works about ninety-nine percent of the time. That's what all the politicians do. I taught this strategy to Linda for her radio and TV interviews, and it has worked like a charm to keep the hosts on track. Before, she would agree to a topic, such as alcoholism, but then the host would take off on a tangent, like how to get their kid to eat liver. This way, she can just invent and answer relevant questions."

The long line of cars on the bridge was moving fast. Larry turned around to look at the trunk, as if he could see through it. "I can't believe you've got Estanislado back there!" he said.

"Believe it, Larry," I said.

"What would Linda be telling to you now?" Mark asked me.

If siblings' nitpicking and backstabbing were tiresome, having them team up against me was worse. Suddenly I pitied Mexican parents. I'd never considered the downside of kiddy alliances.

"Linda would say that she would love to overcome her worrywart ways, and she hopes you two don't follow in her nervous footsteps. Then she'd remind me that you are being ridiculous, because for all the pots I've stirred, I've never been in trouble, not even in school."

My lane of traffic was moving too fast for the officials to be inspecting cars or even passports. Already we were nearing the head of the line. I looked in the rearview mirror and patted my hair into place.

Larry and Mark were silent, but I was on a roll. "And Linda would say that sweating the small stuff has made her old before her time and is a waste of wrinkles. Fretting should be reserved for important issues like and swollen, painful hemorrhoids. "

When I arrived at the immigration booth, the guard signaled me to stop and roll down the window. That was bad. The heat leapt into the car and smacked me in the face. That was worse.

"U.S. citizens?" the guard asked, peering intently at Larry while holding out his hand for our passports.

"Yes," I said.

"The purpose of your visit to Mexico?"

"A vacation." Oops. U.S. and Mexican Easter vacations didn't match. Was he staring at Larry because a school-aged child should already be in school?

"Are you transporting any unwrapped fruits?"

"No."

"Any unwrapped vegetables?"

Estanislado was sealed in metal. "No."

"Any alcohol or other items to declare?"

I shook my head.

"Welcome home, Ma'am," he said, tipping his hat and handing me back our passports.

We'd leapt the first hurdle!

My fingers gripped the steering wheel as I drove on Interstate 35 toward the first security checkpoint sixteen sweltering minutes north of the border. While the air conditioning fought a losing battle to take the edge off the heat, the radio described the outside temperature of one hundred degrees as "a bit warm."

"I would have guessed it was at least one hundred and one," I told Mark and Larry.

A security official lounged in the on a folding chair in the shade outside the inspection booth. As I slowed the car and prepared to brake, he raised an arm and waved me on.

That left Inspection Point Two.

Half an hour later it occurred to me that my contraband hadn't thumped or bumped since I'd stuffed him in the trunk at the border. I screeched onto the highway's shoulder. Hopefully he hadn't been over-marinated in his own juices or asphyxiated by lack of air and his own fumes.

"I've got to check on Estanislado," I told the boys.

We sat in silence as I summoned my courage.

"Do you want me to check on him?" Larry asked.

"No, an adult must do it." I forced myself from the car. If Estanislado's eyes were closed, I might faint.

Fortunately, when I opened the trunk, his eyes were open. His hair and clothes looked like he'd been swimming in a pool but smelled like they'd never touched water.

"*¿Cómo estás?*" I asked.

"*¡Excelente!*" He nodded enthusiastically. "This was my first car ride."

I handed him a drink of water. "There's one more checkpoint ahead. Don't breathe too deeply so you don't run out of air."

My hands gripped the steering wheel as we approached the second inspection station. I slowed down, but the booth was deserted.

Larry and Mark cheered.

"See? I told you everything would be fine," I said. Except that the contraband was still in my trunk. I couldn't leave Estanislado in the South Texas desert—that was how smuggled Mexicans perished. What was I to do with him?

About thirty minutes later the car jiggled as if I had a flat tire. I turned off the radio to listen, heard a thump, and felt another jiggle. Either the tire on the rear passenger side was flat or had a stone lodged in a groove. I pulled off onto the shoulder. The thumping and jiggling intensified as I slowed, so it wasn't a tire problem.

"Oh my God!" I exclaimed, jumping out of the car. How could I have forgotten Estanislado? "No, you two stay here!" I told the boys. But they ignored me.

On opening the trunk, the heavy scent of cow dung made me wince. Estanislado's eyelids were open but his pupils had rolled back into his head. For a horrible moment I thought he was dead. But then he croaked, "*Agua.*"

Larry helped him out of the trunk while Mark ran for the water canteen. While Estanislado drank up, I laid out his plastic bags on the backseat. If he sweated onto the upholstery, no amount of Airwick would undo the damage.

I'd planned to let him out right after the last checkpoint, but did penance for creating a near-death experience by driving him on to San Antonio.

The trip was longer and more miserable than I'd anticipated because rolling up the windows and running the air conditioning intensified the stifling stench. When I turned off the air and opened my window, the South Texas broiler blasts singed my lungs.

I planned to oust Estanislado in the San Antonio suburbs, but on seeing the nice homes and manicured lawns, I couldn't decide exactly where to drop him. He would look so conspicuously out of place, someone would likely call the police.

In downtown San Antonio, Estanislado's head swiveled on his rigid body and his eyes bugged from his head at the strange city sights and big crowds. Every time I settled on a spot to let him out, a policeman suddenly appeared on foot or drove by in a squad car.

Between the marathon drive, immigration dramas, and blistering heat, I was exhausted. My main weapon, my razor-sharp mind, had fuzzed. I felt paranoid about being in such an orderly, law-abiding country. Do and don't signs were everywhere. The national pastime seemed to be punishing citizens for stepping an inch out of line.

I couldn't locate the middle ground between the terror of being caught with my contraband exiting the car and the terror of being caught with contraband in my car. Worrying about such a minor problem wasn't worth the wrinkles. I should be able to come up with a story to exculpate myself. But I worried on.

"Do you have any money?" I asked Estanislado.

He didn't reply.

"It's OK to answer."

He pursed his lips.

"Speak!" I commanded.

"Fifty pesos."

I handed him a twenty-dollar bill to supplement his four dollars.

A few minutes later, I saw a U.S. Department of Immigration sign on an office building. I had an urge to go inside and turn myself over to the authorities. Then, on the building next door, I saw my salvation in a large sign proclaiming, "Day Laborers Wanted."

I swerved to the curb and braked hard. Estanislado, who had been gripping his plastic bags, nearly jumped out of his *huaraches*.

"See that building?" I asked him. "That's immigration. You've already immigrated. See this building? You can get a job right here! So jump out quickly. And good luck."

Estanislado got out, took a few tremulous steps, and then halted. He stood rooted to the sidewalk with a plastic bag still clinging to the seat of his soggy pants.

I wanted to watch him disappear into the safety of the swarming crowd of business-suited men and women, but it parted around him. Pluck him from a farm, and it didn't matter where he landed. He looked and smelled like he belonged in a barnyard.

"I am hoping he is being OK," Mark said.

"Me, too, but I'm very glad he's no longer our concern," I said.

I'd done my good deed for the day. Heck, I'd fulfilled my good-deed quota for life.

When we returned to Irapuato a week later, Lupita was on our doorstep. Obviously something was wrong.

"Have you heard from Estanislado?" I asked.

"*Ay, Señora.* He barely sets a sandal in your country when the immigration police catch him and put him lickety-split on a bus back to Mexico."

I shook my head sadly. "I'm so sorry to hear that."

"Estanislado is very angry. He says you left him by immigration on purpose so they can catch him. I say no, it must be an accident. He says no, nobody could be that *estúpido.*"

I felt the color rise in my cheeks as I muttered an incomprehensible

"Then the ranch boss, Don Guillermo, he fires Estanislado for missing work for two days."

"That's terrible! Whatever will you do?"

"We will sue."

"Who?"

"You."

"What?"

"Even though you do this terrible crime, I still like you, Señora Sonna. I will visit you in the prison."

"WHAT?"

A subpoena arrived a few weeks later. It stated that a lawyer from the state of Guanajuato's Farm Labor Board had filed suit on Estanislado's behalf. I had been officially accused of depriving the Mexican economy of a valuable agricultural worker!

Considering that Mexico's unemployment rate was about thirty percent and millions of desperate men were going to the U.S. to work, it was hard to imagine that losing one strawberry picker would harm Mexico.

The charge was so ridiculous, I wasn't going to bother showing up, but my neighbors insisted. On my way to the courthouse, I decided that the legal shenanigans would likely be interesting to watch, and if the subpoena turned out to be real, I'd have a front-row seat.

After entering the austere courtroom and being sworn in by the serious bailiff, the severe magistrate adjusted his black robe and addressed me in Spanish. "Señora Sonna, do you understand the charges against you?" he asked.

"No, your Honor."

He shuffled through a stack of documents. "You stand accused of kidnapping a Mexican citizen, falsely claiming him to be your husband, forcing him into the trunk of your car, and transporting him across the border into the United States of North America, thereby depriving Mexico of a productive farm worker. If found guilty, you may be sentenced to ten days in jail, and Estanislado's employer will be ordered to reinstate him in his former job."

I chuckled. This was funnier than I had expected.

The Farm Labor Board lawyer snarled, "It was sheer luck that a U.S. policeman recognized Estanislado's plight and rescued him!"

Surely I must be dreaming! But when the odor of cow dung wafted into my nostrils, I knew this nightmare was real.

"What do you say in your defense, Señora Sonna?" the stony-faced magistrate asked.

"Well, your Honor, do I look like the kind of woman who could wrestle a grown man into my car?"

"Do you have evidence to present?"

I paused. "Yes. I want to present Estanislado."

He hobbled to the front of the courtroom. Too many days wearing sandals had apparently afflicted him with the malady of the modern world: blisters.

I stepped out of my high-heeled shoes and stood next to him. "As you can see, we are about the same height. Now, if Estanislado will please make a muscle." Between clenched teeth I hissed at him, "You ungrateful wretch!" I pointed to his ropy biceps. Then I rolled up my sleeve and shook my arm to show off my flab.

"If it please the court, do I look like the kind of woman who could, even if she would, which I couldn't, so I wouldn't, wrestle an unwilling man into the trunk of my car?

"That's your evidence?"

"His height is Exhibit A, his pathetic clothes are Exhibit B. I'm not so idiotic as to think I could pass off this poor peasant as my husband. For Exhibit C, we need to approach the bench."

The magistrate nodded, and Estanislado and I walked forward. "Breathe deeply, your Honor."

The judicial nose twitched and quickly wrinkled in disgust.

"Ah-ha!" I said. "You winced! Let the record show that Estanislado smells like donkey dung. Or maybe cow dung. In truth, I can't tell one kind of barnyard turd from another."

"You may step back," his Honor gasped, attempting to bypass his olfactory glands by breathing through his mouth.

"Now Your Honor," I continued. "I do not question that Estanislado is a dependable man, a hard worker, a devoted father, and an intermittently faithful husband who deserves to have his old job back. But the central facts of this case are as follows: Estanislado's B.O. offends my feminine sensibilities. In conclusion, I have demonstrated beyond the shadow of a doubt why I could never force him and certainly wouldn't allow him into my car! I rest my case in favor of a new one. I want to countersue for this unconscionable assault on my reputation as a classy lady and responsible owner of a clean-smelling car."

"Señora," the magistrate intoned, peering at me over his reading glasses. "Mexico cannot tolerate having our economy deprived of valuable farmworkers. They are the backbone of our nation. I find you guilty as charged!" He struck his wood desk with the gavel. "Estanislado's employer must reinstate him in his previous job. I sentence you to ten days in jail."

My toes went numb, my fingertips tingled, and my mouth went dry as a bone. When I tried to beg for mercy, my tongue stuck to my upper palate. After a strangled moan, my tongue broke free. The loud smack echoed through the court like the gavel that had sealed my doom.

"Does anyone here today speak or understand any English?" the magistrate asked.

No one replied.

"Not even a little bit of English?"

I raised my hand.

"Anyone other than Señora Sonna?" he asked. "No one? OK, Señora. Approach the bench."

When I stepped forward, he said, "I shall address you in English to be sure that you alone understand what I am about to say."

"Yes, your Honor."

"I might be moved to probate your sentence so you don't have to serve time behind bars."

"That would be wonderful!"

"Take my nephew with you the next time you go to the United States. He needs to find work."

I had yet to overcome the trauma of toting Estanislado across the border. There was no way I was going to relive that nightmare. On the other hand, spending even one night in a Mexican jail seemed equally awful.

When I opened my mouth to reply, I had no idea how I would answer. Words came out, and I heard my voice as if from afar. But instead of speaking, I heard myself sing:

> *Happy birthday to you.*
> *Happy birthday to you.*
> *Happy birthday, dear Magistrate.*
> *Happy birthday to you!*

The magistrate began hammering his gavel long before I had finished. The scowl lines on his forehead and around his mouth suggested rage, but his widened eyes and narrowed pupils betrayed fear. "What's going on?" he demanded. "It's not my birthday!" he blustered.

"Not your birthday? I'm sorry, Your Honor. I must have mixed up the date."

"What? You couldn't know my birthday, so how could you get the date wrong? We've never even met before, have we?" The magistrate looked at me as if I were a complete lunatic.

I felt about as crazy as the Mad Hatter, and then I remembered the Disney version of *Alice in Wonderland*. "If today isn't your birthday, then it's your unbirthday. Congratulations, Your Honor!"

"What?"

"It's not your birthday, it's one of the three hundred sixty-four days per year when it's NOT your birthday. You and I need to celebrate."

He was so flustered, one little push should be enough to send him fleeing down the rabbit hole. Linda had told me about a schizophrenic symptom called a word salad that drove the psychiatric personnel bananas, so I decided to give it a try. "I don't like your tone, Sir!" I exclaimed. "Bigotry, bigotry! Everywhere we go, it's the same."

"Bigotry? We who? What are you talking about?" The magistrate's jugular pounded in his neck, turning his fear-whitened face a deep crimson. He might stand up to hardened criminals, but he was clearly a wimp when it came to confronting crazies.

"The road from Acapulco to Nuevo Laredo via Mom's internal tunnel is very long," I continued. "Not that I can tell one kind of barnyard turd from another. I'm a shop-'til-I-drop sort of person, though I'd never out-shop my day pass! But if you want a toilet seat, tube of mascara, or Sarah James' autograph, *mi casa es tu casa*."

"*Dios mío,*" he muttered to his bailiff. "*Es completamente loca.*"

So my word salad had worked—he thought I was insane. "And my car is your car," I continued. "Your nephew is welcome to ride in my trunk as long as he doesn't thump, bump, or die. Have him call me."

The magistrate shook his head. "Never mind," he said. "Just leave. Bailiff, get this woman out of here. NOW!"

I exited to freedom, knowing the nephew wouldn't call.

As I walked home, I thanked my lucky stars that Maridél had shown me how to extricate myself from the biggest Mexican mess I'd ever been in. I instantly forgave her for every trial, tribulation, taunt, and terrible trick she'd ever played on her teachers.

I even wished I could retract my ill wishes for her miserable future. If she was already suffering the scourges of a philandering fiancé, had conceived a child, and had accumulated too much belly fat, I trusted her unhappiness was caused by someone else's hex or evil eye. Fortunately, as an American, all I'd been able to do was send bad wishes and curses her way.

As for my own future, I decided to add people to my list of smuggling no-nos. Unlike my veggie-only vow, I was willing to wager that I could adhere to my newest contraband regulation.

And I won my bet.

CHAPTER 30

MY FEDERAL FRAUDS

"Frugality is misery in disguise."

– Publilius Syrus

How proud I felt to have finally conquered my procrastination and mailed a letter to Linda!

How defeated I felt when the letter was back in my mailbox ten days later with a stamp that said, "Insufficient Postage, Return to Sender" in Spanish.

Every time I had tried to write to Linda in recent months, something had gone wrong. I would decide to write her a letter but wouldn't be able to find my stationery.

Or I'd write a letter but wouldn't be able to find her address.

Or I'd address the envelope but then couldn't find my stamps.

Or I'd forget to put a stamp on the envelope before dropping it into the mail.

The same mix-ups occurred when I tried to write to Larry. Linda had decided he didn't need to graduate from high school, so she had arranged for him to take his college entrance tests at age sixteen. Larry had snagged a full scholarship to attend Southern Methodist University in Dallas and enough college credits to enter as a junior and graduate in two years.

Larry took my lapses in letters in stride. Linda had yet to finish her doctorate in psychology but considered herself the seasoned expert, and she saw hidden meanings everywhere. For example,

> *Dear Mother,*
>
> *It's been so long since I've heard from you! I'm starting to wonder. Don't you want us to stay in touch?*
>
> *Love,*
> *Linda (Your Daughter)*

I didn't want to lose touch with her, even if her letters filled with chitchat about graduate school made me feel that I already had. In my next letter, I had hastened to reassure her.

> *My Dearest Daughter,*
>
> *Of course I want us to stay in touch! I'm not sure why it took me so long to write to you. I promise to do better.*
>
> *Love,*
> *Mom*

My know-it-all daughter couldn't refrain from psychoanalyzing me. Her next letter contained the following comment:

> *Dear Mother,*
>
> *The notable decrease in your letter writing started shortly after I started graduate school. You should ask yourself whether those two events are related.*
>
> *Love,*
> *Soon-to-be Dr. Linda*

When she finished her degree, I hoped she would dedicate herself to analyzing patients and leave my psyche alone. Still, after pondering her letter, I had to admit she could be right. I replied:

Dear Linda,

I admit it's somewhat intimidating to write to an almost-doctor of psychology. I hope you'll confine yourself to reading what I write on the lines and won't poke around between them.

Love,
Your Very Sane & Normal Mother

Linda's reply was not reassuring:

Dear Mother,

I've always read between the lines of what you write, as well as what you say, in order to uncover your real meanings. That's probably why I was attracted to psychology in the first place.

Speaking of which, my major professor said I need to do a statistical study for my dissertation, but I'm hoping to convince him to let me do a case study. I've saved all of your letters, so I've got lots of data. Here's hoping.

Love,
The Next Freud

So having me for a mother had prepared her for a career as a psychologist! Was that a compliment or an insult? And what type of case did she consider me to be? The only kind of psychological case I'd ever heard of was a "mental case." In my next letter, I did my best to thwart her between-the-lines psychoanalysis.

Dear Linda,

The weather is nice. Larry seems to be happy in college. Mark and I are fine. I trust all is well in your world.

Love,
Mother

To which she replied:

Dear Mother,

It took you over a month to respond to my last letter, and what you wrote was so short and terse, you are obviously feeling defensive. Please tell me what's troubling you.

Your Concerned Daughter,
Linda

Now she was even analyzing how often and how many pages I wrote! I'd quickly penned and mailed a long letter, but the Mexican post office had returned it. Who knew what terrible meaning my aspiring psychologist daughter would dredge up from another long silence!

And why had the Mexican post office deemed my eighty-centavo stamp insufficient? Did my letter require additional postage because it was five pages instead of just two or three? I balanced my letter on one hand and my telephone bill on the other. They seemed to weigh the same.

Between the cancelled the stamp and the "return to sender" message, the envelope was a mess. Unfortunately, I was out of envelopes, so I added a new eighty-centavo stamp to the old one.

But because the post office had cancelled my first stamp, I wasn't sure whether it was still good. I affixed a second new eighty-centavo stamp for good measure. Now the envelope was so cluttered, I feared the postman wouldn't be able to find the address. I circled Linda's address and crossed out the "insufficient postage" message. Somehow, that just added to the mess.

Almost-doctor Linda might conclude I'd lost control of my envelopes. I sighed. I supposed her diagnosis would be correct.

I decided to walk my letter to the post office to get a guarantee that my letter would make the full journey north. After standing in line for an eternity, I stepped up to the counter.

"*Buenas tardes,*" I said to the attractive young postal worker. At least, his hair, nose, and mouth were nicely formed. His green-tinted glasses obscured his eyes, upper cheeks, and part of his forehead. As we talked, I found myself focusing on a large dark mole centered just below his bottom lip. "This letter was returned to me for insufficient postage," I explained. "I put two new stamps next to the old one, but the envelope got kind of messy. I want to be sure that my letter will be delivered."

"How many stamps do you want to buy?" he asked.

"None. I just have a simple question. This letter was returned to me for insufficient postage, though it seems to weigh the same as my telephone bill. I don't know why. I know you can't speak for the U.S. post office, but as a postal professional, what is your opinion? Would such a messy letter be considered deliverable?"

The clerk weighed my letter and handed me a ninety-centavo stamp.

"What's this?" I asked.

"There was a postal increase last week. A stamp now costs ninety centavos. Your letter requires two."

"But I mailed this letter last week."

"Last week your letter required two eighty-centavo stamps, not one."

"But see? The envelope now has three stamps worth two pesos and forty centavos. The post office actually owes me sixty centavos."

He pointed to my original stamp. "This one has been cancelled. You need two new stamps."

"How dare the post office cancel my eighty-centavo stamp without taking it to its destination?"

"Because of the postal increase, you need to add twenty centavos."

"So why are you trying to sell me a ninety-centavo stamp?"

"It's the smallest stamp I have left. "Do you want to buy it or not?"

I found myself staring at his mole again. "I didn't bring my purse."

"Next!" he said, gesturing to the woman behind me.

I wasn't about to budge. "The cost to mail this is one-eighty, I already spent two-forty, you're saying I need twenty centavos more, but you're going to charge me ninety centavos more? That's ridiculous!" The difference was only about seven U.S. cents, but there was a principle at stake.

When he gritted his teeth, his mole wobbled. He asked me to step aside.

"This letter is to my daughter. She's studying to be a psychologist, and she analyzes everything. She might have me committed if I don't mail her letter today."

"*Por favor, Señora—*"

"I mailed this before the new rates went into effect. You could see the date, if I hadn't marked through it."

Wobble, wobble.

"Can't you consider that I mailed it last week?"

"No." Wobble, wobble.

"I want to speak to the postmaster!"

"Why don't you talk to the guys in the mail room? I'm sure they'd love to talk to you. They're downstairs."

I nodded curtly and walked off in a huff so the twenty-five people standing in line would understand that the delay was the clerk's fault, not mine.

The only entry to the basement was an outside delivery ramp. I inched down the long, steep ramp in my stiletto heels.

When my eyes adjusted to the dim light in the bowels of the post office, I saw about two dozen men stuffing letters into thousands of cubbyholes in hundreds of giant wooden cupboards. When I coughed to get someone's attention, everyone paused and stared at me.

After an awkward silence, I addressed the crowd. "I've come because I need to get this critical document to the United States immediately," I said, trying not to look as self-conscious as I felt. "Due to an unannounced postal increase, my document was returned for insufficient postage. I added two new stamps, bringing the total to two-forty on a letter that only cost one-sixty last week and one-eighty this week. The clerk upstairs had the audacity to insist that I need to add a twenty-centavo stamp, but the smallest he has costs ninety centavos."

The men continued to stare at me.

"I didn't expect to have to purchase more stamps, so I left my purse at home. This letter has already been delayed for ten days and simply must be in the mail today. Otherwise, there could be a serious deterioration in international parent/child relations. Meaning that if this letter isn't in the mail today, I will be mad as hell at your country, and my daughter may decide I'm deranged."

Two dozen pairs of eyes continued to stare at me.

I cleared my throat. "In conclusion, can anybody spare a dime?"

The men continued to regard me like an exotic zoo animal. I said no more to let the pressure build, and it worked. After a long pause, a pot-bellied gent stepped forward. "Follow me," he said.

He led me through a maze to a back office, opened a desk drawer, and extracted a bulging spiral binder filled with stamps. Most of them were wrinkled; many had bits of envelope clinging to the edges. His mammoth collection of used but uncancelled stamps had obviously been steamed off of people's envelopes. He turned page after page after page. Altogether, his collection must have been worth at least a thousand U.S. dollars!

He closed the binder and shook his head. "I don't have any twenty-centavo stamps," he said.

"But I saw pages of ten-centavo stamps. You could give me two of those."

He pointed to my cluttered envelope. "There's only room for one stamp."

"Then give me a thirty-centavo stamp."

"Why would I donate ten extra centavos to the Mexican government? What has it ever done for me?"

"Well, it feeds, clothes, and shelters you and your family, right?"

"I work long hours for low pay. I hardly ever see members of the public, so I just get a salary—no tips."

"You didn't pay for those stamps, so they're not really yours. The public might be interested to know why so many letters never reach their destination. In fact, one of those stamps looked very familiar. I'm pretty sure it's mine."

He crossed his arms and glared at me. "So is this blackmail or extortion?"

"Neither would be possible. I'm sure that like any other government employee who values his paycheck, your supervisor gave you permission to collect these stamps so you can supplement your paycheck—how? By selling them to friends? Hocking them on the street? Your boss is responsible for what goes on down here. While the powers-that-be are investigating him for corruption, you'd probably just be put on short-term leave and enjoy a much-needed vacation. When the public storm subsides, I'm sure you'd both be back on the job in no time. Or so I assume. Isn't that how things work in Mexico?"

My unhappy civil servant plucked a thirty-centavo stamp from his book, swiped the back with glue, slammed it onto my envelope, and tossed it into a bag on the floor.

"*Gracias,*" I said.

He nodded curtly.

As I hobbled up the steep ramp and made my way back to the sidewalk, it dawned on me that I had been an accomplice in that stamp pimp's federal fraud. In addition, I had blackmailed a foreign official and received stolen goods.

Well, at least a stretch in prison would give me more time to compose thoughtful letters to Linda, though her replies might make me wish for the electric chair.

Meanwhile, I pondered the postal worker's unwillingness to part with a single stamp. Few low- and medium-level employees could survive on a government paycheck, so their bosses and most citizens expected them to supplement their income as best they could, either by charging special fees or by dipping into the public coffer. But to make such a fuss about handing over a stamp worth the equivalent of three measly U.S. cents was disgusting. Well, I supposed every country had a few cheapskates.

At least he had come through for me, and my letter was en route to Linda. Unless he decided to retrieve my envelope from that bag, steam off "his" stamp, and reroute my letter to a waste paper basket. I should have taken it with me and dropped it in an anonymous mailbox on the street!

I had the urge to run back for my letter, but I had already spent half a day, about twenty U.S. cents of my money, three cents of the Mexican post office's money, and had committed two felonies to mail a five-page letter that I could have summarized in a postcard paragraph:

Dear Linda,

The thought of being analyzed for your dissertation gave me the willies when you first brought it up. But then it occurred to me that I am leaving my body to medical science, so why not donate my psyche to social science?

I'd love to be immortalized in a dissertation! I'm sure others can benefit from my uncanny ability to win amigos and influence enemigos.

Also, I thought of a title for your report on me. "From Upstanding American Mom to Mexican Felon: A Case Study.

Love,
Your Slightly Schizzy Mother

Linda did receive my five-page letter, and a few months later I received the disappointing news that she wasn't going to immortalize me in her dissertation:

> *Dear Mom,*
>
> *I decided to do a statistical research project on a REALLY exciting subject. I will compare affective and achievement variables of students enrolled in regular and TV English courses at the Dallas community colleges.*
>
> *Love,*
> *Linda*

Why had she capitalized "really?" Suggesting that my life story was less exciting than an achievement variable must mean I was as boring as cement. Wasn't I wacky enough to interest her?

I dared not risk further trips to the post office. If the postal clerks had posted my picture on the bulletin board, I might be recognized. I couldn't write to Linda again until I found another source or way to purchase stamps.

I finally sent Mark to the post office to buy them for me. Then I wrote to ask Linda what my diagnosis would be. She replied:

> *Dear Mother,*
>
> *I can't legally diagnose anyone until I take the state board exams, but in my unprofessional opinion, you would be classified as normal neurotic.*
>
> *Love,*
> *Linda*

How could my own flesh and blood consider me any kind of normal when I'd dedicated my life to being anything but? What were the professors teaching in that graduate school of hers?

In my next letter, I expressed my opinion of the sorry state of academic psychology. She penned a conciliatory reply:

> *Dear Mother,*
>
> *"Normal neurotic" is a technical diagnosis, but don't despair. I'm sure you also have some narcissistic and sociopathic features. In any case, your kids agree that you're as nutty as a fruitcake. Is that better?*
>
> *Love,*
> *Your Daughter*

Yes. It definitely was.

CHAPTER 31

WAR DANCE

"We'll blast them back into the stone ages,
but then what can we do for an encore?"

— *General W.C. Westmoreland*

Mexico had fallen behind in repaying its international loans, and the foreign financiers were tired of waiting for a *mañana* that never quite arrived. Mexico's president promised to get a check in the mail ASAP. But when yet another debt deadline passed without a payment, the foreign fiends cancelled the country's credit card!

In the ensuing economic chaos, the peso plummeted, losing about eighty percent of its value virtually overnight. After working my brain to the bone for over a decade, the value of my savings was reduced to almost nothing.

My neighbors dealt with their doldrums by complaining about the corrupt politicians, praying for better days in the next world, and attending parties, which were as abundant as ever. The nation had crashed into a financial iceberg, was sinking into the red ink sea, and most everyone I knew was drowning. But just like on the Titanic, the bands played on.

I admired my Mexican friends' steadfast commitment to partying.

Besides celebrating important religious holidays like Three Kings Day, Ash Wednesday, and Virgin of Guadalupe Day, I attended kindergarten and primary school graduation parties, and paid my respects to states at state fairs, to cities at city fairs, and to strawberries at strawberry fairs. I celebrated Children's Day, Postal Employee's Day, and payday. And because every day was someone's Saint's Day or birthday, I was forever up to my hairline in party invitations.

When Catarino, my nerdy doctor friend, invited me to accompany him to a Boy Heroes' Day (*Los Niños Héroes*) ball, I was too caught up in my economic doldrums to feel up to another fiesta honoring anyone. Besides I'd never been a fan of those boys, who weren't exactly the brightest bulbs in the box.

The September 13 celebration commemorated six teenaged soldiers who couldn't quite hold it together against the invading Spaniards during the 1847 battle at Chapultepec palace.

Instead of a sensible surrender, the boys decided to bail out of their besieged Mexico City mountaintop by draping themselves in Mexican flags and leaping, Superman-style, from their fort. Their spirits may have soared, but their bodies catapulted in the predictable direction, landing, kersplat, in the valley below.

My Mexican friends considered the plunge patriotic because of the boys' colorful capes, heroic because they died, and revolutionary because... well, no one could ever quite explain it to me. Given the young soldier's sad situation and suicide jump, I imagined their final words were probably, "This is nuts! I'm getting the hell out of here!"

Though the teens obviously exercised poor judgment in deciding exactly how and where to exit, I do think that a mass decision that war simply isn't worth the time and blood would indeed be revolutionary.

"Thanks, but no thanks," I told Catarino. "I'm a pacifist. It doesn't sound like my kind of party."

"But Lois, this is an once-in-a-lifetime opportunity. Ladies have never been admitted to our military ball before. Who knows if they'll ever be allowed in again."

My feminist hackles rose. "Women are excluded?"

"Women can attend, but not ladies."

From Catarino's ensuing description, the sponsoring organization sounded like a cross between the Moose Lodge, the Elks Club, and the VFW. Back in LaGrange, those groups had also excluded ladies. I'd been appalled when Lee had wanted to join the American Legion. "Those groups are an affront to women and world peace," I'd protested. "Men too old to go to war sit around, discussing its glories. I don't want you to be a part of that."

"I don't need your permission," Lee had snarled.

"Those groups are an affront to women as well," I'd added.

"That's not true! Ladies aren't allowed in."

That was too much. I threatened to infiltrate that bastion of bellicosity and liberate the female entertainment (who supposedly popped out of a giant cake each Veteran's Day clad only in her birthday suit). When I added that I would also collect the male oglers' names and mention them in a newspaper article, Lee had decided not to join.

I decided to be Catarino's date for the Mexican military ball. Partying until the wee hours of the morning would likely improve my mood, and I could make a meaningful contribution to the world by using the time to promote world peace and feminism. The combination seemed *perfecto.*

To prepare for what was to be an elegant bash, I nurtured nature by gussying myself up with false eyelashes, a curly red wig, and a sparkly blue gown. All were genuine imports from my friendly border town J.C. Penney and Woolworth stores.

Catarino didn't want to waste pesos on a taxi since I only lived eight drizzly blocks from the party. We double-timed on over.

Inside the luxurious motel lobby, dozens of military police sipped tequila and chatted. But I quickly realized that they weren't just socializing. They were stationed at carefully selected posts so they could conduct thorough inspections of the arriving women.

I felt uneasy having so many uniformed men look me up and down with their eyes. I tried to remember any recent crimes I'd committed in which an zealous MP might have an official interest, and my kidnapped kids and unpaid import taxes came to mind. I lowered my guilty gaze, hoping to slip through the main checkpoint without getting caught. But when I glanced up, the men were still studying me.

To create a distraction, I licked my ruby reds, batted my plastic lashes, and wiggled my womanly wiles. These were not easy feats. My tongue slid off the slippery lipstick. The rain had turned my eyelash glue to goo, which complicated my attempts to blink. It was hard to wiggle in the dress I had bought two years and two sizes ago.

"Are you all right?" Catarino asked, pointing to the large circles under my armpits.

I explained that being surrounded by so many uniformed men triggered traumatic memories of officials pulling me aside and demanding to see the color of my money.

Catarino nodded. "When I see a policeman, I flee even though he's busy fleecing someone else."

Just as I had anticipated, the dimly lit ballroom brimmed with subliminally bellicose messages.

The air was as smoky as a battlefield.

Spent Howitzer shell casings served as vases for the flowers in the centerpieces.

The waiters wore fatigues.

Although the military men groped their dates as if they wanted to make love, not war, I vowed to expose the potent pro-war propaganda before the night was through.

As Catarino guided me to our table, I sucked in my stomach and tried not to collide with the cuddly couples crisscrossing the dance floor.

Our messmates sat in formation at a table in a corner. The women faced the dance floor with their backs to the wall and facing the stage; the men were lined up in the aisle seats, facing the women's restroom. I desegregated the macho group by taking up a post next to rather than across from Catarino.

After sitting down, I understood why the men had chosen the aisle seats. That put the men within pinching distance of the damsels hurrying to the bathroom. Each time one of them opened the restroom door, rays of light snuck into the twilit ballroom. By looking up on light cue, we glimpsed women adjusting their secrets—the ones that had crept above their waists or wrinkled at their ankles. Catarino, a true gentleman, didn't pinch or peep too often.

I was watching the restroom show when the houselights brightened, a bugle bellowed, and the entire audience leapt to its feet. At first I thought war had been declared, but then uniformed musicians paraded onto the dance floor, belting out the Mexican counterpart of *Stars and Stripes Forever*.

Everyone's face glowed, and the crowd went wild. Well, almost every face. I was grimacing from the bugle blast's initial blow to my ears, and for some unknown reason the young señorita across from me was sobbing.

Because my ears were still ringing I didn't hear the command to be seated, but suddenly the entire entourage sat down in unison, so I did the same. My hearing improved until it was like being in an airplane that had just ascended to forty thousand feet.

While the others at my table sipped drinks, chatted, and traded posts so they could cuddle and nibble on their dates' neck, I held my nose while yawning and poking at my poor ears to try to unplug them.

I wondered why the señorita across from me was still boo-hooing.

Certainly the opening song had been a moving experience—even the chandeliers had marked cadence with the cymbals. Perhaps all the battle hymns and aggressive imagery had upset her?

"*Buenas noches, Señorita.* Quite a bit of pageantry. Very moving, *¿no?*" I asked.

She shook her head as she emptied her sinuses into her paper napkin.

"Are you appalled to see women relegated to sex objects? Are you shocked by the rampant display of hawkish attitudes that will inevitably lead to global conflict or even nuclear annihilation?" I asked.

Again, she shook her head.

"Then *¿qué pasa?*" I asked.

"Every time I hear a military band, I think of my great-grandfather, may his soul rest in peace beside the Blessed Virgin Mary and all the saints, Amen." She crossed herself.

"Was he one of the Boy Heroes? Did he fling himself off that castle and die?"

"No. A tuba fell on my his toe during an Independence Day parade."

I responded like any normal, red-blooded American. I laughed.

She stared at me in horror. So I did what any red-blooded American would do. I coughed. And then I lied. "*Perdóneme.* Good gracious, I seem to have something caught in my throat. So. Well, now. That really is terrible about your grandfather. Seriously injured, was he? (Cough, cough.)"

She nodded. "He never recovered from the humiliation," she sniffled.

I gave a sympathetic nod. "The tuba (cough, chortle, cough) crushed his ego?"

She nodded!

I reached for my goblet and tried to dilute my chuckles with water, but the descending slurps collided with the rising giggles. I accidentally blew noisy bubbles into my glass until I gasped, which sucked the mixture of water and mirth into my nose. As I sputtered and wheezed, I tried to think of a way to console my grieving messmate.

When I recovered from my near asphyxiation, I said, "Well, as I expected my mother to tell me during my darkest hour, 'You're lucky you broke your vacuum and not your back.'"

She paused to consider. "What does that mean?" she asked.

"I guess it means 'Cheer up! Things can always get worse.'"

The maternal words of wisdom that I had feared would undo me worked wonders for her. She nodded, brightened, and was about to speak when a crash of cymbals and snare of drums decimated all hope of conversation.

The military band was at it again. They serenaded us throughout dinner with rousing renditions of our favorite marches and battle hymns. Meanwhile, the men at my table joined in with an impromptu accompaniment. Some played imaginary xylophones, using their knives and forks as mallets. Others pummeled inverted coffee cups. Several played the water glasses with a spoon. Almost everyone toe-tapped. I resigned myself to eating din-din to the din of drums, brass, china, metal, and crystal, chewing on the up-beats and swallowing on the downbeats. The concert didn't end until dessert, at which time the band marched out of the ballroom while playing the sweet, sentimental ditty that used to bring tears to Lee's eyes, *Anchor's Away.*

I was prepared to make an after-dinner toast to nuclear disarmament but got distracted when I noticed that the waiters' white gloves were meant to camouflage their surreptitious finger-licking. My waiter had blown his cover. His left glove had a red thumb that matched the strawberry sauce topping everyone's cheesecake but mine.

Although I had been seated for over an hour, I hadn't learned more about the rank-and-file at my table than whether they preferred cups or plates as drums. If I was going to woo them to the feminist/pacifist cause, I needed to get to know them.

I nudged Catarino, and he commenced the introductions. "This is

Roberto, the night shift cardiologist and his assistant nurse Elena from intensive care. They popped in for a few drinks on their break. The man over there is Carlos, an obstetrician, with Esperanza, his girlfriend. His wife is in the hospital having a baby. Next to him is Miguel—he's into contagious social diseases—and that's Lolita, his mistress. The one sitting next to them is—sorry, I don't know his name."

"It's Juan!" I said, suddenly remembering my macho geriatric womanizer with the social security problem. He hadn't returned to the U.S. to ogle the North American girls; he was in Mexico ogling his date, a scantily-clad woman with dramatic costume jewelry who looked to be in her mid-forties.

At first I was relieved to see that another woman my age was attracted to the ancient codger, but then I felt a bit betrayed. I was supposed to be Juan's one true love; he had promised to carry my picture in his mind forever. If that had ever been true, I had been replaced.

"And next to him is Jaime," Catarino continued, "an orthopedics man, with Irma, his physical therapist."

I nudged Catarino again, and he clinked his glass with his spoon to get everyone's attention. "Señoras and Señores, I'd like to introduce Lois, an American. She is the principal of the *Instituto de Estudios Bilingües*."

The women looked up, but of the men only Dr. Jaime acknowledged my introduction. No one else wanted to be distracted from what appeared to be their central goal: to get drunk. Dr. Jaime had already reached it.

He came over to shake my hand, slurring a Spanish version of "glad ta meecha, teacha." Then he asked, "Have ya ever heard the one about the English teacher who slipped a disk on the way to the office?" Then he emphasized the punch line by laughing too loudly and slapping my shoulder.

I didn't get the joke, so he repeated it with another heavy-handed reminder about when to laugh.

I still didn't get the joke but responded to the third shoulder punch by slugging him back.

As I raised my fist to respond to his next repetition of the punch line and punch, Catarino caught my hand and ushered me onto the dance floor.

As we mamboed I blamed my violent reaction on the bellicose ballroom atmosphere. Otherwise, I wouldn't have exchanged blows after just a few moments' torture at the hands of a drunken orthopedist who had probably just been trying to thud up business.

"Catarino, the men at our table are all wearing wedding rings. Yet they have the gall to show up here with girlfriends and mistresses!"

"Their wives are probably at home, feeding the children and putting them to bed."

"But that's terrible!"

He looked at me blankly. "What?"

"That Mexican women tolerate such philandering!"

He shrugged. "Most wives are probably happy to have their husbands out of the house. It's easier for them to do housework without a man underfoot."

"But that's slave labor! And adultery is a sin!"

"A sin, but tomorrow is Sunday. They can clear their souls tomorrow morning in the confessional."

"It seems to me that Mexican women need to have their consciousness raised."

"Why?"

"So they can throw off the shackles of the patriarchy!"

"And get a divorce?"

"It works in America. After several marriages, most men wise up."

"Mexicans don't believe in breaking up families. We believe divorce is the bigger sin."

I gestured to Juan, who was groping his young date as they mamboed by. "His poor wife!"

Catarino shrugged. "Eventually he'll go home to her. Eventually she will be glad to see him."

"If he got a divorce he could marry his date. As it stands, he and his wife must be very unhappy."

"We have a saying in Mexico," Catarino said. "It goes, '*Más vale lo malo por conocido que lo nuevo por conocer, o tal vez no.*'"

It took me a moment to figure out the literal translation: a known bad is worth more than an unknown good, or maybe not. Then the figurative translation was easy: a bad bird in the hand is worth two in the bush. Or maybe not.

"Well, Catarino, when American wives get divorced, it's because they still believe in the possibility of love."

"But when a Mexican couple takes lovers instead of breaking up the family, it is because they believe in love's reality."

Huh? Guillermo had once said something similar—that Americans don't understand the difference between being in love and loving. I remembered seeing the Responsables holding hands under the table in my kitchen when I'd fed them *pozole a la Yanqui.* That Señor Responsable loved his wife, hairy legs and all, was indisputable. Did he play around? Probably, as that was the general custom.

As if he had read my thoughts, Catarino said, "If lust becomes love, a man may start a second family. But a *macho* man is responsible and dependable. He continues to support his first family economically. He returns for their birthdays and other family celebrations. The children do not lose a parent."

I snorted. "Why not just admit it? Mexican men are macho pigs."

Catarino twirled me, held me in a dramatic dip, and whispered, "Ah, but no man dances alone."

But of course! That was so obvious. Why hadn't I ever considered that before?

"Catarino, I never thought to ask you. Are you married?"

"Well…"

Crashing cymbals announced the next event, and he was off the hook for the moment, though I suspected I already had my answer.

As soon as we had returned to our table, some uniformed men huffed and heaved while pushing a large, squeaky-wheeled cannon onto the dance floor. Apparently no one had thought to apply a bit of grease or splash of oil. I eyed my leftover butter and salad dressing, but had the feeling I shouldn't aid or abet the next event.

A drum roll echoed through the room, and the audience held its collective breath in anticipation. There was a mighty boom, and then the cannon ejected the entertainment. Racy Raquél Rodriguez's Mexican flag unfolded behind her as she flew across the room and landed in a net. After crawling out of the ropy tangle, she strode onto center stage.

The male half of the audience stamped, clapped, and hooted its delight as our blond bombshell's cape dropped to the floor. We women were less enthusiastic. Though the cantaloupe-sized tumors ballooning from the human cannonball's sparkly bikini top were indeed impressive, we could tell that her basic intelligence was deficient. Instead of just putting her flag on, she shimmied and shivered with chill.

We were all amazed by her ability to carry a microphone while balancing on three-inch stiletto heels, but something about her stage presence and the men's ardor rankled. I wished the orthopedist would seize her mic, tell her a joke, and give her a punch line or two.

An hour later it was clear that the show wasn't going to improve, so I raised my water goblet and roused Catarino by dousing him. We tiptoed past the snoozing sentinels stationed at the doors and exited the hotel.

Outside the rain had stopped, and the clean air was refreshing. As I walked and Catarino staggered toward my home, I thought about the evening.

Except for desert, the food had been fine and dancing with Catarino had been fun. Overall the experience had been interesting. I hadn't converted anyone to the pacifist cause, but perhaps war wasn't an issue in Mexico. The Mexican army seemed to spend all its time preparing its soldiers for parades, not battles. Military expertise seemed to consist of crisp marching, loud singing, synchronized drum beating, artful gun-twirling, and a lot of flag-waving.

And despite the hawkish music, dress, decorations, and punch lines, none of the speakers had reminisced about great bloody battles or asked us to applaud the nation's hired killers. The military men had been armed with girls, not guns. Perhaps Lee had merely longed to hum some battle hymns and hoot at a hussy while imbibing booze with buddies at the American Legion. If so, what was the harm?

As for Mexico's "lover" solution for marital misery, maybe it had some advantages over the American "leave 'em" solution. Had Mr. Wrong and I pursued happiness with a lover, perhaps our LaGrange marital nest would have lasted until our birdies were old enough to spread their wings and fly. As best I could tell, Linda, Larry, and Mark hadn't been harmed, but Bill continued flitting across the content in what I feared were aimless circles.

But these were such foolish thoughts! I'd rather have had my toenails pulled out than spend one more night under the roof with Lee.

I regretted not having even tried to convert a sister partier to the feminist cause. Poor Raquél would probably continue as a lowly sex object, though she appeared to relish having a roomful of men fall in love with her chest. And it was hard to tell whether Mexican women actually needed to have their consciousness raised. Mexico's national secret seemed to be that the Madonna Goddess set the example for women to rule the roost, at least at home. Obviously women hadn't penetrated the public patriarchy.

I had a sudden brainstorm about how to help them do that.

I would start a movement to add September 14 to the official holiday calendar so that Mexico could commemorate all the Girl Heroes who had survived the Boy Heroes' Day bashes the day before. All women and ladies would be honored, regardless of marital fidelity, age, or chest size.

CHAPTER 32

CANONIZING SAINT LOIS

"Saint: a sinner revised and edited."

— *Ambrose Bierce*

When Larry finished reading the *World Book Encyclopedia,* he could still recite everything no one had ever wanted to know about aardvarks, thanks to his photographic memory. At age sixteen he aced his SAT exams and headed off to attend Southern Methodist University in Dallas. Linda lived with her husband Tom just a stone's throw from campus, but Larry's scholarship and stipend covered the cost of a dormitory, not to mention everything else.

I was one proud mama!

When Larry finished his Bachelor's degree two years later, he brought a college friend, Greg St. Ville to visit Irapuato. In two days they exhausted the local supply of entertainment. I agreed to a day trip to the nearby city of Querétaro. Claudia, Larry's high school sweetheart, joined us.

Mark and Larry hadn't spent much time together in the previous two years, but on climbing into the car, it was as if they'd never been apart. They delivered elbow jabs and squabbled about who was hogging all the space.

I finally threatened to change the radio to *my* favorite station if they didn't stop. They settled down for a few minutes. Then Larry offered to let me choose the station, which struck me as unusually thoughtful. "He's growing up," I thought. But as soon as I changed it, the arguments resumed.

My nerves were frayed by the time we pried ourselves from the car at the serene Querétaro overlook.

While Claudia and I oohed and aahed over the whitewashed adobe city nestled in the valley below, Greg snapped pictures of Mark and Larry pretending to push one another off the cliff.

As we hiked up The Hill of the Bells to Maximilian's Monument, I said, "Listen up, boys and girl. It's time for your history lesson."

"Aw, Mom," Larry moaned.

Mark frowned at him. "You should always be respecting to the mother," he said.

I smiled. In the Mexican religious hierarchy, every mom is regarded as a veritable saint. Had Larry been younger when we moved to Mexico, he too might have absorbed my favorite foreign family value.

"Several centuries ago," I began, "an Austrian tourist named Emperor Max crowned himself king of Mexico. The Mexican president revoked his visa, ordered his arrest, and Max was captured and imprisoned. Max's wife greased his jailors' palms, and they cooked up an escape plan. Step One was to disguise him by shaving off his beard. Max refused, preferring a dignified death to the shame of a shave. And so it came to pass: he was shot on this very spot."

"Mom, I don't see any soft-drink stands up ahead," Larry said.

"You're supposed to listen to my history lesson! You're in Mexico on a tourist visa, too. Remember what happened to Emperor Max!"

"Yes, Larry! Be behaving yourself!" Mark interjected.

I gave them both my best shape-up-or-else glare. "Anyway, about one hundred fifty years later, the government erected this landmark in Max's honor. See?"

Mark frowned. "But it is with the name of Benito Juarez," Mark said. "He was not being shooted here."

I paused to consider. "Well, public shrines need statues of heroes. Heroes are people who are in the wrong place at the wrong time, with onlookers who brand their bad luck as bravery. Juarez' bad luck of being president when an Austrian emperor took over the country was considered brave. Max's bad luck of being shot due to his vain refusal to submit to a shave was clearly cowardly. Anyway, after so many years, what does it matter who died here? Let's go see the chapel where the assassins said penance for shooting the world's vainest emperor."

Larry squinted up the hill. "Is there a snack bar inside?" he asked.

"Don't be bugging to our mom," Mark said. His view of mother as saint was as Mexican as his view of brother as devil was American. Mark was truly a product of two cultures.

After I purchased tickets to the chapel, Mark looked at his and asked, "Why is it having here a picture of Vicente Guerrero?"

I shrugged. "Maybe they couldn't find a flattering photo of President Benny or Emperor Max? Ask the clerk."

The clerk said that probably explained it.

While Greg and Mark prayed in the chapel, bless their devout Catholic hearts, I retreated to the car. Claudia was Catholic, too, but she had opted to stroll hand-in-hand around the park with Larry.

As they walked, they gazed into one another's love-besotted eyes. They had only seen each other twice during Larry's two-year absence, once in Irapuato and once when Claudia had accompanied Mark and me on a visit to Dallas. Linda had been pushing for me to let Claudia and Larry have a sooner-not-later wedding, but I would not endorse a union of eighteen-year-olds. Larry was scheduled to start medical school in the fall. He couldn't support a wife, and she wouldn't be permitted to work in the U.S.

"Of course I know the statistics on teen marriages!" Linda had said. "But those are macro-level norms. Viewed from a micro-level perspective, they are a perfect match. If Larry doesn't snatch her up, someone else will. As you always say, Mother, 'Absence makes the heart grow fonder, for somebody else!'"

I liked that in Mexico even bright, highly educated daughters honored their mother as wise. Even if they considered her witless, they would be too respectful to let on.

After the kids returned to the car, I drove to the *Convento de la Santa Cruz de los Milagros* in Querétaro.

Greg didn't know the story, so I filled him in on the history of the Convent of the Miracles of the Holy Cross. "Back in the eighteenth century, an elderly priest named Antonio de Margil de Jesús was hobbling along on his staff while taking his daily constitutional, when he decided to bury it."

"Bury what?" Greg asked.

"His staff. That's a walking stick."

"But why?"

I shrugged. "Perhaps he got a new cane, wanted to ditch the old one, but was loath to litter? The reason is buried in the sands of time. All we know for sure is that the buried cane sprouted, took root, and grew into this miraculous thorn tree, the only one of its kind in the world."

Greg was impressed. "Wow! The only one? Really?"

"People have taken cuttings, but the transplants didn't take."

"But why not?"

Mark shook his head and frowned. "Greg, the monks at my school are saying, 'Don't be asking so many questions or you'll be confounding your brain.'"

Mark had embraced the whole Catholic zeal deal host, wine, and stinker. Even my creative religious conversion strategy had failed to woo him from the faith: I had offered to pay him an extraordinary sum to read the entire Bible during the summer. He rose to the challenge, was appropriately shocked and appalled by the utter ridiculousness of the famous stories. But the monks got to him when he resumed school in the fall, and he became an atheist backslider. At least the summer reading project turned him from a reluctant, indifferent reader into an avid, passionate one.

In the convent's garden, Greg snapped pictures of the holy thorn tree. "Cool!" he exclaimed.

"Yes, but take a close-up shot," Larry told him.

Greg zoomed in and saw the three tiny thorns protruding from each little thorn cross. He was flabbergasted.

"Yes," I said. "The three small thorns are positioned exactly where Jesus' wooden spikes would have been driven in, if He had been the size of a grasshopper tacked to a little thorn instead of to a weighty timber."

"A miracle!" Greg said, still agog.

Mark's eyes shone with religious fervor. "Yes, but inside you'll be seeing to the other big cross miracle," he said.

We gathered in front of the ancient painting in the foyer. Donning my tour guide hat, I explained the painting's background. "When the Chichimeca Indians finally agreed to convert to Catholicism, the kindly Spanish missionaries removed their thumb screws. Peace reigned until the Chichimecas' mangled digits healed, and then they teamed up with several other tribes to send the *padres* packing. In 1531, smack dab in the middle of the biggest battle, there was a solar eclipse. The combatants on both sides paused to gawk. Through their seared retinas, they beheld a giant cross high in the sky."

"What they saw as an afterimage," Larry said.

"Oh?" I asked. "I didn't know that. Well, since no ophthalmologist was on hand to explain the consequences of seared retinas, the awestruck

Indians fell to their knees and begged to be baptized. The convent gets its name from the heavenly afterimage as well as the thorn bushes."

Mark's eyes shone with religious fervor. "And that, Greg, is being the biggest miracle here!"

Larry yawned. "Can we go get some lunch now?"

But Greg, bless his Roman Catholic heart, wanted to tour the rest of the convent. While the kids headed into the nave to see the altar, I waited alone in the deserted vestibule.

My only company was a card table stacked with religious pamphlets, buttons, postcards, trading cards featuring different saints, and Convent-of-the-Holy-Cross bumper stickers. Price placards drove home the point that the sacred paraphernalia wasn't free. A wicker basket containing a few coins explained the self-serve purchasing process.

To kill time, I counted the coins. The total came to five pesos and forty centavos, or about forty cents U.S. That was the price of four pamphlets and one big button. Or of one bumper sticker, one pamphlet, and one small button. Or half a pamphlet and five small buttons.

As I nudged the coins around and calculated the possibilities, the kids came out of the nave. At the same moment, the holy relic vendor appeared. "I saw you! I saw you!" the toothless nun screamed at me.

Instead of continuing forward to rescue me, the kids halted, shifted into reverse, shuffled backwards into the nave, and closed the door behind them. I was on my own.

Usually I am embarrassed to be caught with my hands in an alms basket, but this time I was innocent. "I was checking the dates on the coins," I told the toothless nun, figuring that fiction would be more credible than truth.

Her lecture about thievery continued, so I plucked a coin from the basket and placed it in her hand. "This five-centavo piece could be quite valuable," I said. "You don't need to thank me. Consider it a donation." I made the sign of the cross to prove I was beyond reproach and hurried into the nave.

A smattering of the faithful had dropped in for a lunchtime prayer. I didn't see the kids, so I walked to the front of the church and climbed up to the podium to get a better pew view.

A few distracted kneelers were surprised to see me on center stage, so I waved, made those odious middle-finger gestures to pantomime that I had four kids, and then shrugged while looking around to ask if anyone had seen them. No one responded, so I made the sign of the cross to bless them and turned into a small room near the altar to continue my search.

The room was empty except for a jug of water and a card table with a stack of old Order of Service fliers. Suddenly I heard footsteps approaching. Was the vendor after me? I pulled the handle of an ornately carved wooden door. It opened into an ornately carved wooden room the size of a small closet. The only furnishing was a small wood bench. I stepped inside and closed the door behind me. I sat down on the bench in the dark.

While waiting for the footsteps to depart, there was a tap, tap, tap on a tiny wooden door near my right ear. I didn't even try to resist temptation. I quickly opened the door and said, "¿Sí?" in my best baritone.

A tremulous male voice admitted that it had been six months since his last confession. I decided to make the man a deal: "Tell me your sins, and I'll tell you mine, My Child," I suggested.

He listed his. He'd had a few impure thoughts about a neighbor but hadn't tried to convert them into actions. I decided that his boring six-month stretch was enough punishment for one man, so I forgave him for his thoughts and blessed him.

He hurried off before I could share a sample of my sins. Realizing what he was missing might have helped him toward a more interesting life path.

Suddenly the sound of multiple foot shuffles penetrated the confessional's thick door.

I heard Claudia wonder where I was.

I heard Mark fear I was getting myself into trouble.

I heard Larry wager that I already had.

I stood up and threw open the confessional door. "Honor thy *mamacita!*" I exclaimed. "Take not her humor in vain!" To ward off their evil, I extended my arms and crossed my index fingers in the anti-Dracula sign.

Mark looked horrified.

Claudia's brown face paled.

Larry's face whitened.

Greg's white face reddened. "Mrs. Sonna," he said, as nervous perspiration accumulated above his brow. "You shouldn't be in there."

I made the sign of the cross over his head. "I forgive you, my Son, for not getteth-ing my joke."

"Can we leave, now? Please?" Greg begged.

"We shall depart forthwith. First I needeth a drink of water."

Greg sprinted to the water jug. There were no chairs in the room, so I sat back down on the confessional bench. There were no glasses, so Mark used his origami expertise to fold a church flier into a cup.

"Please, Mrs. Sonna. You shouldn't be in there," Greg pleaded.

"If you've anything to confess, this is your chance," I told him.

"And I don't think you should drink that water," the poor soul continued.

"It's OK, Greg. "Bottled water is safe."

"No, I mean you shouldn't because—"

"Greg, please stop shoulding all over me!" I had been dying to use that line since reading it in one of Linda's self-help books years ago.

I drank from Mark's origami cup while Larry poured, but the water eked out of the flimsy flier faster than I could guzzle. "I guess God doesn't want me to drink the water, either. Let's go get a Coke."

As we passed through the vestibule, I responded to the holy relic vendor's glare with a cheerful wave. But then her pupils contracted into shocked pinpoints and her eyes widened into awe as she stared at my raised palm.

I checked for an oozing stigmata, but the wet church flier's ink had bled onto my skin. My decal said, "Order of Mass" in Spanish. I rubbed my hands together to smudge the evidence and hurried outside.

As the kids and I walked the cobblestone path to the parking lot, Greg continued to fret about my soul. "I can't believe you drank the convent's holy water, Mrs. Sonna!"

I continued to reassure him. "Yes, Greg. That probably makes me a saint!" I placed my palm on his forehead. "You can be my first disciple."

Greg scanned the heavens for lightning bolts.

Claudia's lips curved into a wan smile.

Larry guffawed.

Even Mark laughed.

I was proud of my boys' mirth. Mark had inherited the Sonna sense of humor, but it was nevertheless impressive that he could enjoy iconoclastic comments about religious absurdities without feeling compelled to defend his faith. And after a slow start, Larry had evolved into a master humorist. Besides getting my jokes, he entertained us with incisive observations, unexpected quips, and complex wordplays.

I was immersed in thought when suddenly a black-suited young man with a white priest's collar approached us from behind and said, "Excuse my poor English, Señora. Did I hear you correctly? You drank the holy water in the small room behind the altar?"

"It must have been divine providence, Father. I must be as holy as thou now," I joked.

"No, I do not think so," the priest said, shaking his head. "That water is for the baptisms and the blessings. We are taught never to drink the water."

That wiped the smile off my face faster than I could say "typhoid." If a full-fledged man of the cloth lacked the power of water purification, how could I, a saint with questionable qualifications, expect to defeat damnable dysentery?

As we window-shopped our way around Querétaro's downtown plaza, Larry and Mark dickered about this and quarreled about that. Their tits for tats and barbs weren't funny, but I bore their endless sparring with equanimity.

Maybe it was the holy water moving within me, gracing me with Christ-like tolerance. Probably I was too busy searching out restrooms to try to keep my cup from runneth-ing over. For sure I was too intent on praying for a miracle to deliver me from diarrhea and prove my sainthood. As if having endured a family outing wasn't proof enough!

CHAPTER 33

CAUGHT IN THE ACT!

"One man's trash is another man's treasure."

— Anonymous

It was a well-known fact that whenever the U.S. sneezed, Mexico got a cold. So it shouldn't have been surprising that when the U.S. contracted a cold in 1979, Mexico came down with pneumonia.

As the Yankees' economic ills ballooned into Mexico's financial crisis, the value of the peso plunged again, so low this time that I suited up and joined the run on the banks.

When I reached the end of the long line at the finish, the teller relayed the bad news: to share the misery among the hordes of dedicated contestants, the governmental referees had capped withdrawals and made it illegal to take dollars out of Mexico. I gasped when the teller placed my paltry prize in my palm—a check for a few measly U.S. dollars.

So as not to do anything illegal, I inserted the check into an envelope, addressed it to Linda in Dallas, took it to the post office, and let the Mexican postal service commit the crime of taking money out of the country. A week later I again joined the throngs outside the bank, withdrew the maximum allowable pittance, and took a second envelope to that same criminal postal organization.

After bank run Number Two, I returned home and collapsed on the couch. While Mark watched dubbed Bonanza re-runs, the horror sank in. I'd lost my contraband, school uniform, and textbook profits virtually overnight due to the currency devaluation, while triple-digit inflation was gobbling up my *Instituto* salary faster than a clutch of hungry hens. I could barely afford to keep us in tortillas, much less peanut butter.

I was still reeling from the blow when the phone rang. "I don't know how else to say this, Mom, so here it is," Bill began. "You need to move back to the States. NOW."

I braced myself for news of an emergency.

"You need to get Mark back here while there's still time," Bill warned.

"Time for what?"

"To learn English. Otherwise, he'll have to attend college in Mexico or some other Spanish-speaking country—he won't get into a U.S. school. Don't you want to keep his options open?"

I was mystified. "Whatever are you talking about? Mark's English is the second best in town."

"Yours is best. Now that Larry's in college, Mark is the only other American in Irapuato. That makes him second and dead last."

"I've got other troubles now. We'll talk later." I handed Mark the phone. "It's Bill," I said.

As I collapsed back onto the sofa to continue mourning my lost savings, I heard Mark say, "Good afternoons, Big Brother. How are doing you?"

I bolted upright. "WHAT? Mark! Why are you talking that way?"

Mark looked perplexed. "How way?"

"Your grammar is atrocious!"

His lower lip trembled. "I am telling good-bye to you now," he said to Bill.

Larry called from Dallas a few days later to beat the same drum. "If

Mark is going to survive in a U.S. college, he will need to know more than English. You need to move back now so he can learn the ins and outs of American cool."

"What's that?"

"It's acting like the popular kids. The students teach one another in junior high and high school what to do to be accepted. For instance, if you make good grades, everybody avoids you like the plague. It's better to lie and say you failed a test or to be vague and say you're trying to put that test out of your mind. So actually, it's OK to make good grades so long as nobody finds out. Wearing the wrong clothes is the same. You can only wear white socks with sneakers or you're shunned as a dork. On a button-down shirt, you have to leave the top one open or you're a social pariah."

"You are exaggerating."

"I'm OK, 'cause I got into SMU's nerd heaven, Letterman's Dorm. It's a haven where uncool eggheads can discuss science, philosophy, literature, and etc. in the cafeteria. It's not like a regular dorm, where guys engage in jock talk about sports, drunken parties, and who's sleeping with whom. But Mark isn't enough of a scholar. He'll be in a regular college dorm. Mr. Social will be miserable as an outcast."

"Mark will rise above sock-and-shirt superficiality, Larry."

"If you move back to the U.S. now, he'll have time to learn about Americans."

"That's ridiculous! Uncle Sam is in his genes."

Larry sighed. "Yes, and Mark's popularity will be largely dictated by where he buys pants. You grew up during the depression and live where lots of kids don't even have shoes. You can't imagine the social repercussions of wearing the wrong brand of expensive designer jeans. Genes/jeans. Get it? Never mind. Can I talk to Mark?"

"*Hola*, Larry," I heard Mark say. "Not much. I was taking the siesta and doing some stuffs. I am to be reading *El Cid* for the class of the literature. In this evening I am seeing to a cinema containing my favorite actor, Cantinflas."

How had I not noticed Mark's English before tonight? I tried to retrace his linguistic journey, but after tracking it from "Batman" to "Wa-wa" to "Wa-wa, Batman" to *"agua,"* the trail went cold. I didn't pick up the scent again until he was about four, when I clearly remembered him saying, "Grab to me the water" at the dinner table. It had taken me a moment to figure out he wanted someone to pass him the water.

Had I been a proper mommy and corrected Mark's errors? Probably not, because he still said things like, "Grab to me the water." But what I did remember was looking up "grab" in my bilingual dictionary, discovering that it meant *agarrar,* and realizing that Mark was translating Spanish phrases and sentences into literal English.

After that revelation I had begun using Mark's verbal oddities as markers to guide me through the complex Spanish syntax terrain. Hearing him say "please tell to her" instead of "please tell her" meant that "to tell" in Spanish, *decir,* required an indirect object, not a direct object like in English.

By the time Linda and Bill pointed out that Mark had veered from the proper English grammatical path, I'd heard his quirky turns of phrase so often that they sounded normal to me.

I had noticed that his intonation was more Mexican than American, but I had written off Linda and Bill's criticism of Mark's English as their weakest talking point in their decade-long campaign to convince me to move back to the U.S. Impossible as it now seemed, I hadn't noticed a problem with Mark's English until overhearing him through Bill's ears on the phone.

When Linda phoned a few nights later, I knew that Mark's three elder siblings had formed an alliance, and a conspiracy was afoot. "It's time to return to Yankee Doodle Land," she began. But after her upbeat

introduction, her tone darkened. "It's. Time. To. Come. Home. NOW,"
she said. She sounded like a mother rounding up her teenaged curfew
criminal.

"I am home," I said.

"Home to the U.S. Before. It's. Too. Late."

"Too late for what?"

"For you."

Then she hung up.

Her ominous words haunted me. I hadn't noticed Mark's English
until a few nights ago. Had my eleven-year Mexican vacation also
affected me in ways I couldn't see?

I made the decision to move like my other major life decisions: fast.
After a two-week garage sale, Mark and I packed our personal treasures
and left for Dallas. Bill still lived in LaGrange, and Larry was en route
to Johns Hopkins medical school. But at least Mark and I would be near
Linda and her husband. And the threat of that kidnapping charge was
over. Mark was thirteen—old enough to choose his guardian.

I knew I'd find employment at the drop of a job application. I had a
decade of solid administrative experience, and María Luisa Gonzalez
would gladly attest to my outstanding work as a trapeze artist, CEO
of a multinational corporation, or anything else. My stunning success
during that interview for the marketing research job in Chicago had not
been an anomaly, as I'd believed at the time; my seventeen-year failure
to charm Lee had killed my confidence. I no longer doubted my gift for
gab.

On the long drive north, I began Mark's crash course in American
culture. "Listen carefully, Son. At the end there will be a quiz. You
will need to explain why Americans persist in eating greasy hot dogs

in stale buns, though they know they will have to swallow vile pink medicine—I can't remember what it's called—to soothe their heartburn afterwards."

"I was once eating a hot dog. It was making my gas to stink."

"You must not say that! Americans don't talk about their gas or about anything that comes out of their intestines."

"Why?"

"It's impolite."

"Why?"

"It's just a social rule. I'm going to teach you as many as I can so you don't suffer culture shock."

"That sickness is sounding terrible to my ears. Tell to me about her."

I paused. "You do know how to say those two sentences correctly, don't you?"

He looked out the window.

"Culture shock is when Mexicans are shocked by American culture."

Silence.

"Are you listening to me?"

"I am counting the poles of the telephones so that my mind is calming itself."

I hadn't told him that I had used the exact same method to relieve stress during my long-distance run from LaGrange years ago. He really was a chip off the maternal block. Had he also embraced Scarlett O'Hare's philosophy? "You may prefer to think about this tomorrow, Mark, but your lessons in U.S. culture begin today. Number One: Americans do everything as fast as possible."

He nodded. "Linda was telling to me how the Americans hurry themselves even when they are doing the nothing. Is it true the policemans are catching the peoples for doing the nothing outside?"

"That's called loitering. And yes, it's illegal."

"If my English is so much terrible, I am better to just be guarding the silence."

"No, now listen. We'll work on English a little at a time. Right now we're discussing culture. Americans consider loitering a crime because they think people should always be busy, that relaxing is a kind of sin. Kids are taught that 'idle hands are the devil's workshop.' "

"Busy in doing the what?"

"It doesn't matter. Also, Americans are very finicky about germs, real or imagined. If Americans can smell someone, they think the person must be dirty or diseased. We must wear deodorant every single day to mask our scent. A favorite topic of conversation is how to get yellow scum off everything from shirt collars to no-wax floors to teeth. Anything that looks like it might be dirty is also considered a bit sinful. Kids are taught that 'Cleanliness is next to godliness.' "

"You are saying these stuffs to be a joker!"

"I swear it's true! Americans also worry endlessly about their health. There's a disease spreading through the country called 'the heartbreak of psoriasis.' It's too dreadful to show on TV, so your heart could be breaking without you knowing."

"Is it catchable?"

"I don't know if it's contagious."

"The life, she is not being the same there."

"I think we should try to obey the laws, but there are so many it will be hard. When we cross the border, you may have noticed that if a light is red, Americans stop even at night at empty intersections."

"Why for?"

"A red light means it's someone else's turn, even if nobody else wants one."

"Why this?"

"The U.S. needs lots of laws to keep the police busy. If they just walked around in uniforms to prevent crime like in Mexico, they wouldn't look busy. If they just punished people by having them pay bribes, there wouldn't be enough paperwork to keep the police busy."

"I am confounded."

"Yes, it's confusing. And you must be very careful not to break any garbage laws. Putting trash in the wrong place is called 'littering.' People who commit that crime are called 'litter bugs.' "

"Bugs like *cucarachas?*"

"I guess. Linda says that Dallasites must put their trash in expensive, government-approved plastic bags. Otherwise, the garbage men won't haul it to the dump. And that's big trouble, because it's also illegal to leave trash outside except on garbage collection day."

Mark looked overwhelmed. "What if I am not having the approved types of bags?"

"Store your trash in a pocket until you can dispose of it properly."

"And at the cafeteria in the school? Where am I putting the box for the milk after I am drinking her?"

"School cafeterias have special bins lined with legal bags."

Mark chuckled. "*Ay*, Mom, you are being such an exaggerator. Americans cannot be bending themselves out of their shapes for these types of stuffs."

"No, they are fingerprinted, fined, jailed, or worse—sued."

Mark opened his window.

"Wait," I said when I realized he was going to pitch his apple core out of the car. "Let's practice. Wrap the core in a napkin and put it on the floor until I can come up with a trash bag for the car."

Over tacos and warm Coke in Zacatecas, I outlined some other cultural differences in the two countries' solutions for pressing problems:

Taxes

U.S.: *Vote for whomever promises to cut them, complain about the increases, pay them, & support whoever promises to cut them in the next election cycle.*

Mexico: *Don't pay them. To get public servants to serve, bribes* *work better than paychecks.*

Gasoline Prices

U.S.: *Blame the Arabs, criticize oil company profits, protest pump prices, buy a $10,000 car, & drive across town to a station to save 10 cents a gallon on gas.*
Mexico: *Take the bus.*

Marijuana Use

U.S.: *Imprison the users, fine the sellers, harass the importers, & threaten the growers.*
Mexico: *Grow it, transport it, & let the Americans decide what to do with it.*

Crime

U.S.: *Pass more laws, hire more police, build more prisons, & arrest more people.*
Mexico: *Have few laws so that most everything is legal. Then, if someone breaks one, pay the police to look the other way.*

Unemployment

U.S.: *Wait for job hunters to give up & then declare the problem solved, or start a war to jumpstart the economy.*
Mexico: *Declare more holidays so no one can tell who doesn't have a job.*

Corrupt Officials

U.S.: *Pardon the president, parole the senator, re-elect the governor, support the mayor, & ignore the city councilors.*
Mexico: *Elect the candidates that collect the most bribes.*

Inflation

U.S.: *Impose price controls, increase taxes, & print more money.*
Mexico: *Declare the problem solved.*

Garbage Disposal

U.S.: *Store it in regulation bags & cans, then dump it in lakes & rivers.*

Mexico: *Drop it in the gutter to keep street sweepers employed.*

Mark bit his lower lip.

"In time you may come to love living in a land with laws for most everything. Most Americans obviously do, because they keep passing new ones. I'll ask for a doggy bag so we can store our trash in the car."

"What is this 'doggy bag?'"

"Americans think it's wrong to waste good food. They carry their restaurant leftovers home in a bag, pretending it's for their dog, whether or not they have a dog. They put the bag in their refrigerator and forget about it. When the food spoils, they can throw it away without feeling guilty."

Suddenly Mark was excited. "The peoples are keeping the dogs at their houses? Can I—"

"Let's talk about dating," I said quickly. But what to say? Linda's dating preparation lecture had been a version of my moms-have-eyes-in-the-back-of-their-heads speech from when she was about age four:

Wherever you go,

Whatever you do,

I will be peering over your shoulder,

Watching you.

Years later Linda accused me of having ruined her life with my poetic lecture. She couldn't shake the feeling that I was looking over her shoulder, observing her bedroom and bathroom movements. She blamed me for her disappointing honeymoon and chronic constipation.

I decided to postpone my talk with Mark until I'd had time to think it through.

During the our long post-lunch drive, Mark and I chewed gum, sucked hard candy, munched apples, grazed on bananas, and guzzled Cokes. Our doggy bag ended up with an impressive collection of wrappers, cores, peels, and soda bottles.

As we approached the border, I was overcome by sadness. How to say good-bye to my wonderful life? I wanted to make a grand speech to thank Mexico, but that would require me to harrumph away the lump in my throat, which would likely unleash more tears than words. So I batted away my tears and said nothing.

After being waved through U.S. immigration, we pulled up to the U.S. customs booth. A full-body search of our car's eleven-year accumulation of treasures would have taken hours, so I was on my best behavior when the official ran through the standard questions: "What was the purpose of your visit to Mexico? Do you have anything to declare? Do you have any drugs in your possession? Are you transporting any unwrapped vegetables, fruit, or other produce? Did you spend more than two hundred dollars during your visit?"

I thanked my lucky stars when I finished the twenty-second interview and could proceed to rest my weary tailbone on a squishy bed in a Brownsville motel. But none of them would accept Mexican money. The peso's value was still fluctuating wildly, the banks were closed for the day, and I didn't have enough U.S. dollars on hand to cover the cost.

"We'll have to drive back into Matamoros to change money at an all-night currency exchange," I told Mark wearily. "Or we could just spend the night there."

"If we are driving back, we will have to be getting the new tourist visas and passing through the customs on the going and the coming back." He pointed to a poster for *Alien* outside a movie theatre. "Can I be staying and seeing to that cinema while you are changing the pesos to the dollars?" he asked. "You can be leaving the car and walking yourself across the border so you are not needing a tourist visa, and the *aduana* is

325

not searching to the car during the both crossings."

I'd spent eleven years teaching English to other people's kids while neglecting my own son.

As if he had read my mind, he said, "I am speaking my own way, and this is this."

"You mean, 'that's that.' "

He glared at me.

"I just don't want you to have social problems in school. Apparently U.S. kids are picky about proper English and attire. You can't wear ironed slacks and shirts to school. The uniform is blue jeans with holes at the knees and faded tee-shirts."

"The other childrens can be liking to me or lumping me."

I unearthed enough U.S. coins from my purse for his movie ticket and snack. "And here's an extra dime. You'll need to exit the theatre and feed the meter in an hour."

"Why so?"

"To park here, we have rent the space by the hour. Parking without paying the rental fee is theft. The government pays meter maids four dollars an hour to fine squatters about ten dollars for staying after their hour is up. During the second hour, the police can tow the car to free up the space for someone who will pay the ten-cent rental fee. Then the police charge about sixty dollars a day to rent a space in their lot."

Mark put his head in his hands. "I'm getting a shock from this culture."

"Customs are just personality quirks carried out on a national scale. Americans want their quirks hammered into laws. As long as most locals are OK with them, it doesn't matter that foreigners find them foolish. Not that we'll be foreigners, exactly."

Mark left for the theatre. I was about to toss the doggy bag into the gutter when I remembered the many "Fine for Littering" signs littering the lovely Texas highways. The costs for making a mistake in the U.S. could really add up fast. I decided to carry the trash bag with me and dispose of it properly.

At the gateway to the International Bridge, I dropped a dime into a metal slot, hip-bumped through the turnstile, and re-entered Mexico. I quickly located a currency exchange and traded pesos for enough dollars to hold us until the U.S. banks opened in the morning.

I was walking back across the darkened bridge toward the U.S. side when I spotted the glimmer of a metal trashcan. I was about to toss in the doggy bag when some stickers on the side of the can caught my eye. They said, "LEAVE YOUR DRUGS IN MEXICO!" and "DEPOSIT YOUR ILLEGAL DRUGS HERE!"

I paused. Apparently I hadn't crossed the border yet, but I must be very close, and the can's sign was in English. If it was a U.S. can, was it OK to use it for run-of-the-mill garbage? Or was it exclusively for drugs?

I pushed open the can's little metal door and peered inside, but it was too dark to see anything. Suddenly a movement up ahead caught my eye. A uniformed official was pointing something at me. A gun? No, he was taking my picture with a hand camera! But why? To use as evidence that I had put general garbage into a drug-designated receptacle? I decided it was better to be safe than sorry. I stuffed the doggy bag into my purse and continued on my way.

The official appeared to be waiting for me. The best defense is a good offense, so when I got close enough to read his identification tag, I paused to greet him. "Good evening, Mr. Humberto Mateos of the U.S. Drug Enforcement Agency. You should have warned me you were going to take my picture so I could have combed my hair and powdered my nose. How about a re-do?"

Hubert was not amused.

"Do you have a mirror I can borrow for another photo shoot?"

Silence. Not even a smile.

"Humberto, do you speak English?

"Sí," he said.

"If you think you can use that photo you took to blackmail me, you're probably right."

No smile.

"You must be very tired, poor man," I said. "Have a good night." I felt his eyes boring into my back as I walked away.

The official sitting outside the U.S. immigration booth was reading a newspaper. He didn't check my passport, welcome me back to the U.S., or even look up as I passed by. I was just a few blocks from the theater—so close to finding a motel and falling into bed, I could taste it.

But when I stepped into the little U.S. customs office and saw the throngs of foot traffic waiting to be processed, I wanted to cry. After standing in line long enough to see why it wasn't moving, I wanted to scream.

A lone bureaucrat was conducting slow-motion interviews. I was disgusted by the waste everyone's time and my tax dollars, should I ever pay any. Again and again he asked the exact same questions, as if reading from a script, even though every traveler gave identical answers, as if they were reading from a script, too:

"Welcome to the United States. What was the purpose of your visit to Mexico?"

"Tourism."

(Pause. Pause. Put a check mark on the customs form. Pause. Pause.) "Do you have any alcohol or other items to declare?"

"No."

(Pause. Pause. Put a check mark on the customs form. Pause. Pause.) "Are you transporting any unwrapped fruits or vegetables?"

"No."

(Pause. Pause. Put a check mark on the customs form. Pause. Pause.) "Do you have any drugs in your possession?"

"No."

(Pause. Pause. Put a check mark on the customs form. Pause. Pause.) "Did you spend more than two hundred dollars during your visit?"

"No."

I glanced at my watch. In thirty minutes he had only processed three people. With nine people still ahead of me, I would be here until close to midnight. Mark would be frantic. The car would be ticketed, perhaps towed.

I was powerless to save myself, but at least I could spare the hapless hostages in line behind me. I put check marks by the correct answers on my customs form. When my turn came, I handed the official my form, glanced at his nametag, and spoke loudly enough to get everyone's attention as I handed over my custom's form. "Ready Pedro? On your mark…get set…go!"

Pedro stared at me quizzically. He clipped my customs form to his clipboard, carefully aligning it, paused, cleared his throat, and began, "What was the purpose of–?"

I floored my verbal accelerator and took off, leaving him in the dust as I zoomed full speed ahead. "The purpose of my visit to Mexico was TOURISM. Do I have any alcohol or other items to declare? NO. Am I transporting any unwrapped fruits or vegetables? NO. Do I have any marijuana in my possession? NO. Did I spend more than two hundred dollars during my visit no Mexico? NO." I spun around, tapped my watch, smiled broadly, opened my arms to my admiring crowd, and announced, "That took just thirty seconds. Next!" I added, stepping aside to make room.

Instead of smiling, nodding, and clapping, the crowd just stared at me quizzically. The next person in line didn't step forward. Apparently no one was going to follow my admirable lead.

I turned back to my bureaucrat. "Now you can enjoy a nine-minute break, Pedro. And not to worry—you'll still be right on schedule."

"Why did you say 'marijuana?'" he asked.

"What?"

His hooded eyes were inscrutable.

I tightened my cheek muscles to hold my smile in place. "Because you were going to ask me that."

"What?"

"If I had any marijuana in my possession."

"Why would I ask you about marijuana?"

"Because that's what the customs officials always ask me!" I sounded a tad defensive. To compensate, I batted my lashes a few times to enhance the sparkle in my eyes. Eyelash batting at this late hour was a bit risky. Despite the adrenaline rush from my high-speed performance, after closing my eyelids, lifting them back up was difficult. I was that exhausted.

Pedro squinted at my customs form as if he might have overlooked a question the last ten thousand times he'd read them aloud to tourists. "No, the question is about drugs in general, not about marijuana in particular." He looked me up and down. "That's not a standard question. The officials must have had a reason to ask you about marijuana." He tapped his pen on his clipboard. "I'll need to run a background check." He picked up the phone on his desk and dialed.

Within seconds a door slammed in the hall, and Humberto, my photographer from the bridge, arrived. He escorted me into a small, drab room.

After lowering my poor coccyx onto the hard metal folding chair, Humberto read me my rights. An alarm sounded from somewhere inside my fuzzy brain. I tried to focus my thoughts, but nothing about this surreal scene made sense. My interrogator's name was Mexican, and his dark brown skin, black hair and eyes, mestizo features, and heavy Spanish accent were Mexican. But his employee nametag said U.S. Drug Enforcement Agency. I was obviously in the U.S.

"Now, Señora, I'm going to be asking to you some questions. Telling the lies to a customs official, this is a federal offense."

"Please, call me Lois," I said lightly.

"What's inside to that paper sack, the one that is hiding in your purse?"

"What sack? Oh, you mean the doggy bag? Nothing." I pulled it out of my purse and placed it on the metal table. "It's just trash."

"It is to your advantage to make the confession."

"Really, Humberto. Just trash. Garbage. *Basura.*"

He humphed. "I saw you outside, on the bridge, at the depository for the drugs. And you cannot deny this evidence!" He slapped the Polaroid onto the table.

When I saw myself poised by the trashcan on the bridge, I gasped. My hair looked even worse than I had imagined. "I was going to throw away the doggy bag."

"But you did not."

"No, because I didn't want anyone to think I was throwing away drugs."

"Why would anyone be thinking this?"

"Because the stickers on the can said—. But this is ridiculous. If you're concerned about the contents of my doggy bag, just look inside."

"First I will be asking you some questions. Telling the lies to an official of the government during investigations is a crime. If you are telling any lies, you will be presented to the judge tomorrow. Tonight you will be spending in our little jail cell."

This was not someone to antagonize. I bobbed my head, hoping for humble.

He picked up his clipboard. "What was the purpose of your visit to Mexico?"

"Tourism."

He checked off a box on the customs form. "Do you have alcohol or other items to declare?"

"No."

He checked off a box on the customs form. "Are you transporting any unwrapped vegetables or fruit?"

"No."

"Did you spend more than two hundred dollars during your visit?"

"No."

He opened my doggy bag and plucked out the rubbish, piece by piece. As the pile grew, I felt a tad embarrassed by all the candy wrappers. "Gee, Humberto. I never imagined we would become this intimate. I hope I'm more to you than just another wad of bubble gum."

He plucked out my blackened banana peel, smacked it onto the desk, and growled, "How do you explain this?"

I stared at him, mystified. "I don't know what to tell you, Humberto. I was trying to get my son hooked on nutritious snacks. Or did I eat the banana? I'm sure that after we finished the candy, my son did eat the apple. Its browned remains should also be in the doggy bag, probably under the gum wrappers."

"You lied to a U.S. government official!"

"Oh? Well, perhaps my son only ate half the apple, and I ate the rest. I can't quite remember."

"Your sack contains two unwrapped pieces of fruit. You lied during the first customs interview, and you lied to me."

"Fruit? Where?"

"One unwrapped banana peel. One unwrapped apple core."

Surely he was joking!

Humberto pulled out a set of handcuffs.

He wasn't joking!

"Why does customs care about a blackened banana peel and a brown apple core?"

"The importation of the produce is strictly controlled. The agriculture in the U.S. must be protected."

"The U.S. government is afraid—of what? That I'll flood the market and erode the price of fruit?"

"That's ridiculous! Of course not."

"What danger do my peel and core pose to U.S. agriculture?"

"The smell is very attractive to the fruit fly."

"A fruit fly is dangerous?"

"Just one fruit fly could begin an infestation if she is pregnant. The infestation could decimate the Texas fruit crops, and then devastate the agriculture across all of the country."

"There aren't any fruit flies in the U.S.?"

"Your Mexican fruit fly could be a different species."

"I see." It was good to know that Mexican fruit flies were too law abiding to simply flit across the border when an official's back was turned.

"The imported produce must be wrapped," he said severely.

"Mine was contained in a sack."

"Your sack is insufficient to prevent the odor of the fruit from escaping to the nose of a fruit fly. A pregnant fruit fly might—"

I finished his sentence. "—be attracted to the smell and follow the bag across the border into the U.S."

Humberto nodded.

I'd heard a lot of bogus bases for bribes, but his topped them all! I was far too tired to play Humberto's silly game. So I nodded, pulled out my wallet, and asked, "How much do you charge to look the other way?"

Humberto leapt to his feet. "Do you know of the penalty for the bribing a U.S. official?"

U.S.? Oops. Poor Humberto had either lost touch with his ancestors' noble roots, or they had withered away. How sad. Despite his looks and light accent, he was a Heinz-57 American.

"I wasn't trying to bribe you, Humberto. I asked you a question. I'm a teacher, and I was giving you a test. Because I sprang it on you unannounced, it probably came across more like a pop quiz, which everyone hates. As a law-abiding U.S. citizen, I was checking your integrity. Congratulations, Humberto! You passed."

Humberto spent an hour conferencing with colleagues and running background checks while I dozed on my metal torture chair.

If the computer contained any troubling information about me, it kept its data to itself, but passing the background checks wasn't enough to regain my freedom.

Humberto had to complete various forms. I even had to sign a form to acknowledge the legal confiscation of my banana peel and apple core, and my understanding of the steps I'd need to go through to appeal if I wanted to regain custody of my goods.

When we finished, Humberto handed me my paper sack.

"I don't want it," I said.

"Only the banana peel and apple core are in federal custody. If you don't take the sack back, I will have to do more forms for the other items—the candy wrappers, the soda bottles, the gum wrappers, and the chewed gum. And then you will have to sign the documents."

I agreed to take my sack. I dozed again when he left to Xerox the paperwork so I could have copies for my records.

Mark was hysterical when I finally got back to the car. "Here you are finally being! It's after twenty-four hours o'clock! I am out here all these times, looking busy so the policemans are not seeing me doing the loitering!"

"Mark," I said wearily. "I was detained at customs for failing to dispose of my garbage properly. Promise me that you will be very, very careful with any trash you become involved with!"

"Mom, let's return ourselves to Irapuato."

I shook my head. "I've got to turn you into a full-fledged American, or your siblings will never forgive me." I started the motor.

"My only dinner was being the popcorn in the cinema. Do we have something for to eat?"

"Check the picnic basket."

He lifted it into the front seat. "Only tortillas and the butter of pea-nuts. Mom, you know I am hating these stuffs. You promised to be buying for me a Big Mac, remember?"

Any kid who craved Big Macs in the middle of the night was des-tined to make it in America. "I'm so very tired, Son. Couldn't we go tomorrow?"

"You were promising to me."

"There won't be *pico de gallo* for your burger, Mexican cream for your bun, *salsa* for your fries, or *limón* for your watered-down, over-iced Coke."

"I am adjustable."

"Yes, I know you are." He might whine from time to time, but he was basically easygoing. His disposition was almost as sunny as mine.

As I searched for the golden arches, I suddenly wondered about how "adjustable" I was. After eleven years in Mexico, I also liked lime in my sodas, and little or no ice. I preferred *pico de gallo* to pickles, *salsa* to catsup, *bolillos* to Wonder bread, and Mexican cream to mayonnaise. My mouth watered at the mere thought of charcoal broiled goat, though I had never summoned the courage to taste the testicles.

Why had Linda said I needed to move back to the U.S. before it was too late for me? Did she think I had become so Mexicanized that I was nearing the point of no return? Considering my border brouhaha, perhaps I'd already surpassed it.

In Mexico everyone instantly pegged me as American. Everyone in the U.S. assumed I was just another white American. But I didn't feel like one. Who was I? Not a Mexican. Without a Mexican ancestor, I couldn't claim to be Mexican-American, either.

Larry had chosen "other" as his ethnicity on his medical school application, and then explained during his admissions interview that he was an American-Mexican. Was that now my ethnicity, too? But who besides Larry and his admissions committee had ever heard of that?

And what did it even mean?

The bigger question was my future. After trading my mundane peanut-butter-and-jelly-on-white-bread life for a grand peanut-butter-and-tortilla adventure, I'd concluded that happiness required a good match between personal chemistry and cultural geography.

In Mexico the match had been *perfecto*. More than the warm, friendly people and the endless parties, I'd loved the live-and-let-live attitude and unremitting good cheer. My Mexican friends and even total strangers had enjoyed my outrageous sense of humor. If at times people had laughed at me rather than with me, I didn't mind. Shared smiles were what mattered, not what triggered them.

Could I be happy in such a serious, judgmental society? Well, I had laughed a lot in the U.S. before I'd married Lee. Actually, I'd laughed a lot while married to him, but my brand of merriment had been his irritant.

Soon I would find what the U.S. held for me without Lee.

CHAPTER 34

THE NACHO SOLUTION

*"Nothing so needs reforming as other
people's bad habits."*

– *Mark Twain*

"**L**ook!" Mark said, pointing to the darkened arches and empty parking lot. "McDonalds already closed himself."

We ended up at Dennys Restaurant. The hard orange plastic seats glared beneath the fluorescent lights, searing my aching eyes and torturing my coccyx. The visual onslaught and hard chairs energized Mark.

A greasy busboy brought us beverages and a menu without greeting us or returning my smile, but Mark didn't seem to notice. He thanked him and eagerly flipped through the massive tome. "Look at all of the so many choices!" he enthused.

With a Mexican "psst," he summoned our gum-chomping, fingernail-polish-picking waitress.

I needed to teach Mark American restaurant etiquette, as soon as I could remember the proper way to get a U.S. restaurant worker's attention.

"Pardon me, waiter lady," he said. "Can you be telling to me, please, what are these on this card, that she is calling the 'nachos?' "

The waitress sunk her Bic pen into her towering platinum blond hair-sprayed hive. The foot-high stack of hair moved like it was made of metal when she wiggled her pen up and down to scratch her head. "I reckon y'all ain't from 'round these parts, then," she drawled. "Nachos is melted American cheese on tortilla chips. Real tasty."

Mark and I exchanged quizzical glances. "You reckoned correctly," he said, mimicking her drawl. "We ain't from 'round these parts."

To think I'd worried about him mastering English. In less than five seconds he'd mastered Texan! I should have taken him to more sit-down restaurants on our many previous trips to the border. Conversations at McDonalds rarely progressed beyond, "Y'all come back now, yah hear?"

A small pink bubble emerged from between the waitress' bright orange lips. She popped it with a resounding smack and sucked it back inside her mouth. "Y'all oughta truck on down to Mexico and check it out. I hear nachos is real popular down there."

Mark and I exchanged glances.

"But we cannot," Mark said. "We are not having a truck." He ordered a Dennyburger and turned to me. "What are you to be ordering for yourself?" he asked me. "Maybe trying the nachos on for your size?"

Suddenly I had my answer to the Big Question. "That's it!" I exclaimed. "Nachos!"

"Comin' right up," the waitress said, poking the pen behind her ear.

Mark rested his head on my shoulder. Hopefully he wouldn't absorb American touching taboos any time soon. "You are being very happy in your heart, Mom," he said.

"Yes! I just realized that tortillas can be flattened for tostados, folded for tacos, or chopped and fried into chips, but they continue to be what they are. The same goes for peanut butter. No matter how thin you spread it, it's still Skippy."

"I am not understanding the meaning."

"That tortillas-and-American cheese combination sounds like the perfect metaphor for my new life. I'll be a resident nacho."

"I am not being certain of what you are telling to me, Mom."

I tousled his hair. "All that matters is what I'm telling myself."

The waitress reappeared. "Y'all want jalapeños on yer nachos?" she asked me.

I laughed with delight. "Yes! A nacho needs lots of pizazz!"

"No, Mom," Mark said. "That's a lot of too much spiciness for having in your stomach."

I nodded like a compliant child, but then I heard the *tin* and *tan* of alarm bells sounding in my mind.

I had tried to accommodate my family's wishes back in LaGrange, but I had never succeeded in getting along for long. My desire to turn up the flame on each golden moment until it sizzled kept winning out. In the end, it had fueled my flight to a land without peanut butter and jelly. I'd found happiness in Mexico because I'd been thoroughly, unapologetically me.

As the waitress awaited my momentous jalapeño decision, Mark explained the problem. "My mom cannot be eating too much spiciness," he told her. "It is making her gas to stink."

The waitress' eyes widened and her mouth dropped open.

Mark apparently remembered that lower GI sounds and scents were U.S. taboos, because he hastened to explain. "What I am meaning is that my mom cannot eat so much spiciness or her stomach will be needing the pink *medicina*. She is hating that taste."

"Pepto Bismol?" the waitress asked. She blew, popped, and sucked in another small pink bubble. "Yeah. That stuff tastes like shit."

Mark looked at me. "She is saying about the shit."

I shrugged. "I guess American etiquette has changed a lot since I lived in the U.S. I guess we'll have to learn the new rules together. Then we'll decide which ones we want to follow."

Suddenly Mark gasped and turned to the waitress. "But how are you knowing of the taste of the *caca?*" he asked. "You were putting it inside your mouth? For why? For to be eating it? You are boggling to my mind!"

I didn't hear how the waitress explained her excretory simile because I was too busy pondering a happy revelation: Mark had tried to nix my jalapeño order out of genuine concern for my well-being. My kids lectured me, just as I lectured them, to protect, not to thwart. Problems heated up when I strove to stop being me in hopes of pleasing others. That was a mistake I simply must not repeat. In the future, if I wanted to be as outrageous as a giant helping of jalapeño peppers on a plate of tortilla chips and melted cheese, well, watch out, Dallas! A nacho was coming to town!

"I do want jalapeños," I told the waitress. "Though my son is right. They'll probably make my gas stink."

The waitress' mouth rounded into an O and she actually took a step back, as if in addition to mentioning anal air, I'd unleashed a puff.

Using my napkin as a shield, I whispered to Mark, "Apparently it's OK to say 'tastes like shit,' which to me sounds crude, but not 'stinky gas,' which to me sounds cute." We stifled giggles. "Perhaps your sister and brothers can explain the modern mindset to us."

The waitress remained rooted in place, not even chomping her gum.

"I think she is having a bad suffering from the culture shock," Mark whispered. "Go ahead," he told her. "You can be bringing to my mom the jalapeños, please."

I smiled. "Yes, I need enough hot peppers to spice up a whole new life. But I don't want to alienate everyone on my first day in the country, so please serve them on the side, waiter lady."

EPILOGUE

*"Few things are harder to put up with
than a good example."*

— *Mark Twain*

Most children are products of their parents' upbringing, but I was a product of my children's. All four worked hard to turn me into a responsible adult. Much to their relief, I belatedly acquired the trappings of an upstanding citizen.

I obtained a U.S. driver's license, car registration, voter's card, and apartment lease with names that matched. I took an office job that paid an over-the-table salary. I calculated my income taxes with what I assumed to be the average amount of finagling, and I filed them every year.

Then, when I was old enough to gauge the passage of time by the waxing and waning of my social security checks, I finally fulfilled my children's ultimate dream for me: I became stark raving conventional.

Yes, it's true. I moved into an ordinary (ticky-tacky) Dallas apartment complex, avoided illegal (exciting) sidelines, eschewed dangerous (fascinating) pastimes, and steered clear of wild (interesting) friends.

I married an ordinary (boring) elderly Jewish gentleman with a heart condition and many lovely assets (high-yield investments). After our bank accounts were joined in unholy matrimony, I came to admire Abe's character (he laughed at my jokes) and indifference to home-cooked meals (he didn't mind eating out a lot). In short, I fell in love

THE SONNA FAMILY, 1985

Back Row: Cheryl (Bill's darling wife), Nancy (Dr. Larry's ex – no comment), Dr. Larry (ICU doc, still a genius), Dr. Linda (psychologist, author, artist, and a bit of a know-it-all), Tom Agler (Dr. Linda's ex – no comment).

Front Row: Bill (errant hippie teen turned workaholic), Lois Sonna Mark (peanut-butter-and-jelly mom turned hot-tamale smuggler turned nacho queen), Mark (cute *niño* turned dancer, choreographer, award-winning playwright, director, actor, screenwriter, and owner of MBS Productions theater company in Dallas).

Not Pictured: My kids' pet dogs, cats, parakeets, cockatiels, newts, horses, skinks, turtles, gerbils, and goldfish.

with him. When we traveled to the Orient, I wanted to stay on indefinitely. But when the tour ended and Abe said it was time leave, I went home with him.

After Abe died Linda comforted me by giving me a Shih Tzu dog for Christmas. I welcomed little Cha-cha (short for *Muchacha*) into my life with as much enthusiasm as her teenaged *I Hate to Cook Book* present. Though Cha-cha and I became close, my feelings about pets and cooking remained unchanged.

Now, at age eighty-seven, I spend the mornings wowing fellow exercisers with my physical prowess during daily torture sessions at the Dallas Jewish Community Center's gym. I spend the afternoons yukking it up with friends at my bridge, Mahjong, and book clubs. In the evenings I sew raggedy Anns and Andys for young inpatients at the Texas Scottish Rite Hospital for Children in Dallas. I've donated well over a thousand.

Although none of my children chose to follow in my hallowed footsteps, I have caught occasional glimpses of my influence. Despite their mundane lives, I don't view them as completely lost causes. I still have hope.

D r. Linda readily acknowledges that she learned more about deviance from me than from her college textbooks and professors. In her psychology practice she teaches children how to raise better parents, and in her many parenting books she teaches parents how to be the kind of mom she wanted me to be.

Linda moved to San Miguel de Allende, Mexico, in 2005. I was proud as *ponche* that she had followed my example and stepped off the well-trod suburban path. But even in the lawless land south of the border she has remained as straight as the highway in the Sonora desert. In fact, she went so far as to conduct training sessions for the San Miguel and State of Guanajuato police, which felt like a very personal and pointed betrayal. I felt better when I learned that she was teaching them how handle mentally ill members of the public during emergency calls, but then she upgraded my diagnosis from "normal neurotic" to "a lovable sociopath." If I get caught committing an unlawful no-no in San Miguel, I guess the police will know how to manage me.

Hippie Bill eventually traded his beard for a briefcase and turned into a full-fledged yuppie. He married a high school Spanish teacher, completed several university degrees, and has maintained a successful career as a civil engineer. After spending his childhood trying to restructure me, he said that re-vamping the Chicago White Sox' home, Comiskey Park, was a breeze by comparison. He and his wife Cheryl raised Tanya, David, and multiple designer dogs in their home in LaGrange, just a short donkey ride from Lee.

Then, for Bill's dramatic midlife crisis, he sold their home in LaGrange and moved his family into a Chicago condominium ten miles away.

Bill's wild-and-crazy hobbies include working long hours, bike riding, jogging, spending time with his wife, and cooking the Thanksgiving turkey. His car, home, and the rest of his life are registered, licensed, and approved by the city, county, state, and federal governmental powers that be. I tried to teach him better. But, oh well.

I'm not sure that Larry ever forgave me for nixing his plan to autopsy our dead pet burro and dog. (Yes, I buckled under Linda's relentless "kids need a pet" campaign and allowed little Dog to move into our Irapuato home.) Despite that extreme educational deprivation, Larry obtained a double doctorate from Johns Hopkins medical school and then taught at Harvard for many years.

Dr. Larry gave up his pocket protectors, polyester pantsuits, and white socks to marry Nancy, a proper pretty preppy WASP. At their wedding I offended her New England sense of decorum with my jokes, plunging neckline, and glittered chest. She regarded me as the tumor on the family tree throughout their twenty-year marriage. I should have followed Linda's advice to let him marry his Irapuato sweetheart.

Since reconnecting with Dr. Larry after his divorce from Nancy, he has continued to wow me with his genius and jokes. Despite his humor, he has a decidedly serious dark side. He has threatened to use modern medicine to keep me on a healthy track if my life threatens to go haywire again. Given my advanced age, I doubt I'll do much more traveling. But if I decide to live out my China fantasy, I won't tell Dr. Larry until I'm safely on the plane.

————

After a year in junior high school, Mark's English progressed from comprehensible to absolutely *perfecto*. After a year of ballet lessons, his feet progressed from flat to arched.

At the Arts Magnet high school in Dallas, Mark thrived socially due to his classmates' admiration for his talent and delightful personality. He went on to complete a double major in anthropology and dance at Southern Methodist University, and then received a master's degree in Spanish literature at the University of California at Whittier.

I like to think that he used the wheeling-and-dealing skills I'd taught him when he ordered merchandise for the two upscale Dallas boutiques he owned with his partner, Larry Groceclose. Despite my sparkly pink tennis shoes and purple slacks, the boys occasionally allowed me inside their stores to shop.

Mark danced, acted, and directed plays as a sideline until 2005, when he opened MBS Productions at the Stone Cottage theatre in Addison,

Texas. He continues to write, direct, act, and sometimes dance in his award-winning plays. One hit, *Persistence in Memory*, is a play that he first wrote and produced at age twenty-one. In it he recounts his experiences growing up in Mexico with Yours Truly.

The mystery of why Mark called me "Batman" as a baby remains unsolved.

Clearly, my smuggling sideline had a tremendous influence on all four of my children and left indelible scars. It scared them permanently straight.

That is unfortunate, because Mexico taught me that crime does pay—and quite well. Although the Mexican economy's financial glitches wiped out my contraband profits, I retain a wealth of memories. With them (and my darling late husband's fortune), I am rich!

DISCUSSION QUESTIONS

"If there is anything in the universe that
can't stand discussion, let it crack."

— *Wendell Phillips*

1. How did the cultural revolution of the 1960s affect the Sonna family? Have you or anyone you know experienced personal, marital, or other conflicts due to conflicting values, roles, and expectations?

2. How have U.S. and Canadian slang, fashions, products, attitudes, values, and family relationships changed since the 1960s? Do you consider the changes positive, negative, or neutral?

3. What is your ethnic background? Have you experienced being a minority because of your religion, language, age, sex, ethnic background, or appearance? If so, what was that experience like for you?

4. Describe Lois' motivations, personality, and choices. What do you like and/or admire about her? What do you dislike and/or disapprove of?

5. Should immigrant parents encourage their children to learn their parents' language, follow their customs, and/or embrace their values?

Why or why not? Or should parents dedicate themselves to helping their children integrate into the new culture? Why or why not? What are the benefits and drawbacks of having children remain faithful to their cultural heritage on the one hand, or fully assimilating into the new culture on the other?

6. What did Lois like about living in Mexico? What did she perceive as the main drawbacks of living outside of the U.S.? What would be the benefits and drawbacks for you of living in a foreign country?

7. What differences in attitudes, values, beliefs, and customs between the U.S. and Mexico did Lois encounter? Do you consider the differences to be positive, negative, or neutral?

8. Would the Americans and Canadians benefit from embracing some Mexican customs, beliefs, values, attitudes, laws, or practices? If so, which ones might enhance your life or be good for your country as a whole, and how would they make life better?

9. Would Mexico benefit from embracing some American or Canadian customs, beliefs, values, attitudes, laws, or practices? If so, which ones? How might Mexicans' lives be better?

10. Do you anticipate any cultural changes as the population of U.S. and Canadian Hispanics grows? If so, what types of changes might occur? Do you think the changes will make life better or worse for you, your descendants, and/or the country as a whole? In what ways?

ABOUT THIS BOOK

"The road to hell is paved with works-in-progress."

– Philip Roth

Because I was the first child ever t o attend t he L aGrange Public Library's Writers Group, the members weren't sure whether to allow a thirteen-year-old to join. After a short debate, they decided to let me give it a try. I ended up attending for three years.

I took copious notes during the presentations about writing and publishing. "Don't underestimate your talent," one speaker admonished us. "When you send out a book proposal, aim for a top publisher!" I thought that sounded like excellent advice. I couldn't wait to become a famous book author.

At age fifteen, while attending a six-week summer program in Saltillo, Mexico, I came up with a title, *Tortillas & Peanut Butter: Adventures of an American Teen in Mexico.*

After returning to LaGrange, I wrote the cover letter, book outline, three sample chapters ("Bargaining Basement Prices," "Mexican Plumbing," and "Fernando the Fearful"), as well as my (very short) author biography.

I mailed my book proposal to Bennett Cerf, the chief editor at Random House, the world's biggest publishing company. I "knew" him from watching him host a TV game show called *What's My Line.*

Another Random House editor replied. She said she liked my proposal, could not promise publication to an unknown author, but wanted to see the rest of the manuscript ASAP, and asked me not to send it to any other publisher.

I floated in a cloud of joy for hours as I envisioned my book climbing onto the best-seller list. Then I realized I needed to write the rest of the book. I crashed down to earth and got busy.

After nine months of blood, sweat, and intermittent bouts of tears, I mailed the finished manuscript to "my" Random House editor. Soon after, I began calling home from my high school's public telephone each day at lunchtime to find out if the mailman had delivered my publishing contract or (oh horror of horrors) a rejection letter. Six months later, I decided to end the suspense by calling New York to find out what was going on.

"This is Linda Sonna," I told "my" editor.

"Who?"

"Linda Sonna."

"I'm sorry, but I don't recognize that name."

Obviously she had disliked my book was so much, she hadn't bothered to reject it and had simply put it out of her mind. The sudden lump in my throat prevented me from speaking. I hung up so she wouldn't hear me sob.

I buried my manuscript and my dreams in a drawer for a decade, limiting my writing to school papers and, after college graduation, to psychological reports.

Meanwhile, my mother wrote weekly letters during her eleven-year Mexican holiday in which she detailed her antics. When she returned to the U.S., she attempted to convert her stories into a book, and I gave her my *Tortillas & Peanut Butter* title. After writing a draft, she turned her attention to her new job at GTE-Sprint and concentrated on writing office memos.

Around age thirty I re-wrote and expanded my mother's draft by adding scenes and chapters. I also added scenes and chapters from my original manuscript by revising them to reflect my mother's point of view. "You know me so well," she said in amazement when she saw the results.

But instead of seeking a publisher, I put the book on hold to work on other projects. In the blink of an eye, another decade passed.

At age forty I spent a year ushering each chapter of *Tortillas & Peanut Butter* through the Dallas-Fort Worth Writers Workshop's read-and-critique process. After revising the entire manuscript, I turned my attention to writing psychology self-help/parenting books. In the blink of my other eye, another decade flew by.

At age fifty I spent yet another year doing chapter-by-chapter revisions with the help of my Taos Writers' critique group. Life again became complicated, and I set aside the manuscript for what I expected to be a few months. Another decade hurtled past.

Around age sixty I resumed working on *Tortillas & Peanut Butter* while presenting writers' workshops in the small coastal town of La Manzanilla in Jalisco, Mexico, during the winter. For the next five years, I returned to the same lovely town each winter and presented chapters to the La Manzanilla Writers Group, reading segments during meetings and revising them afterwards.

Finally, at age sixty-five, a serious illness drove home the message that I wouldn't live forever. At age eighty-six, my mother was in perfect health and would likely outlive me. But despite her continuing intention to find the keys to eternal youth, I suspected that her time was also limited. I determined to finish multiple books that I had started and worked on over the years, and to finish this book by Mother's Day, 2016.

After more months of revision, I hired Lynne Willard to do a final professional edit, created a cover, and researched the world of self-publishing paperbacks, eBooks, and audiobooks.

Now that my half-century-long project is complete, I can finally say the word "smuggler" with a smile.

Happy Mother's Day 2016, Mom!

THANKS!

If you enjoyed this book, please post your five-star rating and rave review to **www.Amazon.com**, and be sure to recommend it to your cyber friends.

However, if you didn't love this book, please don't bother! Instead, you can submit your concerns, complaints, rants, and tirades to me at www.drsonna.org. I promise to read every message with a closed mind and a cold heart.

Sincerely,

Dr. Linda Sonna

Made in the USA
Columbia, SC
31 December 2017